GW00778022

VALVE DESIGN

VALVE DESIGN

G H PEARSON
CEng FIMechE FInstF

MECHANICAL ENGINEERING PUBLICATIONS LTD
LONDON

ISBN 0 85298 404 9

Printed in England by Staples Printers St. Albans Limited at the Priory Press.

Contents

PREFACE

Basically there are only four types of valve – rotary, lift, slide and piston – and their evolution was undoubtedly in this order.

There are many variants, however, of these four basic types, as may be expected; yet all are alike in concept and, despite the present-day trend for greater simplification and standardization, it seems clear that the advent of new industrial processes and techniques, and the discovery of new, and sometimes exotic, materials of construction, will promote these variations, perhaps with increasing intensity.

Four fundamental designs, and their variants, in common usage, all reliant on manual operation, are dealt with in the first four chapters. The alert designer should, however, have no trouble adapting the reasoning used to designs having similar characteristics to those chosen by way of example.

The sequence of the first four chapters is in order of evolution of the valves, but it is of interest to note that the timescale is somewhat logarithmic. For example, the earliest valve – the cock – was introduced before the Christian era; the screw-down valve, *circa* 1790; the wedge-gate valve in 1839 and the parallel slide valve in 1884. All are basically stop valves arranged for manual operation, and, in more recent times for operation by some form of motive power.

Valves which function automatically, such as safety or relief valves, reducing valves, non-return valves, steam traps and similar devices, are in a class apart and are dealt with in the remaining five chapters. These valves are automatons in the strict sense of the word. Correctly designed and installed, each may be relied upon to perform its appointed function, unostentatiously maybe, day-in, day-out, more likely year-in, year-out.

The safety or relief valve, an essential adjunct to any piece of equipment which can justly lay claim to being a pressure vessel, is particularly note-worthy by reason of the essential role it plays in the safeguarding of life, limb and property. By 'pressure' we infer 'absolute pressure', since vessels operating at sub-atmospheric pressure generally require some means of automatic protection if they are liable to collapse under the crushing effect of the atmosphere should a vacuum be created inside them from any cause whatsoever. The other examples, important as their respective function might be, would be less likely to engender such doleful consequences should they fail in their appointed function; but no less care should be lavished on their design on this account.

For those students, engineers, designers and draughtsmen alike, who are confronted with the design or installation of these devices, and who are aware of their necessity, it is hoped this present volume will prove to be a vade mecum.

G H Pearson
Newport, Gwent
November 1978

Acknowledgments

Grateful acknowledgment is made to the following for supplying information:

The American Society of Mechanical Engineers,
United Engineering Center,
345 East 47th Street,
New York,
NY 10017

The British Standards Institution,
British Standards House,
2 Park Street,
London W1

Delta (Manganese Bronze) Ltd,
Ipswich

Holo-Krome Ltd,
Dundee

Spirol Industries Ltd,
Sunbury-on-Thames

Drayton Controls Ltd

Hopkinsons Ltd,
Huddersfield

Spirax-Sarco Ltd,
Cheltenham

Chapter 1
Cocks

UNDOUBTEDLY the cock was the very first fluid closure device conceived by man. It has sufficed for well over 2000 years and will continue to do so since it is the essence of simplicity, normally fully opened and closed in one quarter of a revolution of the plug. By rotating the plug the port is alternately made to line up with its counterpart in the body and to the blank wall of the body to give open and shut conditions respectively.

Unquestionably its origin is attributed to the Roman workers in metal and many of their early examples have survived to intrigue engineers and others alike.

The idea of a conical plug rotating in a conical shell or body and retained in intimate—but not too intimate—contact with it was a distinct 'breakthrough' on the part of its originator, whoever that might have been. It must have become of pressing necessity when the open conduit gave way to the metal pipe originally made of rolled sheet lead, folded into near circular form, and sealed longitudinally in the manner practised by present day plumbers (lead burning).

Cocks are mainly designed empirically rather than by the results of any mathematical investigation into their behaviour. The included angle of the plug is generally made 10°. A substantially smaller angle would result in the plug and body becoming 'seized up' entirely or at best the plug would prove difficult to turn.

PLUG PORT DESIGN

Whatever pattern of cock is under consideration, the ports should be proportioned in the manner advocated below, unless, of course, circular ports presenting a flow passage of uniform cross-section are required. A plug with circular port requires to be of larger diameter than a plug featuring the trapezoidal section port. Figs. 1.1, 1.2, 1.3, 1.4 and 1.5 illustrate simple cocks commonly employed for a variety of low pressure applications, all of trapezoidal section.

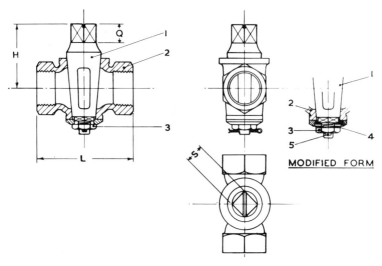

All dimensions in mm

Nom. pipe size		6	10	12	20	25	30	40	50	60	75	100
Length	L	48	57	64	73	86	98	114	127	165	190	240
Height	H	30	35	38	48	64	70	76	95	108	127	203
Size of square	S	9·5	10	11	13	16	18	20	24	30	35	50
Length of square	Q	11	11	12	14	19	22	24	28	31	35	40

All dimensions in inches

Nom. pipe size		$\frac{1}{4}$	$\frac{3}{8}$	$\frac{1}{2}$	$\frac{3}{4}$	1	$1\frac{1}{4}$	$1\frac{1}{2}$	2	$2\frac{1}{2}$	3	4
Length overall	L	$1\frac{7}{8}$	$2\frac{1}{4}$	$2\frac{1}{2}$	$2\frac{7}{8}$	$3\frac{3}{8}$	$3\frac{7}{8}$	$4\frac{1}{2}$	5	$6\frac{1}{2}$	$7\frac{1}{2}$	9
Height	H	$1\frac{1}{4}$	$1\frac{3}{8}$	$1\frac{1}{2}$	$1\frac{7}{8}$	$2\frac{1}{2}$	$2\frac{3}{4}$	3	$3\frac{3}{4}$	$4\frac{1}{4}$	5	8
Size of square	S	$\frac{3}{8}$	$\frac{13}{32}$	$\frac{7}{16}$	$\frac{17}{32}$	$\frac{5}{8}$	$\frac{11}{16}$	$\frac{27}{32}$	$\frac{15}{16}$	$1\frac{1}{8}$	$1\frac{3}{8}$	2
Length of square	Q	$\frac{7}{16}$	$\frac{7}{16}$	$\frac{1}{2}$	$\frac{9}{16}$	$\frac{3}{4}$	$\frac{7}{8}$	$\frac{15}{16}$	$1\frac{1}{8}$	$1\frac{1}{4}$	$1\frac{3}{8}$	$1\frac{5}{8}$

Fig. 1.1 *Taper ground plug cock; nut and washer bottom pattern*

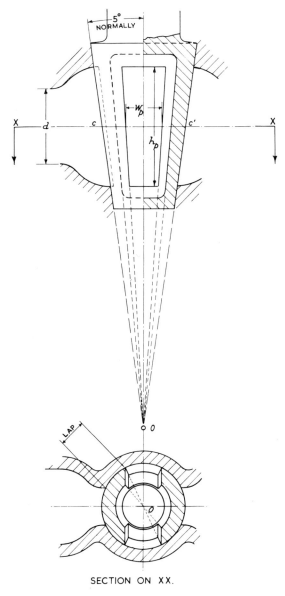

SECTION ON XX.

Fig. 1.2 *Geometry of cock plug design*

Obviously the cross-sectional area a of the ports in both the body and the plug should be at least equal to the cross-sectional area of the bore of the pipe, i.e.

$$a = \pi d^2/4$$

where d is the bore of the cock.

For all practical purposes, the area of each port may be taken as the product of w_p and h_p in Fig. 1.2, although due allowance should be made for the loss of area caused by the fillets (deliberately omitted in the figure in order not to complicate the geometry). The angularity in Fig. 1.2 is exaggerated in the interests of clarity.

The mean width of the port w_p taken on the central plane cc' should be made equal to one half the bore of the cock, an easy rule to remember. We may then readily determine h_p, the length of the port, as follows:

$$w_p h_p = \pi d^2/4 \qquad (1.1)$$

whence

$$h_p = \pi d^2/4 w_p$$

but since $w_p = d/2$, eqn (1.1) may be written

$$h_p = \pi d/2 \qquad (1.2)$$

Some allowance may be made for the small loss of area due to the fillets by extending h_p slightly.

Referring to Fig. 1.2 it should be noted that the near-vertical edges of the ports when projected should converge on the common apex 0. In this way the width of the port will bear the same relationship to the diameter of the plug at any point in its length, as it must do in order to avoid the possibility of reducing the lap (or even eliminating it entirely) to such an extent as to induce short-circuiting of the line fluid. By *lap* is meant that portion of the circumference of the plug and of the body cavity remaining in mutual contact when the cock is in the closed position, i.e. with the plug port at right angles to the ports in the body shown in Fig. 1.2 and as at a in Fig. 1.3.

Taking an extreme case, if there was no lap—as at b in Fig. 1.3—leakage would be inevitable to a lesser or greater extent from the body port to the plug port, and this condition might easily occur at some point along the plug if the geometry advocated in Fig. 1.2 is not rigorously adopted.

There is one particular case, however—despite the foregoing—where

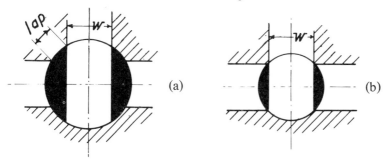

Fig. 1.3 *Transverse section through ports of body and plug. Three-way cock.*
      (a) with lap; (b) with no lap

even *negative* lap is most desirable! This aspect will receive consideration in
the section on multiway or multiport cocks.

GROUND PLUG COCKS

Reverting to Fig. 1.1 this is a simple plug cock destined for low pressure
service and generally intended for insertion in a straight run of piping. Fluid-
tightness is entirely dependent upon the correct intensity of the wedging
effect between the plug 1 and the body 2, the requisite amount of 'bite' being
achieved by tightening the base nut 3. In a more 'refined' version the nut is
tightened against the compressive resistance of a spring washer 4, shown as
a separate detail alongside.

The base nut 3 is prevented from slackening back by locking it to the plug
1 with the split pin 5. In some models the spring washer is omitted entirely,
the bottom nut arranged as a somewhat tight fit in the threads as a
precaution against working loose.

Proportions are based more on expediency than on any mathematical
premise and the proportions indicated in Fig. 1.1 based on gunmetal as the
material of construction should aid design.

GLAND PACKED GROUND PLUG COCK

A somewhat more refined version is the gland packed cock illustrated in Fig.
1.4. Usually the gland is of the two bolt/stud pattern. In this design, unlike
the former, the plug 1 does not protrude through the base of the body. At
least one avenue of escape of the working fluid is thereby prevented.

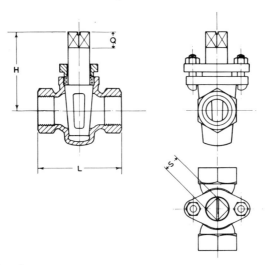

All dimensions in mm

Nom. pipe size		6	10	12	20	25	30	40	50	60	75	100
Length	L	48	57	60	73	86	97	111	127	158	190	235
Height	H	48	54	64	70	83	95	108	127	146	165	203
Size of square	S	9·5	10	12	14	16	19	22	25	29	32	50
Length of square	Q	11	11	12	14	16	19	22	25	31	35	40

All dimensions in inches

Nom. pipe size		$\frac{1}{4}$	$\frac{3}{8}$	$\frac{1}{2}$	$\frac{3}{4}$	1	$1\frac{1}{4}$	$1\frac{1}{2}$	2	$2\frac{1}{2}$	3	4
Length	L	$1\frac{7}{8}$	$2\frac{1}{4}$	$2\frac{3}{8}$	$2\frac{7}{8}$	$3\frac{3}{8}$	$3\frac{13}{16}$	$4\frac{3}{8}$	5	$6\frac{1}{4}$	$7\frac{1}{2}$	$9\frac{1}{4}$
Height	H	$1\frac{7}{8}$	$2\frac{1}{8}$	$2\frac{1}{2}$	$2\frac{3}{4}$	$3\frac{1}{4}$	$3\frac{3}{4}$	$4\frac{1}{4}$	5	$5\frac{3}{4}$	$6\frac{1}{2}$	8
Size of square	S	$\frac{3}{8}$	$\frac{13}{32}$	$\frac{1}{2}$	$\frac{9}{16}$	$\frac{5}{8}$	$\frac{3}{4}$	$\frac{7}{8}$	1	$1\frac{1}{8}$	$1\frac{1}{4}$	2
Length of square	Q	$\frac{7}{16}$	$\frac{7}{16}$	$\frac{1}{2}$	$\frac{9}{16}$	$\frac{5}{8}$	$\frac{3}{4}$	$\frac{7}{8}$	1	$1\frac{1}{4}$	$1\frac{3}{8}$	$1\frac{5}{8}$

Fig. 1.4 *Taper ground plug cock. Two-bolt oval gland pattern*

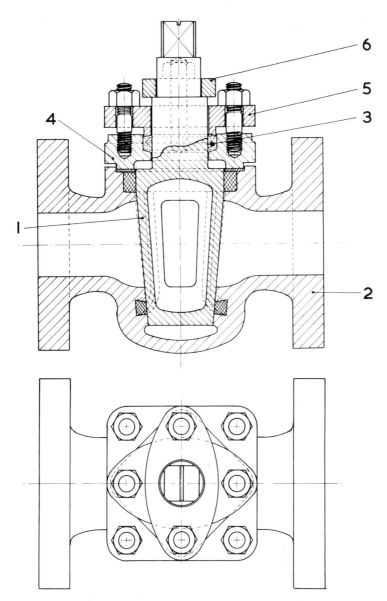

Fig. 1.5 *Typical asbestos groove packed cock. Straightway pattern*

Proportions for gunmetal cocks are as indicated on the drawing but may be modified according to individual requirements and to the kind of materials employed, again assumed gunmetal in the present case.

ASBESTOS GROOVE PACKED COCKS

Originally intended for boiler blow-down duties this is one of the most sophisticated forms of cock (see Fig. 1.5).

Instead of relying for fluid-tightness on metal–metal affinitive contact between the plug 1 and the body 2, as in previous models, the plug surface (in a correctly packed cock) just clears the body metal by reason of two U-grooves circumscribing each of the two ports in the body. The body, when tightly rammed with asbestos packing of a kind which is self-vulcanizing under the influence of the steam heat*, tends to force the plug out of metallic contact and to 'ride' on the slightly raised surface of the packing. The U-grooves are shown to advantage in Fig. 1.6.

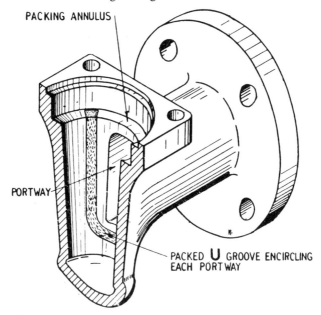

Fig. 1.6 *Section of asbestos-packed cock body showing packing grooves*

*Only if the steam pressure does not fall below 50 psig

This arrangement also makes for easy operation because the frictional resistance to rotation is reduced.

The particular packing employed is known as *indurated asbestos* and is in flake form.

Reverting to Fig. 1.5, a stuffing box 3 prevents leakage via the clearance between the plug shank and the cover plate 4. The plug is held down by the oval plate 6 secured to the cover plate by two studs and nuts shown.

A commendable feature of this arrangement is that the whole assembly of cover plate 4, oval gland 5 and holding down plate 6 may be lifted entire with the removal of the plug 1, therefore leaving the packing undisturbed.

MULTIPORT COCKS

The examples so far described have all been of the straight-through variety, i.e. for insertion in a straight run of pipework, the cock merely acting as a stop cock for arresting or permitting flow unidirectionally.

There are innumerable applications, however, where it is desirable to divide the flow, and no array of screw-down valves can effect this requirement so simply as the single, three, or even four-way cock.

To describe and illustrate each and every variant would take up too much space in a volume of this nature, but the reader is referred to the Author's other work *Applications of Valves and Fittings** in which these are described and illustrated in detail. In passing, however, it is pertinent to point out that the plug of a multiport cock normally requires to be greater in diameter than its straight-way counterpart where positive lap is essential.

Negative lap is most desirable when the discharge derived from a constantly running positive displacement pump is required to be diverted through a multiport cock. In short, there must be no complete shut-off during the transition of the ports or otherwise the pump will be endeavouring to pump against a closed outlet and damage to the pump or ancillaries will inevitably result.

Designers and users alike should be alerted to this possibility. The provision of a relief valve (on the outlet side, of course), although commendable, may not provide the safeguard it might appear to be since it may not open promptly enough to take care of any shock wave created. An air vessel (see *Applications of Valves and Fittings*, p.140) is advocated in these cases.

Modern counterparts of the age-old cock principle are the grease

*PEARSON, G. H., *Applications of Valves and Fittings*, 1968 (Pitman, London)

lubricated cock, the sleeve packed cock, and the ball 'valve'. (Various examples are featured in *Applications of Valves and Fittings*).

The ball 'valve' cited above should rightly be termed a ball *cock* since in principle it is exactly similar to its progenitor, differing essentially in the plug which is spherical instead of conical, a simple typical example of which is portrayed in Fig. 1.7.

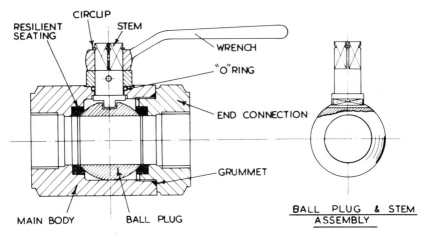

Fig. 1.7 *Simple ball cock (or valve)*

This type of fitting is characterized by its extreme freedom from perceptible frictional restraint, comparing most favourably with the conventional plug cock in this respect. The 'frictionless' feature is achieved by the much diminished area of rubbing contact and by the low frictional characteristics of the finely lapped surface of the spherical metallic plug working in conjunction with a seating of ptfe, the usual material employed.

Chapter 2
Screw-Down Stop Valves

INTRODUCTION

Although the cock has sufficed as a closure device for more than 2000 years, the screw-down stop valve is a relative newcomer! It is virtually a revised form of vice or clamp and owes its inception as we know it today to two closely related events—the introduction of the screw-cutting lathe *circa* 1795–1800 and the increasing use of steam prompted by the engines of Watt and Trevithick. It was not until 1768 that Watt devised the rotative steam engine, in consequence of which boilers became in increasing demand, and the ground plug cock in common use soon proved inadequate to deal with the steadily increasing steam pressures—although these by present-day standards would appear near atmospheric!

The screw-down stop valve is available in different guises. It may take the form of a *globe* stop valve (Fig. 2.1) for use in horizontal or 'in-line' mains; as a *junction* stop valve (Fig. 2.2) enabling a right-angle change in direction of the main to be made, or to sit on the standpipe of a boiler; or as a controllable feed check valve wherein the valve member is arranged free of the stem (but whose lift is controlled by it) to cater for unidirectional flow (Fig. 2.3).

Only the outside screw pattern valve will be considered, having flat faced seat contacting faces as illustrated in Fig. 2.4. The proportions given relate to seatings of the permanent pressed-in type.

FACTORS GOVERNING ULTIMATE EFFECTIVE CLOSURE

The point at which pressure-tightness of a seating is ultimately achieved is on a relatively narrow raised annulus and this should be ground and lapped to a mirror-like finish.

If this annulus be made too narrow, the contact pressure may prove so excessive as to induce 'galling' (scuffing); if too wide, the contact pressure is insufficient to ensure pressure-tightness across the seating face.

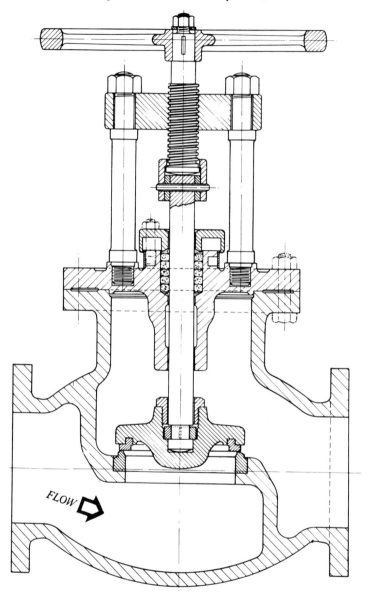

Fig. 2.1 *Typical screw-down globe stop valve, two-piece stem pattern*

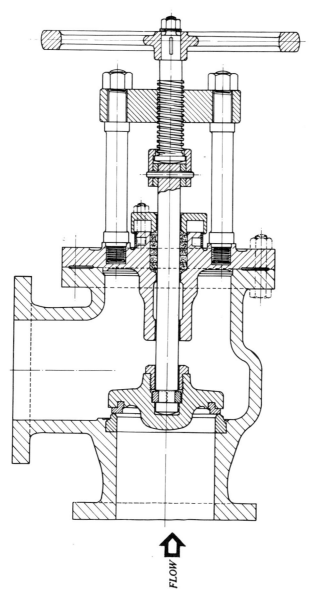

Fig. 2.2 *Typical screw-down junction valve, two-piece stem pattern*

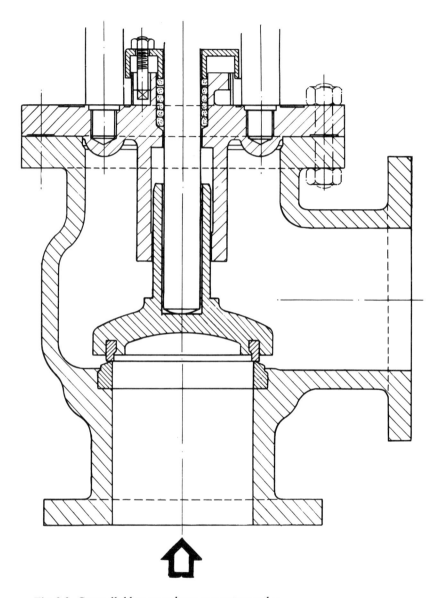

Fig. 2.3 *Controllable screw-down non-return valve*

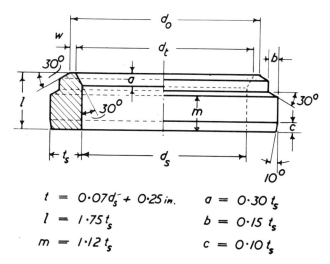

$$t = 0.07d_s + 0.25\,in. \qquad a = 0.30\,t_s$$
$$l = 1.75\,t_s \qquad\qquad b = 0.15\,t_s$$
$$m = 1.12\,t_s \qquad\qquad c = 0.10\,t_s$$

Fig. 2.4 *Stop valve seatings*

The width w of the seating face referred to in Fig. 2.4 is given by the relationship

$$w = pd_o/4\,(u - 2p) \tag{2.1}$$

where p = working pressure

d_o = *outside* diameter of the seating face

u = allowable unit contact clamping pressure.

For values of u see Table L of the Appendix.

Of course a value of d_o must be assumed prior to a more precise determination later. It will be noted that w is a function of the outside diameter, the permissible unit stress and the working pressure.

At first sight it might be supposed that the axial force to be exerted by the stem to secure closure tightness is solely that which is sufficient to counter the upthrust due to the line pressure exerted on the underside of the valve member*. Even were this a valid assumption (and it is far from being one),

---

*In the initial stages, that is in the process of running down the valve member, it would be appreciably less than this (the friction of the gland packing apart), consisting solely of the force to overcome the effect of the line pressure acting on the cross-sectional area of the lower stem.

some extra downthrust would be advisable if only to avoid marginal effectiveness.

There are three constituent resistances to be overcome in order to close down effectively a screw-down stop valve against a known line pressure. These are:

(i) the force to resist the line pressure upthrust on the valve member, and denoted by P_o;
(ii) the axial clamping force at the seating to maintain fluid tightness and denoted by P_c;
(iii) the frictional resistance imposed by the embracing effect of the gland packing on the stem and denoted by P_f.

If P_T denotes the *total* axial force to be imparted by the stem to overcome these three resistances acting in unison then:

$$P_T = P_o + P_c + P_f \qquad (2.2)$$

Dealing with these constituent resistances in turn we have:

$$P_o = (\pi/4)\, d_o^2 p \qquad (2.3)$$

Now it has been demonstrated that a clamping pressure at the seating faces of from $1\frac{1}{2}$ to 2 times the line pressure is required in order to secure fluid-tightness: for design purposes it is advisable to adopt the higher value, i.e. $2p$, then:

$$P_c = 2\pi\, d_o wp \qquad \text{very nearly} \qquad (2.4)$$

The last-named resistance, the frictional resistance of the gland packing, is one open to some conjecture. Undue tightening down of the gland nuts could impose an incalculable resistance to the free travel of the stem through the packed stuffing box; on the other hand the employment of 'automatic' packings used in conjunction with shims to restrict their initial compression would impose the minimum of frictional resistance.

It is customary, however, to employ 'block' packing or shredded packing (the former for preference) compressed through the agency of the gland plate, and the gland bolts or studs and design must cater for these accordingly.

Certain assumptions will require to be made in a (vain) attempt to evaluate the frictional resistance P_f, but before proceeding, a word or two regarding the proportions of the stuffing box will be desirable.

Suppose that the packing is so compressed as to exert a minimum pressure on the stem equal to the line pressure p and that this is constant throughout the length of contact l_s of the packing (see Fig. 2.5) then*:

total grip of packing on stem = unit pressure × exposed area

$$= \pi \, d_s l_s p$$

and if μ_s be the coefficient of friction between the packing and the stem, then

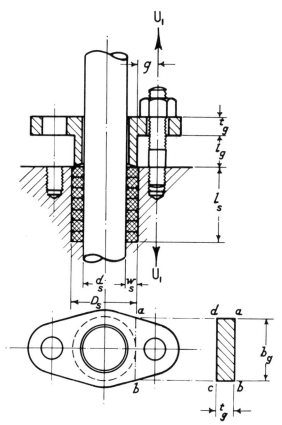

Fig. 2.5 (a) *Stuffing box and gland*

*For a more detailed study of the behaviour of packed glands of various composition see THOMSON, J. L. 'Packed glands for high pressures: an analysis of fundamentals', Proc. Instn mech. Engrs, 1958, **172**, 471–86.

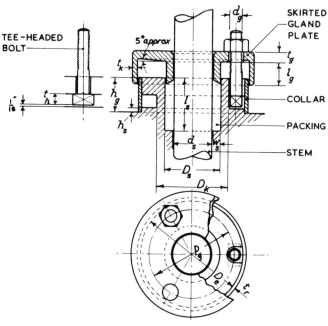

$D_e = p_g + d_g + \frac{1}{4}$ in approx.

$D_k = D_s + 2w_s$

$h_g = 1\frac{1}{4}d_g + t_h + \frac{1}{4}$ in

$h_s = d_g/4$

$p_g = d_s + 4w_s + d_g + \frac{1}{8}$ in

$t_g = \frac{2}{3}d_g$

$t_k = \dfrac{d_g}{8} + \frac{1}{8}$ in

$t_r = \dfrac{d_g}{8} + \frac{1}{16}$ in

$l_g = 2\frac{1}{2}w_s$ to $3\frac{1}{2}w_s$

For l_s and w_s see text.

Fig. 2.5 (b) *Three-bolt stuffing box and gland, for screw-down stop valves and parallel slide valves*

the frictional resistance to axial displacement P_f will be given by:

$$P_f = \pi \mu_s d_s l_s p \qquad (2.5)$$

Then combining eqns (2.3), (2.4) and (2.5), eqn (2.2) may be resolved:

$$P_T = (\pi/4)p \{d_0^2 + 8d_o w + 4\mu_s d_s l_s\} \text{ (approx.)} \qquad (2.6)$$

STEM DIAMETER

Only the two-piece stem form of construction as featured in Figs. 2.1 and 2.2 will be considered.

Dealing firstly with the lower plain stem, this will be subjected to direct compressive stress in the process of closing down the valve, namely the total axial force P_T for bringing about complete closure. In the process of *opening* the valve the stem will be subjected to *tensile* stress of less intensity since the line pressure (for 'under and over' flow) will *assist* the opening process. Consequently, we are only concerned with the force P_T required for securing positive closure*.

The stem cannot assume any semblance to a strut in the engineering sense of the word since it has so little unrestrained length, namely that denoted by the lift, even in the large sizes. The exception might be in certain types of tank outlet valves where the lift needs to be in excess of the usual amount of one quarter the diameter of the seating in order not to impede the free efflux of the contained media. But such valves almost invariably work at fairly low pressures and therefore the stems have no appreciable thrusts to impart.

It would seem, therefore, that the diameter d_s may be determined simply by equating the maximum compressive force P_T to the moment of resistance. Now if reference is made to Fig. 2.6 it will be seen that the stem 2 is weakened at its upper extremity by the hole for receiving the pin 5. If this pin is made of a diameter equal to one quarter the stem diameter (the adequacy of the pin diameter can be checked later but in most cases will be

---

*It could be argued that, in the very final stages of closure, the seating members having made contact and in the process of being progressively squeezed together, the force due to the frictional grip of the gland packing will have no bearing on the resistance to closure since there is no apparent movement of the stem. In the absence of experimental evidence about this, it is advisable to take this force into account in all calculations if only to err on the right side.

found sufficient) then the cross-sectional area of the stem will be given by:

$$a_s = (\pi/4)d_s^2 - d_s^2/4$$
$$= 0.535d_s^2$$

then

$$P_T = 0.535d_s^2 f_c$$

where f_c is the allowable direct compressive stress, whence

$$d_s = \sqrt{(P_T/0.535f_c)} \qquad\qquad (2.7a)$$

Suitable values for the allowable compressive stress may be obtained from Appendix J or K, appropriate to the material selected for the stem (see also *Applications of Valves and Fittings*).

Experience suggests that to cater for low pressures this formula would yield results incompatible with practical requirements, the diameter working out unreasonably small. Consequently, it is suggested the formula becomes an empirical one such that:

$$d_s = \sqrt{(P_T/0.535f_c)} + C \qquad\qquad (2.7b)$$

where C is a constant and equals

$0.5/\sqrt{d_o}$ where d_o is the *outside* diameter of the seating, or $12.5/\sqrt{d_o}$ in metric units.

Note: Sizes of screw-down stop valves in excess of 8 in (or 200 mm) bore are not looked upon with favour as they can become cumbersome where high pressures are concerned. They are admissible, however, for low pressure gas duties for example.

The foregoing data relates to the lower stem of a two-piece stem arrangement irrespective of the form the actuating mechanism may take.

The two-piece assembly has every commendable virtue, principally that of the actuating screw being located outside the valve casing and, therefore, immune from the prevailing temperature of the working media and being actually out of contact with it.

Additionally, the construction permits dimensions for the screw such as to secure the ideal relationship of mean diameter and pitch as will yield the desired mechanical advantage and efficiency.

ACTUATING SCREW

Consider the screw-cum-stem assembly shown in Fig. 2.6. In the process of *closing* down the valve the rounded end of the actuating screw bears on the flat top of the stem 2 to impart the full thrust P_T. The collar 3, sleeve 4 and pin 5 play no part whatsoever in this process, other than in maintaining their ordained positions, and carry no load. They are mere passengers.

On opening the valve, however, the actuating screw lifts the stem and it is then that the parts 3, 4 and 5 come into operation. The rising screw lifts the collar 3 which in turn lifts the stem 2 since it is pinned through 3 and 4.

The line pressure acting on the underside of the valve member assists in the opening process. Should the valve be opened to its fullest extent, and the maximum effort still be applied to the handwheel, then the pin 5 could be called upon to resist an upwardly applied shearing force of extent P_T. It is at this stage, therefore, that the validity of the previously assumed diameter of one quarter the diameter of the stem could be checked and any adjustments made accordingly.

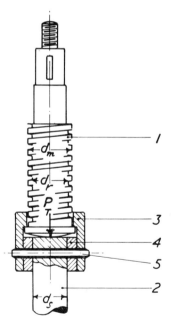

Fig. 2.6 *Actuating screw assembly*

One or other of the many proprietary high shear strength spring pins is recommended for this duty in preference to the out-dated (and more expensive) solid turned pin sometimes employed. Details of allowable loading for typical spring pins of varying qualities are given in Appendix Z.

The actuating screw could, therefore, be called upon to sustain a *compressive* force in the *closing* process and a *tensile* force in the ultimate *opening* process, each of intensity P_T. We are concerned only with the compressive force.

Let d_r denote the root diameter of the threads (see Fig. 2.6), then equating the axial force to the moment of resistance we have:

for compressive load

$$P_T = (\pi/4)\, d_r^2 f_c$$
$$d_r = \sqrt{(4P_T/\pi f_c)} \qquad\qquad (2.8a)$$

f_c being the allowable compressive stress.

The value of d_r will always work out less than d_s (as derived from eqn 2.7) if equal values for f_c are adopted since there is no reduction in the cross-sectional area of the upper stem due to intrusions. An examination of Fig. 2.6 will reveal that from practical considerations the root diameter d_r might be made larger than theoretical conditions indicate and at least equal to d_s previously determined, or:

$$d_r = \sqrt{(4P_T/\pi f_c)} + C \qquad\qquad (2.8b)$$

where C is a constant, again equal to $0{\cdot}5/\sqrt{d_0}$ (or $12{\cdot}5/\sqrt{d_0}$ in metric).

Some designs of screw-down stop valves feature the 'rotate spindle' device illustrated in Fig. 2.7. This enables the valve member to be rotated on its seating without accompanying axial displacement; this clears the seat contacting faces of any trapped scale, for example, and also gives the faces an occasional burnish. The valve member is slackened off slightly by giving the main handwheel a partial turn and the inner spindle (the 'rotate' spindle) then rotated by manipulating the cross-bar handle situated above the operating handwheel.

This arrangement necessitates a somewhat larger diameter actuating screw, as will be seen, because it now requires to be made hollow to accommodate the rotate spindle.

Proceeding as for a solid actuating screw, let d_1 and d_2 represent the *root* diameter of the screw and the diameter of the plain axial hole, respectively

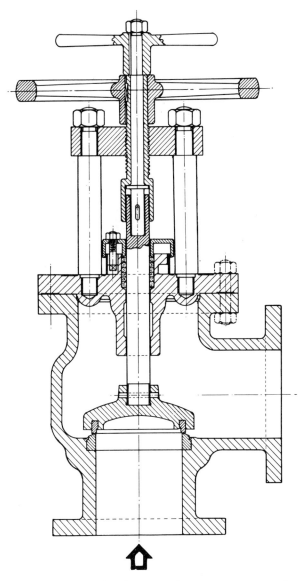

Fig. 2.7 *Actuating screw assembly for screw-down junction stop valve, featuring 'rotate spindle' device*

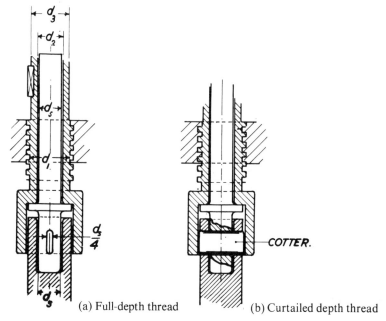

(a) Full-depth thread   (b) Curtailed depth thread

Fig. 2.8 (a) and (b) *Actuating screw assembly featuring 'rotate spindle' device*

(see Fig. 2.8), then:
   for *compressive* load

$$P_T = (\pi/4)f_c \{d_1^2 - d_2^2\}$$
$$d_1 = \sqrt{(4P_T/\pi f_c + d_2^2)} \qquad (2.9)$$

   Since the diameter of the stem (d_s) will have been already calculated (from eqn 2.7) the diameter of the axial hole d_2 can be readily assigned a suitable value (say d_s + 1/32 in. or 1 mm), whence d_1 will be the only unknown, and:

   for *tensile* load

$$d_1 = \sqrt{(4P_T/\pi f_t + d_2^2)} \qquad (2.10)$$

DIAMETER OF HANDWHEEL

The best designs feature the two-piece stem, as exemplified in Figs. 2.1 and

2.2, the lower stem usually and preferably of stainless steel, the upper of gunmetal or manganese bronze for the following reasons.

It is most desirable for the actuating stem to have a 'slow' thread in the interests of obtaining the optimum mechanical advantage and in order to achieve the best relationship between mean diameter and pitch of threads. This necessitates an increased diameter which, if adopted in the case of a one-piece stem, would mean excessively large stem and gland.

Let H_w be the effective diameter of the handwheel (i.e. the outside diameter), τ the net manual effort applied, consisting of a push and a pull each of intensity $\tau/2$, the common radius of application being $H_w/2$ (see Fig. 2.9), η the efficiency of the screw thread, and p_t the true pitch of the screw thread (single start thread), then, considering one complete revolution of the handwheel:

work done on screw = work done on handwheel

Now 'work done' is *force* times *distance* through which the force acts, therefore,

total axial force on stem × pitch of screw
= net manual effort × circumference of handwheel
× efficiency of screw

or

$$P_T p_t = \tau \times \pi H_w \times \eta$$

whence

$$H_w = P_T p_t / \pi \tau \eta \qquad (2.11)$$

For η substitute η_1 or η_2 according to the type of thread (see eqns 2.12a and 2.12b which follow).

Note that η is always a fraction of unity. If percentage values are employed multiply right-hand side by 100.

We must now determine the efficiency η_1 or η_2 of the actuating screw, either by calculation or from the appropriate graph in Appendix P, Q, R or S. By calculation,

for square threads

$$\eta_1 = \tan a / \tan (a + \varphi) \qquad (2.12a)$$

where $a = $ lead angle (see Fig. 2.10) and $\varphi = $ friction angle. Note than

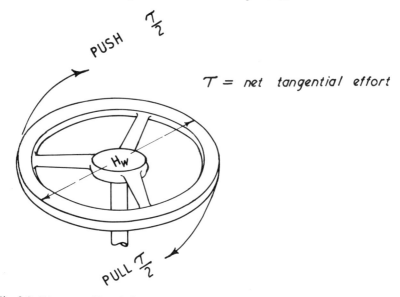

T = net tangential effort

Fig. 2.9 *Diagram of handwheel and mode of application of manual effort*

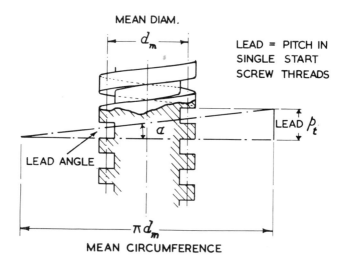

Fig. 2.10 *Relationship between the true pitch (lead) and mean diameter of screw thread*

$\tan\varphi = \mu$, the coefficient of friction of the thread materials. For gunmetal on mild steel, the usual combination, μ may be taken as $0 \cdot 15$ where no means of lubrication is provided. (The best designs feature a crosshead fitted with a Stauffer or similar lubricator.)

For Acme threads, included angle of $29°$ (see Fig. 2.11(a) and 2.11(b)):

$$\eta_2 = \tan a / \tan (a + k\varphi) \tag{2.12b}$$

where $k = 1/\cos\beta$ where $\beta = $ half the included angle of the thread flanks, i.e. $14° \, 30'$ in the case of true Acme threads, whence $k = 1 \cdot 033$.

This value of k is near enough to unity to give no appreciable variation from results obtained from the expression for square threads (i.e. eqn 2.8). At best the final evaluation of our calculations can only be closely approximate.

In view of the difficulty normally associated with the threading of the many grades of stainless steel, especially with dies of Acme form, it is most advisable to restrict the cutting depth to two-thirds that of the normal depth of $p_t/2$. This also permits an increased core diameter which is an advantage. Both standard and substandard depths are shown at (a) and (b) respectively in Fig. 2.11. The practice may be adopted in the case of square section threads with similar advantage.

Having evaluated H_w the diameter of the handwheel, useful proportions may be obtained from Appendix V and W, giving details of both 'flat' and 'dished' handwheels which have proved satisfactory in a variety of applications. The dished pattern is to be advocated for the smaller valves where the pillar ends (or their nuts, to be more precise) are more likely to encroach on the rim on the handwheel than is the case on the larger valves, this type of wheel being less likely to cause damage to the knuckles of an unwary operator on account of the increased clearance it provides.

ACTUATING SCREW TERMINATION

This extreme portion of the actuating screw is subject at least to torsional stresses and to the additional possibility of some bending, and both facts require to be taken into account. Compression or tension arising from the manipulative axial thrust is restricted to that portion under the crosshead and cannot be transmitted beyond that point by reason of the restraint imposed by the threads in engagement.

Valves of this type (and other handwheel operated valves) often suffer

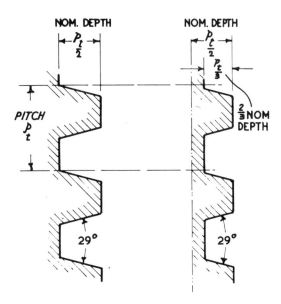

Fig. 2.11 *Elements of Acme thread*

damage in transit by being allowed to fall over on to their handwheels—with the result that the shank end on the screw is often found to be bent.

Although design should not really cater for *every* contingency of handling likely to arise, some account should be taken in the final analysis of the *bending* stress (as well as the *torsional* stress) which could be incurred in normal operation, but it is difficult to compute because most of the manual effort applied will be tangentially directed. The amount absorbed in bending of the stem is practically indeterminate, especially at this stage in the design process. We have seen from Fig. 2.9 that the tangential effort is comprised of a *push* and a *pull* each of intensity $\tau/2$ where τ is the net tangential effort expended. Then the twisting moment will be given by

$$M_T = \tau H_w/4 \qquad (2.13)$$

where H_w is the effective diameter of the handwheel.

Now the torsional moment of resistance of a solid shaft is $f_s Z_t$ where f_s is the shear stress induced and Z_t the polar modulus of a solid circular section and equal to $(\pi/16)d_t^3$

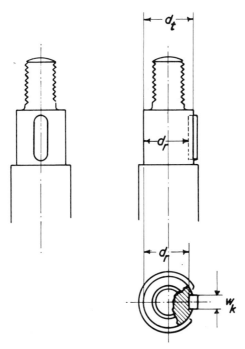

Fig. 2.12 *Typical stem termination*

Then equating the twisting moment M_T to the moment of resistance:

$$M_T = f_s Z_t = (\pi/16)\, d_t^3 f_s \tag{2.14}$$

whence

$$d_t = \sqrt[3]{(16\, M_T / \pi f_s)} \tag{2.15}$$

For a hollow shaft (as in the case of the rotate spindle pattern illustrated in Figs. 2.7 and 2.8) the torsional moment of resistance is similarly given by $f_s Z_t'$ where Z_t' is the polar modulus of a *hollow* circular section and is given by

$$(\pi/16)\,(d_{max}^3 - d_{min}^3)$$

Again

$$M_T = f_s Z_t' = (\pi/16) f_s \{ d_{max}^3 - d_{min}^3 \} \tag{2.16}$$

Some amount of trial-and-error calculations may be the best course to adopt to determine the maximum and minimum diameters d_{max} and d_{min}.

We must not lose sight of the fact that the shank is weakened to some extent by the intrusion of the inevitable keyseat (note: key*seat* in the shaft: key*way* in the wheel) and the diameter as calculated by any of the foregoing formulae must be adjusted accordingly in order to compensate effectively for this weakening effect.

A reasonably valid approximation is to adopt a torsional sectional polar modulus (for a solid shaft) Z_t of $(\pi/16)\, d_t d_r^2$ where d_r is the distance from the bottom of the key or keyseat to the opposite edge of the stem termination (see Fig. 2.12): then

$$M_T = f_s Z_t$$
$$= (\pi/16)\, d_t\, d_r^2 f_s \qquad (2.17)$$

whence

$$d_t = 16 M_T / \pi\, d_r^2 f_s \qquad (2.18)$$

Inevitably this calls for some amount of trial-and-error calculations based on an assumed tentative value of d_r.

Since the depth of the keyseat is usually made one-twelfth the diameter of the shaft, then d_r may be taken to be $11 d_t / 12$. Substituting in eqn (2.17):

$$M_T = (\pi/16)\, d_t f_s \left(\frac{11}{12} d_t\right)^2 = 0 \cdot 165 f_s d_t^3$$

whence

$$d_t = \sqrt[3]{(6 \cdot 06\, M_T / f_s)} \qquad (2.19)$$

In the case of the hollow screw (Fig. 2.7) and the formulation leading to eqn (2.16) proceed as for a plain termination (i.e. no key) and make an allowance for the depth of the keyseat since otherwise the mathematics becomes involved.

PILLARS

In the process of *closing* down the valve, the pillars are subject to pure tension in both their screwed extremities; in the process of *opening*, the plain portions underneath the crosshead are subject to compression. The latter form of loading we can ignore since the middle portions of the pillars are

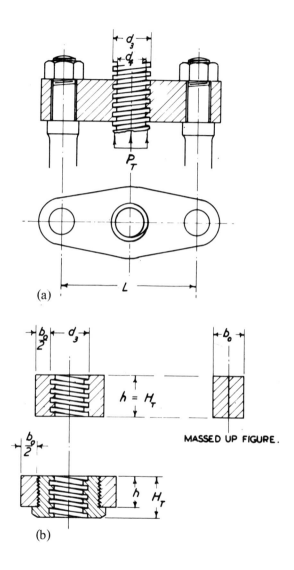

Fig. 2.13 *Screw down stop valve crosshead*

substantially larger in diameter than the screwed terminations and, therefore, amply strong.

It is advisable, therefore, to so proportion the upper extremities to cater for the tensile forces imposed and to make the lower extremities a shade heavier in order to cater for any bending stresses which might be imposed in tugging at the handwheel.

The tensile force to be resisted by each pillar extremity is $P_T/2$.

If a_c = core area of each upper screwed extremity, and

f_t the allowable stress in the material of the pillar, then

$$a_c f_t = P_T/2$$

or

$$a_c = P_T/2f_t \qquad (2.20)$$

from which an appropriate size of screwed extremity may be determined, using any tables relating to the preferred form of thread—BSW, BSF, ISO-metric, for example. It is recommended that a pillar termination of 5/8 in (16 mm) should be regarded as minimal.

CROSSHEAD

This item will be subjected to bending and shearing forces under the influence of the maximum axial force P_T centrally applied, the crosshead being supported by the two pillars.

Strictly speaking, the loading is not applied at the geometrical centre of the 'beam' but along a periphery denoted by the outside diameter d_3 of the actuating spindle threads (Fig. 2.13 (a)), or even further away if the crosshead is bushed (as in Fig. 2.13 (b)).

Since the beam is neither 'simply supported' nor '*encastré*' and the loading is not truly centrally applied, it is customary in applying the beam theory to adopt a modified bending moment M of $P_T L/5$ (as distinct from $P_T L/4$ for ideal loading, simply supported).

Hence

$$M = fZ = P_T L/5 \qquad (2.21)$$

where Z is the section modulus, L the 'span', and f the stress in the remote 'fibres'. Therefore

$$Z = P_T L/5f \qquad (2.22)$$

Now Z for a solid rectangular section is $b_o h^2/6$ (see Fig. 2.13 (a)) where b_o is the effective width of the crosshead and h the depth. Then

$$b_o h^2/6 = P_T L/5f \qquad (2.23)$$

whence

$$b_o = 6 P_T L/5fh^2 \qquad (2.24)$$

Alternatively, one could determine h in terms of b_o, bearing in mind, however, that h is governed by the length of thread engagement that will give adequate bearing area having regard to the axial thrust it is called upon to sustain.

Let a_b denote the required bearing area, d_3 and d_4 the outside and root diameters respectively of the stem, H_t the length of thread engagement, p_s the true pitch of the screw threads, n the number of turns or threads contained in the desired length H_t, and p_b the allowable intensity of bearing pressure on the engaging surfaces of the screw threads, then:
very approximately,

Bearing area per turn, or pitch, of screw $= (\pi/4) \{d_3^2 - d_4^2\}$

Required bearing area

$a_b = $ load imposed/allowable bearing pressure $= P_T/p_b$

Therefore number of turns, or pitches is

$n = $ required bearing area/bearing area per pitch
$= a_b/(\pi/4) \{d_3^2 - d_4^2\}$
$= 4P_T/\pi p_b \{d_3^2 - d_4^2\} \qquad (2.25)$

whence

$$H_T = np_s \qquad (2.26)$$

A value of $p_b = 1000$ lb/in^2, or 7 N/mm^2, is recommended. Any value of H_T less than $1\cdot5d_3$ should be rejected.

Note that H_T is the length of thread engagement whether a plain or bushed crosshead be employed. If the latter, then the effective depth h of the crosshead will be H_t *minus* the thickness of the flange on the bush. To allow for wear due to repeated manipulation, a value for H_T of $d_3 + \frac{1}{4}$ in (or 6 mm) should be regarded as minimal. Obviously, if eqn (2.26) was rigorously obeyed in the case of a valve requiring a small amount of axial force in its operation, the resulting value of H_T would work out absurdly small.

Equation (2.24) may now be exploited to determine b_o, bearing in mind that the *total* width will be $b_o + d_3$.

STUFFING BOX AND GLAND

Screw-down globe and junction stop valves are rarely called for (or advocated) in the very large sizes for steam service at pressures much in excess of 250 lbf/in² (1·72 N/mm²). Smaller valves, however, especially of forged steel construction, are currently employed for much higher pressures.

For stems up to 1 in diameter (25 mm) the two bolt/stud oval gland featured in Fig. 2.5(a) will suffice; thereafter the three bolt/stud circular gland shown in Fig. 2.5(b) is invariably preferred.

Consider the two-bolt stud form of 'oval' one-piece gland and attendant stuffing box in Fig. 2.5(a).

It is suggested that the length l_g of the annular projection of the gland entering the stuffing box be made $2\frac{1}{2}w_s$ to $3\frac{1}{2}w_s$. In order to determine the requisite size of the studs it is reasonable to assume that *at least* they could be called upon to sustain an upthrust U_p occasioned by the line pressure p acting on the packing annulus bounded by D_s and d_s:

$$U_p = (\pi/4)\, p\, (D_s^2 - d_s^2) \qquad (2.27)$$

In addition, there would be the 'drag' of the packing on the surface of the stem, and this will be taken into account in due course.

Nothing would appear to be more open to speculation in valve design than the proportioning of the stuffing box and its gland. If the 'box' is shallow in depth (more often in a bid to economize in packing material than in overall height), then the chances are that the packing will lack that degree of resilience so essential to creating a wiping action on the stem, and inevitably the valve will prove stiff in operation and possibly the stem will be prematurely scored and leakage will result.

Various empirical relationships between stem diameter, width of packing annulus w_s and its depth l_s have been formulated by various authorities (originally prompted by the needs of the steam engine) and most of which yield results on the high side for the near-static stems of screw-down and other valves.

The following empirical rule is recommended for determining the width w_s

of the packing annulus where d_s is the diameter of the stem and where steam is the intended working medium (see Fig. 2.5 (a) and (b)):

$$w_s = d_s/8 + 3/16 \text{ in } (5 \text{ mm})\qquad(2.28)$$

This value of w_s should be taken to the nearest 1/16 in or 1 mm upwards.

The depth of the packing l_s should vary according to the working pressure:

$l_s = 4w_s$ for steam pressures up to 100 lbf/in² (0·70 N/mm²) (7 bar)

$\quad = 5w_s$ for steam pressures from 100 to 250 lbf/in² (0·70 to 1·75 N/mm²) (7 to 17 bar)

$\quad = 6w_s$ for steam pressures from 250 to 500 lbf/in² (1·75 to 3·5 N/mm²) (17 to 34 bar)

We have seen (eqn 2.5) that this 'drag' $P_f = \pi \mu_s d_s l_s p$

Combining these two expressions we have:

Total load U_T to be shared by the two studs will be

$$\begin{aligned}
U_T &= U_p + P_f \\
&= (\pi p/4)\{D_s^2 - d_s^2\} + \pi \mu_s d_s l_s p \\
&= (\pi p/4)(\{D_s^2 - d_s^2\} + 4\mu_s d_s l_s)
\end{aligned}\qquad(2.29)$$

and load per stud, say U_1:

$$U_1 = (\pi p/8)\{D_s^2 - d_s^2\} + 4\mu_s d_s l_s\qquad(2.30)$$

It must be remembered that the foregoing applies only to a two-stud gland, the number commonly employed on stems up to, say, 1 in (25 mm) diameter; thereafter three or four studs (or bolts) are necessary.

A suitable size of stud may be selected from Appendix N, appropriate to the calculated value of U_1 above.

Adjustments will require to be made if the stud is of a material other than the steels given in the Appendix. For example, for marine service, phosphor-bronze studs are often demanded because of their enhanced resistance to corrosion in a salt-laden atmosphere or even to the sea-water itself!

The thickness of the gland plate may now be determined.

Reverting to Fig. 2.5(a) the plate will be subjected to a bending moment due to the force imparted by the studs, the maximum intensity of which will occur at the plane marked abcd in the plan and in the projected view alongside.

Let M_g denote this maximum bending moment,

$$M_g = U_{1g}$$

Denoting the sectional modulus of the section at the plane abcd by Z_s we have:

$$Z_s = b_g t_g^2 / 6$$

and, since $M_g = f Z_s$ where f is the stress induced in the remotest fibres,

$$U_{1g} = f b_g t_g^2 / 6$$

or

$$f = 6 U_{1g} / b_g t_g^2 \qquad (2.31)$$

or

$$t_g = \sqrt{(6 U_{1g} / f b_g)} \qquad (2.32)$$

An appropriate value for f may be taken from Appendix J or K.

With regard to the three-bolt gland (Figs. 2.3 and 2.5 (b)) previously advocated for stems in excess of 1 in diameter, the proportions of the stuffing box itself may be as for a two-bolt gland, as also the length l_g of the annular projection entering the box.

By similar reasoning to that for the two-bolt gland, the load to be resisted by *each* stud will be two-thirds that which would require to be resisted if two studs were used or

$$U_1' = (\pi/12) p \{D_2^2 - d^2\} + 4\mu_s d_s l_s \qquad (2.33)$$

To determine the thickness of the plate t_g by analytical means would be futile since the exact line of fracture would be difficult to forecast.

Resort is made, therefore, to empiricism and the proportions in Fig. 2.5(b) are the very embodiment of successful practice.

BODY CONFIGURATIONS

We have seen (Figs. 2.1 and 2.2) that the screw-down stop valve may be of two types, the *globe* and the *junction* pattern. The globe pattern might be more aptly described as the *lemon* pattern, since the bodies generally more closely conform to this shape than to an orange for reasons which will be more apparent when the flowpath through the body of a globe valve is examined in close detail.

Taking first of all the globe pattern body, it is essential that the area presented to flow at the throat portions (see Fig. 2.14) should be at least equal to that presented by the bore of the valve or pipe, preferably more so in order to compensate for frictional resistance. The design work necessary to achieve this gives rise to an intricate problem in solid geometry; space does not allow an outline of the solution*.

In the interests of moulding, the chest thickness t_s will be constant throughout the casting, and the weakest part of the shell will be on a transverse vertical plane passing through the mid-point O of the bottom of the body (Fig. 2.14).

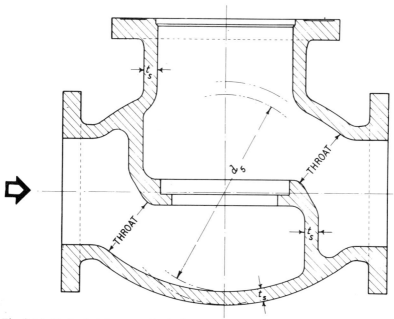

Fig. 2.14 *Typical globe stop valve body*

*PEARSON, G. H., *The Design of Valves and Fittings*, 1953, pp. 48–51, (Pitman, London)

The section at this point may be regarded as a transverse section through a circular cylinder, although it is interrupted by the vertical neck of the body. This will be ignored and an unbroken cylindrical section assumed.

Adopting the well-known thin cylinder formula (really applicable only where the diameter is very large in comparison with the shell thickness), and adding a constant to bring it into line with practical requirements, mainly those of moulding, we have:

$$t_s = (p d_s / 2f) + C \qquad (2.34)$$

where t_s = shell thickness

p = working pressure

d_s = internal diameter of body at largest point

f = maximum allowable working stress

C = a constant 5/16 in (8·0 mm) for cast iron, 1/4 in (6·5 mm) for cast steel, 1/8 in (3·3 mm) for gunmetal

As an additional check the designer is advised to compare the results obtained by eqn (2.34) with those derived from Lamé's well-known formula for thick cylinders and from the empirical formula prescribed under the Indian Boiler Regulations, taking note of the difference in nomenclature adopted in the case of the latter (thicknesses in thirtyseconds of an inch).

Lamé's formula:

$$t_1 = \frac{d_s}{2} \sqrt{\left(\frac{f+p}{f-p} \right) - 1} \qquad (2.35)$$

where t_1 = shell thickness

p = working pressure

d_s = diameter of body (as above)

f = maximum allowable working stress.

Indian Boiler Regulations:

$$t_{32} = \frac{p d_s}{C_i} + X \qquad (2.36)$$

where t_{32} = shell thickness in 1/32nds of an inch. p and d_s are as before (inch-lb units) and C_i and X are constants as outlined in the table on p. 40.

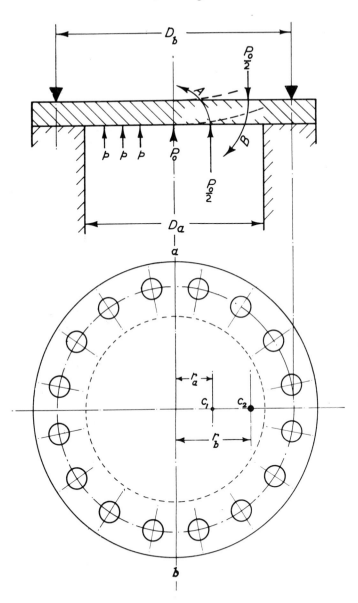

Fig. 2.15 *Forces acting on cover plate*

Casting Material	C_i	X
Cast Steel, 28–35 tonf/in² UTS (432–540 N/mm²)	400	8
Cast Iron, at least 9 tonf/in² UTS (139 N/mm²)	160	6
Bronze, at least 14 tonf/in² UTS (217 N/mm²)	175	4

Constants for use with Indian Boiler Regulations formula for shell thicknesses of valves

Equation (2.36) will apply equally well to the junction pattern valve body featured in Fig. 2.2, the shell thickness as before being based on the largest diameter of the body (d_s).

COVER FLANGES AND BOLTING

The proportioning of the cover flange provides an excellent example in 'flat plate' design and one which has intrigued many designers and engineers.

There is no simple formulation whereby the thickness appropriate to the diameter and the line pressure may be determined exactly since in a loaded cover plate as ordinarily constituted the degree of fixity cannot be accurately defined. In terms of beam theory, it is neither 'simply supported' nor 'encastré'. For purposes of design, however, it may be regarded as being 'simply supported' by the cover bolts. As a preliminary investigation the number and size of the securing bolts should be determined and this will enable the outside diameter of the plate to be established.

It can be shown that

$$P_n = p(A + a_f \eta_3)/n \qquad (2.37)$$

where n = number of bolts

p = line pressure

P_n = load to be imparted by *each* bolt to contain the line pressure

A = area of plate subjected to line pressure

a_f = area of joint face

η_3 = average unit contact pressure at joint face *divided by* internal pressure p appropriate to the mode of jointing adopted. Values of η_3 are given in Appendix M.

Having evaluated p_n a suitable diameter of bolt may be selected, according to the preferred grade of steel, from Appendix N.

The outside diameter of the cover plate may then be fixed.

DETERMINATION OF COVER PLATE THICKNESS

Assume the plate to be of uniform thickness t_c (see Fig. 2.15) and ignore the intrusion of the stuffing box which would unnecessarily complicate the problem. (The reader is referred to *The Design of Valves and Fittings*, 2nd Edition, in which Chapter 18 is wholly devoted to the subject of cover plate design, or to C. C. Pounder's *The Design of Flat Plates**.)

The underside of the plate is subjected to a uniform pressure of intensity p tending to lift it against the restraining influence of the bolts/studs. The bolts/studs collectively exert a downward thrust diagrammatically represented by the imaginary knife edges shown bearing upon the pitch circle D_b of the bolts/studs. (The image would be complete if the bolts were replaced by a circular ring of V-section.)

Let P_o = the total load acting on the whole of the exposed surface whose diameter is D_a

$$= (\pi/4) \, D_a^2 p$$

Take moments about any diameter ab and consider one half of the plate, the one to the right of ab. The force acting on half the plate will be $P_o/2$ and it can be supposed to be concentrated at the centroid of the semi-circular area distant r_a from ab where $r_a = 0.2122 D_a$.

Now this force $P_o/2$ will tend to 'rotate' the half plate in an anticlockwise direction (as indicated by the inwardly and upwardly curved arrow A) and to produce curvature in the plate shown exaggeratedly by the dotted lines in the sectional elevation. Then, anticlockwise moment M_A due to line pressure is given by

$$M_a = \frac{P_o}{2} \times \tau_a$$

$$= \frac{P_o}{2} \times 0.2122 D_a$$

The expression M_a is best left in this form, meanwhile, for better understanding.

If the force exerted by the bolts/studs exactly matched the upward force due to the line pressure, then the effect would be to produce bending of the plate in the reverse direction (see inwardly and downwardly curved arrow

*POUNDER, C. C., *The Design of Flat Plates*, 1919 (DATA, Richmond, Surrey)

B). Again if we consider one half of the plate, then the restraining force of the bolts/studs will be $P_o/2$ and this can be supposed to be concentrated at the centroid of the half circumference of the pitch circle distant r_b from ab where $r_b = 0.3183D_b$. Then, clockwise restraining moment M_b due to bolts/studs is given by

$$M_b = \frac{P_o}{2} \times r_b$$

$$= \frac{P_o}{2} \times 0.3183D_b$$

Again, the expression for M_b is best left in this form.

The average bending moment Mv across the plane ab will be the algebraic sum of the moments acting to the right (or left, for that matter) of the plane, i.e.

$$M_v = M_b - M_a$$
$$= 0.3183D_b P_o/2 - 0.2122D_a P_o/2$$
$$= P_o(0.3183D_b - 0.2122D_a)/2 \qquad (2.38)$$

Now from 'beam' theory,

$$M/I = f/y \text{ or } M = fI/y = fZ$$

where $Z = I/y =$ the section modulus

$M =$ the bending moment

$I =$ the second moment of area (often styled moment of inertia)

$f =$ the skin stress in the plate

$y =$ the distance from the neutral axis of the section to the outermost 'fibres'

$= t_c/2$ in the case considered.

Now for a plate or beam of uniform thickness

$$Z = bd^2/6$$

where b is the breadth and d the depth.

Then

$$f = M/Z$$

$$= \frac{P_o(0 \cdot 3183 D_b - 0 \cdot 2122 D_a)/2}{D_b t_c^2/6}$$

$$= \frac{3P_o}{D_b t_c^2}(0 \cdot 3183 D_b - 0 \cdot 2122 D_a) \tag{2.39}$$

but $P = (\pi/4) p D_a^2$ and therefore

$$f = \frac{3 \pi p D_a^2}{4 D_b t_c^2} (0 \cdot 3183 D_b - 0 \cdot 2122 D_a) \tag{2.40}$$

As we have assumed the plate to be 'simply supported', D_a and D_b should be equal in order to comply with the definition. Then

$$\text{Average stress } f = \frac{3 \pi p D_a}{4 t_c^2} (0 \cdot 1061 D_a) \tag{2.41}$$

$$= 0 \cdot 25 p D_a^2 / t_c^2 \tag{2.42}$$

But it was found that the maximum stress f_m occurs at the centre of a uniformly loaded symmetrical flat plate and is equal to $1 \cdot 25$ times the average stress; hence we may rewrite (2.41) thus:

$$f_m = 0 \cdot 3125 p D_a^2 / t_c^2 = 5 p D_a^2 / 16 t_c^2 \tag{2.43}$$

Transposing:

$$t_c = D_a \sqrt{(5p/16 f_m)}$$

$$= \frac{D_a}{4} \sqrt{(5p/f_m)} \tag{2.44}$$

Practical considerations decree that a constant be added to this expression to satisfy casting requirements:

$$t_c = \frac{D_a}{4} \sqrt{(5p/f_m)} + C \tag{2.45}$$

when it is suggested that

$C = 1/4$ in ($6 \cdot 5$ mm) for cast iron

$= 1/8$ in (4 mm) for gunmetal and cast steel.

Since we have assumed that D_a and D_b are equal, eqn (2.45) can only be regarded as a very close approximation and the addition of the constant C makes it empirical. Since in practice D_a and D_b are not coincidental it would be advisable in any calculations to adopt a mean diameter, say

$$D_m = (D_a + D_b)/2$$

in which event we may rewrite eqn (2.45) thus:

$$t_c = \frac{D_m}{4}\sqrt{(5p/f_m)} + C \tag{2.46}$$

The thickness adopted should not be less than that of the pipe connecting flanges, if only for the sake of appearance.

There would appear to be no further aspects of design calling for detailed examination for a valve so simple in concept and so it is fitting to conclude the present chapter with a worked example.

WORKED EXAMPLE

Determine the essential characteristics of a 150 mm diameter Screw-down Junction Stop Valve suitable for a working saturated steam pressure of 1 N/mm^2. The design should favour the two piece type of stem, both the upper and lower portions being of gunmetal. Adopt flat faced seating faces.

Solution

Seating. For this pressure and corresponding temperature the body and cover may be of cast iron and the seating and valve-member of good quality gunmetal.

We have seen from eqn (2.1) that the width of contact w of the seating face is given by:

$$w = pd_o/4 \ (u - 2p)$$

where p = working pressure

d_o = *outside* diameter of seating face

u = allowable unit contact clamping pressure

Throughout these calculations SI notation will apply.

Take d_o to be 160 mm and from Appendix L, $u = 13\cdot7$ N/mm^2 for gunmetal. Then

$$w = (1 \times 160)/4(13\cdot7 - 2 \times 1) = 160/(4 \times 11\cdot7) = 3\cdot41 \text{ mm}$$

Axial force to close valve From eqn (2.2) the *total* axial force to be imparted by the stem is given by

$$P_T = P_o + P_c + p_f$$

where P_o = upthrust on underside of valve member due to line pressure

P_c = clamping force at the seating

P_f = frictional resistance of stem in packing.

For better understanding these three forces will be determined separately rather than by the combined formula given in eqn (2.6).

From eqn (2.3), the force to resist the upthrust:

$$P_o = (\pi/4)\, d_o^2 p = (\pi/4) \times (160)^2 \times 1 \text{ N}$$
$$= 20\ 100 \text{ N}$$

and from eqn (2.4), clamping force at seating:

$$P_c = 2\pi d_o w p = 2 \times 3\cdot142 \times 160 \times 3\cdot41 \times 1$$
$$= 3\cdot430 \text{ N}$$

and from eqn (2.5), force to overcome embrace of packing on stem:

$$P_f = \pi \mu_s\, d_s\, l_s p$$

where d_s = stem diameter at stuffing box.

Before this expression can be evaluated we need to assign values both to μ_s, the coefficient of friction between the packing and the stem, and to l_s, the length of contact of the packing. We have seen (eqn 2.28) that the annular width w_s of the packing is given by:

$$w_s = \frac{d_s}{8} + 5 \quad \text{mm}$$

but we have yet to determine d_s by calculation. At this stage, d_s will have to be assumed, later checked for validity and adjustments made accordingly.

Assume $d_s = 32$ mm, then

$$w_s = 32/8 + 5 = 9 \text{ mm}$$

Also assume length of contact l_s of packing is five times w_s or

$$l_s = 5 \times 9 = 45 \text{ mm}$$

We can then proceed to evaluate P_f.
Assume $\mu_s = 0\cdot15$

$$P_f = 3\cdot142 \times 0\cdot15 \times 32 \times 45 \times 1 = 678\cdot5 \text{ N}$$

Total axial force required:

$$P_T = P_o + P_c + P_f$$
$$= 20\,100 + 3\,430 + 678\cdot5$$
$$= 24\,208\cdot5 \text{ N}$$
$$\text{say } 24\,208 \text{ N}$$

Stem diameter. Let us now determine the least diameter of the lower stem from consideration of the approximate force P_T imposed. Take the allowable direct compressive stress $f_c = 60$ N/mm². From eqn (2.7b)

$$d_s = \sqrt{\{P_T/(0\cdot535 \times f_c)\}} + 12\cdot5/\sqrt{d_o}$$
$$= \sqrt{\{24\,208/(0\cdot535 \times 60)\}} + 12\cdot5/\sqrt{160}$$
$$= 27\cdot46 + 0\cdot98$$
$$= 28\cdot44 \text{ mm, say } 30 \text{ mm}$$

which is very close to the figure originally assumed, so no adjustments to the calculations so far would appear justifiable.

Actuating screw. From eqn (2.8b)

Minimum root diameter $d_r = \sqrt{(4P_T/\pi f_c)} + 12\cdot5/\sqrt{d_o}$
$$= \sqrt{\{(4 \times 24\,208)/(3\cdot142 \times 60)\}} + 12\cdot5/\sqrt{160}$$
$$= 23\cdot65 \text{ mm}$$

This would suffice from a strength point of view but this is not the sole criterion of design. We must select a combination of mean diameter and pitch that will yield an acceptable Mechanical Advantage.
Assume a mean diameter d_m of 35 mm.

Diameter of handwheel. Adopting square threads, 5 mm pitch (single start), the next step is to determine the *mechanical efficiency* of the screw, having regard to the dimensional characteristics and the materials in engagement and the probable extent of lubrication of the engaging surfaces.

From eqn (2.12a)

Efficiency $\eta_1 = \tan a / \tan(a' + \varphi')$

$\tan a' = p_T / \pi d_m$

$\qquad = 5/(3 \cdot 142 \times 35) = 0 \cdot 0455$

whence, from trigonometrical tables,

$$a' = 2° 36'$$

Also the friction angle φ' is determined from the relation $\tan \varphi' = \mu$, the coefficient of friction of the screw elements. For gunmetal on mild steel (the usual combination) μ may be taken as $0 \cdot 15$, then:

$$\tan \varphi' = 0 \cdot 15$$

whence again from trigonometrical tables $\varphi = 8° 32'$.

Then from eqn (2.12a)

Efficiency $\eta_1 = \tan 2° 36' / \tan(2° 36' + 8° 32')$

$\qquad = \tan 2° 36' / \tan 11° 8'$

$\qquad = 0 \cdot 0455 / 0 \cdot 1967$

$\qquad = 0 \cdot 2313$ (or $23 \cdot 13\%$)

This is an obvious agreement with the value derived from the curves in Appendix Q.

From eqn (2.11)

Diameter of handwheel $H_w = P_T p_t / \pi \tau \eta$

Assuming a man can exert a net tangential effort at the rim of a handwheel of medium proportions of 350 N (80 lbf), intermittently applied (as has been proved experimentally), then:

$H_w = (24\ 208 \times 5)/(3 \cdot 142 \times 350 \times 0 \cdot 2313) = 475$ mm (say $18\frac{1}{2}$ in)

The tentatively assumed mean diameter of the screw of 35 mm would appear to have been justified.

Actuating screw termination. Taking the net manual effort applied to the handwheel as 350 N, then

$$\text{Twisting moment } M_T = \tau H_w = (350 \times 475)/100 \text{ Nm}$$
$$= 167 \text{ Nm}$$

whence, from eqn (2.15), and taking f_s to be 55 N/mm²

$$\text{Diameter of stem termination } d_t = \sqrt[3]{(16 M_T/\pi f_s)}$$
$$= \sqrt[3]{\{(16 \times 167 \times 1\,000)/(3 \cdot 142 + 55)\}}$$
$$= 23 \cdot 07 \text{ mm, say 23 mm}$$

Now this would be the diameter of a *plain* termination, with no fastening device; consequently, the diameter as calculated above must be increased in order to compensate for the weakening effect of the keyseat.

From eqn (2.19), substituting known values:

$$d_t = \sqrt[3]{\{(6 \cdot 06 \times 167 \times 1\,000)/55\}}$$
$$= 26 \cdot 4 \text{ mm}$$

There would be no point in machining down the termination to this diameter when the root diameter of the threads selected is $35 - 5/2$ mm = $32 \cdot 5$ mm. The termination recommended, therefore, would be 30 mm diameter leaving a 'landing' of $(32 \cdot 5 - 30)/2 = 1 \cdot 25$ mm.

Pillars. From eqn (2.20) the core area of each upper extremity is given by

$$a_c = P_T/2f_t$$

Take $f_t = 45$ N/mm².

Substituting known values,

$$a_c = 24\,208/(2 \times 45) = 269 \text{ mm}^2$$

where root diameter

$$d_{rp} = \sqrt{(269/0 \cdot 785)} = 18 \cdot 5 \text{ mm}$$

Adopt 20 mm diameter termination. The screwed-in base terminations should be 4 mm in excess of the upper terminations to cater for some amount of bending stresses induced by pulling upon the handwheel.

Crosshead. We will assume that the actuating screw engages with a screw cut into the crosshead, i.e. no bush (Fig. 2.13 (a)). The depth h will depend upon the length of thread engagement to give adequate bearing area and this will be determined from eqn (2.25) and eqn (2.26).

Firstly, from eqn (2.25)

$$\text{Number of turns (or pitches) } n = 4P_T/\pi p_b (d_3^2 - d_4^2)$$

Adopting an average value for the allowable bearing pressure p_b of 7·5 N/mm^2 for gunmetal on steel, $d_3 = 36$ mm, $d_4 = 33$ mm, we have

$$n = (4 \times 24\,208)/\{3 \cdot 142 \times 7 \cdot 5 \times (36^2 - 33^2)\}$$
$$= 19 \cdot 86$$

and from eqn (2.26)

$$H_T = np_o = 19 \cdot 86 \times 2 \text{ mm} = 39 \cdot 72 \text{ mm say } 40 \text{ mm}$$

Since there is no bush, because the actuating screw is screwed directly into the crosshead, the depth of the crosshead $h = H_T = 40$ mm.

We may now revert to eqn (2.24) in order to determine the effective width b_o of the crosshead:

$$b_o = 6P_T L/5fh^2$$

It is assumed at this stage that design has proceeded sufficiently to enable the span L to be decided, say 170 mm. Take the allowable tensile stress f_t for mild steel as 70 N/mm^2, then

$$b_o = (6 \times 24\,208 \times 170)/(5 \times 70 \times 40^2) = 44 \cdot 1 \text{ mm, say } 44 \text{ mm}$$

Then, *total* width of crosshead $= d_3 + b_o = 36 + 44 = 80$ mm

Stuffing box and gland. From eqn (2.28) the annular width of the packing space w_s is given by

$$w_s = d_s/8 + 5 \text{ mm}$$

Substituting known values:

$$w_s = 30/8 + 5 = 8 \cdot 75 \text{ mm, say } 9 \text{ mm}$$

Therefore, diameter of stuffing box

$$D_s = d_s + 2w_s = 30 + 2 \times 9 = 48 \text{ mm}$$

and from the recommendations which followed, the depth of the box

$$l_s = 5w_s = 5 \times 9 = 45 \text{ mm}$$

Gland bolts or studs. From eqn (2.30), the load per bolt or stud (for a two-bolt gland) is

$$U_1 = (\pi/8) \, p \, \{(D_s^2 - d_s^2) + 4\mu_s d_s l_s\}$$

Substituting known values:

$$U_1 = (3 \cdot 142/8) \times 1 \times \{(48^2 - 30^2) + 4 \times 0 \cdot 15 \times 30 \times 45\}$$
$$= 871 \text{ N}$$

From Appendix N, an M12 ISO metric (or a 1/2 in BSW) bolt or stud of 430 N/mm² (or 28 tons) UTS respectively would be suitable.

Thickness of gland plate. Before eqn (2.32) can be exploited, the plan view configurations of the gland will require to be established and also the appropriate width of the relevant section, together with the dimension *g* scaled off the drawing.

Body configurations. The maximum internal chest diameter in a correctly designed junction stop valve body will be the diameter near to the valve member, since the body requires to 'bulge' at this point in order to provide a sufficient annular area to the passage of the working medium when the valve is opened up. It is customary to make this annular area equal to that of the bore and this errs, to some advantage, on the high side since there is quite an appreciable escape area presented in the vicinity of the outlet branch.

In this example, the internal diameter of the chest works out at 235 mm. From eqn (2.34)

Shell thickness $t_s = (pd_s/2f) + C$

Take allowable stress *f* as 38 N/mm² (from Appendix K) for cast iron. Then

$$t_s = (1 \times 235)/(2 \times 38) + 8 = 11 \cdot 09 \text{ mm, say } 12\text{mm}$$

Let us see how this result compares with that derived from the Indian Boiler Regulations empirical formula given in eqn (2.36). We must at this point revert to Imperial units; the working pressure *p* will be 145 lbf/in² and the shell diameter d_s will resolve into $235/25 \cdot 4$ in or $9 \cdot 25$ in.

$$t_{32} = (p d_s / C_i) + X$$
$$= (145 \times 9 \cdot 25)/160 + 6$$
$$= 8 \cdot 4 + 6$$
$$= 14 \cdot 4/32 \text{ in or } 0 \cdot 45 \text{ in}$$

which is in close agreement with the previous calculation, namely

$$0 \cdot 45 \times 25 \cdot 4 = 11 \cdot 43 \text{ mm}$$

Cover flanges and bolting. The first essential is to determine the number and size of the bolts securing the cover plate to the body. Experience suggests that eight bolts be adopted in a valve of this size; then from eqn (2.37) the load p_n to be imparted by each bolt is given by:

$$P_n = p(A + a_f \eta_3)/n$$

But before proceeding, some clarification of the terms A = the area of the plate subjected to the line pressure, and a_f = the area of the joint face, is desirable. The area A is taken to be that of an imaginary disc dropped *inside* the bolts and just touching them; in short, the area of a cricle whose diameter is equal to the pitch circle *minus* the diameter of one bolt.

In our case the pitch circle works out at 254 mm.

Tentatively assume 16 mm diameter bolts (these may be checked later for size); then the area A subject to the line pressure will be that of a circle 254 $- 16 = 238$ mm in diameter, the area of which is 44 500 mm^2 or 445 cm^2 approximately.

Now the area of the joint face a_f is the area of the annulus bounded on the outside by the inside of the bolts and on the inside by the spigot, in this case 238 mm and 190 mm respectively, or

$$a_f = (\pi/4) (238^2 - 190^2) = 16 \; 135 \text{ mm}^2 \text{ or } 161 \cdot 35 \text{ cm}^2$$

say 160 cm^2 for purposes of design. Note that n_3 for graphited sheet asbestos (recommended in the present case) is $0 \cdot 26$, from Appendix M.

$$P_n = (44 \; 500 + 160 \times 0 \cdot 26)/8$$
$$= 5 \; 567 \text{ N}$$

Adopting bolts of 430 N/mm^2 UTS, the 16 mm diameter bolts tentatively assumed would be inadequate, whereas 20 mm would be acceptable but there is every justification for adopting the lower size but of steel of higher UTS.

Proceeding, the thickness t_c of the cover plate (taking it to be a simple flat plate) may now be determined:

From eqn (2.46) we have

$$t_c = \frac{D_m}{4} \sqrt{(5p/f_m)} + C$$

Now

$$D_m = (D_a + D_b)/2 = (184 + 254)/2 = 219 \text{ mm}$$

We have seen that C is equal to 6·5 mm for cast iron.

Take f_m, the maximum allowable stress, as 19 N/mm² for cast iron, then:

$$t_c = \frac{219}{4} \sqrt{\{(5 \times 1)/19\}} + 6·5$$

$$= 34·6 \text{ mm}$$

Chapter 3
Wedge-Gate Sluice Valves

THE invention of the wedge-gate sluice valve by James Nasmyth in 1839 ranks in importance with that of the taper plug cock, whose origin is lost in antiquity. History records that the wedge-gate valve of Nasmyth was inspired by the shortcomings of certain waterworks cocks reported to him in the hope that he could devise a more reliable alternative.

Both these fluid control devices share the common feature, however, of relying on a wedging action between the mutually contacting seating surfaces to effect a seal. One surface is a flat plane, the other conical or circumferential, and both have withstood the test of time yet have been regularly modified in their detailed design and materials of construction.

In the following only the wedge-gate sluice valve will command our attention.

An examination of such a valve as the simple one in Fig. 3.1 will reveal that simultaneous closure-tightness of the *two* seating faces may be achieved, which makes for double security against leakage, a commendable virtue and one which certainly appealed to James Nasmyth.

Dual closure-tightness can be secured *only* if

(*a*) the angularity of both wedge and body seating faces are coincidental and both these faces are coplanar transversely;

(*b*) the axially applied closure force imparted by the stem (spindle) is of *more* than sufficient intensity to overcome not only the force imparted to the wedge (and thence to the downstream face) by the line pressure, but also that of the frictional resistance to sliding of the wedge-gate over the seatings;

(*c*) the seating faces themselves are in pristine condition, i.e. well lapped-in.

Simultaneous closure-tightness of the two opposing seating faces is not an absolute essential for a valve of this type. On the contrary, so long as one face is adequately preventing flow taking place the valve is a 'stopper' in the strict sense of the word. At all events the screw-down stop valve and the

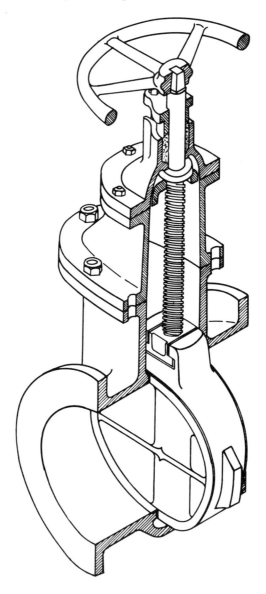

Fig. 3.1 *Wedge-gate sluice valve, a typical arrangement. Inside screw pattern*

parallel slide valve (spring disk type) rely for their closure-tightness on *one* seating face only.

The possibility of securing dual closure-tightness is very much in the wedge-gate valve's favour, however, but in the following treatment it will be assumed that design conditions are fulfilled when closure-tightness is secured at the downstream seating faces only.

The behaviour of such a valve for varying conditions of installation will now be examined in detail and followed by a worked example relative to a large bore wedge-gate valve.

Case I(a). Valve installed in vertical main (friction and weight of gate neglected)

The mechanics of operation will be best understood first by considering the valve to be installed in a vertical pipe-line with the line pressure acting down-wardly on the top face of the gate, as shown in Fig. 3.2(a).

This is not the most favoured method of installation, but often the most suitable.

Let $d =$ the diameter of the valve, or to be more precise, of the seating;

$p =$ the line pressure on the upstream side
(Note: the downstream pressure is assumed to be atmospheric for purposes of design);

$a =$ the angularity of each seating face with respect to the centre line of the stem or that of the body in a direction at right angles to the bore.

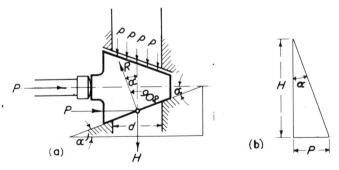

(a)   (b)

Fig. 3.2 *Case I(a) Valve in vertical main; pressure on top side; friction and weight of gate neglected*

Now the downwardly acting force on the gate imposed by the line pressure will be determined by the product of the line pressure and the transverse cross-sectional area of the seating of diameter d. This force may be regarded as a single collective force H (see Fig. 3.2 (a))* assumed concentrated at point 0, where

$$H = (\pi/4) d^2 p \qquad (3.1)$$

It must be remembered that we have ignored the weight of the gate and its frictional resistance to sliding.

It is required to move the gate from left to right in order to close the valve through the influence of a horizontal force P to be imparted by the stem. If there were no frictional resistance between the two seating contacting surfaces (an impossibility, of course), the downwardly acting vertical force H and the horizontally acting force P would be jointly counteracted by a resultant reactionary force R acting in a direction normal to the seating faces.

This is best illustrated by reference to the triangle of forces diagram, Fig. 3.2 (b).

Then, neglecting friction and the weight of the gate, we have

$$P/H = \tan\alpha \qquad (3.2)$$

or

$$P = H \tan\alpha \qquad (3.3)$$

Case I(b). Valve installed in vertical main (friction considered)

Now consider the conditions portrayed in Fig. 3.3 (a). Because of the frictional resistance of the seating faces, the resultant force will not act in a direction *normal* to the seating faces but its line of action will now be deflected towards that of the axial force through some angle φ (the *friction angle*) such that $\tan\varphi = \mu$, where μ is the coefficient of friction for the contacting material and degree of 'lubrication' of the seatings.

As in Case I(a) we may now draw the triangle of forces for these conditions (Fig. 3.3 (b)), from which it will be seen that the axial force P

---

*In this force diagram—and subsequent similar ones—for better understanding the wedge angle a has been grossly exaggerated. Almost invariably it will be found that the friction angle φ will be very much in excess of the wedge angle

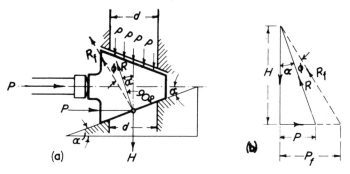

Fig. 3.3 *Case I(b) Valve in vertical main; pressure on top side; friction considered: weight of gate neglected*

previously determined has now increased to some value P_f.

Obviously, $P_f - P$ will denote the *additional* axial force required just to overcome the frictional resistance of the seatings.

Proceeding as in Case I(a), from the triangle of forces in Fig. 3.3 (b), we now have:

$$P_f/H = \tan (\alpha + \varphi) \tag{3.4}$$

and

$$P_f = H \tan (\alpha + \varphi) \tag{3.5}$$

Case I(c). Valve installed in vertical main (friction and weight of gate considered)

Let W = weight of gate; then the total downwardly acting force directed on the 'downstream' face will be $H + W$ (see Fig. 3.4 (a)). The force diagram is as Fig. 3.4 (b) where P_f is the axial force to overcome force H, as in the previous example, and P_{fw} is now the axial force required to overcome the combined resistances imposed by the line pressure, the frictional resistance to sliding of the wedge-gate, and the weight of the wedge-gate.

Proceeding as before

$$P_{fw}/(H + W) = \tan (\alpha + \varphi) \tag{3.6}$$

or

$$P_{fw} = (H + W) \{\tan (\alpha + \varphi)\} \tag{3.7}$$

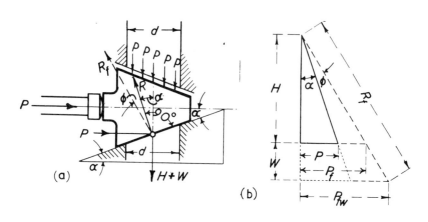

Fig. 3.4 Case I(c) Valve in vertical main; pressure on top side; friction and weight of gate considered

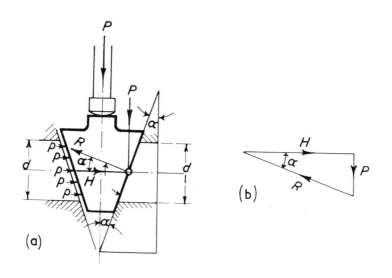

Fig. 3.5 Case II(a) Valve in horizontal main; pressure exerted horizontally; friction and weight of gate neglected

Case II(a). Valve installed in horizontal main (friction and weight of gate neglected)

Now consider the case of a wedge-gate valve installed in the more orthodox position, the axial force required to open or close it being applied vertically, upwardly or downwardly, according to whether the valve is being opened or closed. The line pressure will be taken as acting from left to right as portrayed in Fig. 3.5 (a).

Again the effect of the line pressure will be to urge the wedge-gate onto the downstream face.

The forces acting on the gate (remembering that we are neglecting frictional resistance and the mass effect of the gate meanwhile) will be shown in Fig. 3.5 (b) from which

$$P/H = \tan\alpha$$

or

$$P = H\tan\alpha \tag{3.8}$$

which is exactly what applies to a valve lying on its side. We may rightly conclude from this that, if we neglect frictional resistance and the mass

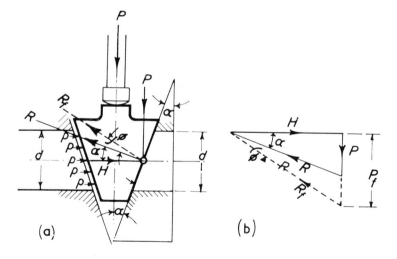

Fig. 3.6 *Case II(b) Valve in horizontal main; pressure exerted horizontally; friction considered*

effect of the gate and its attendant unrestrained parts (if any), the same expression will apply for *all* angular positions of the valve.

Case II(b). Valve installed in a horizontal main (friction considered)

Now consider the conditions portrayed in Fig. 3.6 (a). Again due to the frictional resistance of the seating faces, the line of action of the resultant force P_f will be deflected towards that of the applied axial force P as in Case I(b) and the appropriate modified force diagram (Fig. 3.6 (b)) constructed, whence:

$$P_f/H = \tan (\alpha + \varphi)$$
$$P_f = H \tan (\alpha + \varphi) \qquad (3.9)$$

which is exactly as determined for a valve installed in a vertical main (see eqn 3.5). Again we may conclude that this expression will apply whatever the positioning of the valve body.

The mass effect of the wedge-gate, etc, will break the sequence of coincidental formulae, however, as will now be seen.

Case II(c). Valve installed in a horizontal main (friction and weight of gate considered)

In this the last case to be considered, it will be seen that the mass effect of the wedge-gate acting downwardly will *assist* the closing process and *resist* the opening process.

Taking P_{fw} to denote the net axial force to seat the gate, having regard to the pressure loading, frictional resistance, and weight of wedge-gate, we might readily adopt a short cut by modifying eqn (3.9) to meet the present case.

The downwardly acting axial force required to close the valve against all three resistances and to *unseat* the wedge-gate is given by

$$P_{fw} = P_f - W = H \tan (\alpha + \varphi) - W \qquad (3.10)$$

Figs. 3.7 (a) and 3.7 (b) complete the sequence of force diagrams.

From the foregoing results, it will be seen that it makes very little difference to the closure force required whether the valve is installed on its side or in the more conventional upright position when all three factors of line pressure, frictional resistance and weight of moving parts are taken into account.

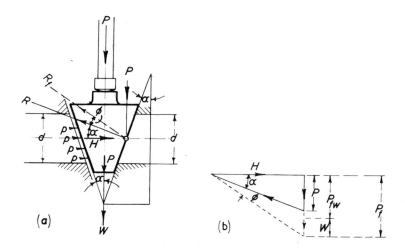

Fig. 3.7 *Case II(c) Valve in horizontal main; pressure exerted horizontally; friction and weight of gate considered*

Moreover, this force will only be required in the very final stages of closure. Meanwhile, in the preliminary winding-down process, the only purely axial force to be countered is that from the influence of the line pressure which is exerted on the unbalanced cross-sectional area of the stem where it passes through the stuffing box. Obviously, the line pressure will tend to force the spindle out of the valve (much in the manner of the rod of a steam engine), the only opposition being that of the atmospheric pressure acting in the opposite direction and exerted on the same cross-sectional area.

Denoting this force by P_s and the diameter of the stem at the point indicated by d_s we have

$$P_s = (\pi/4)pd_s^2 \qquad (3.11)$$

The other force to be overcome *at all stages* leading to closure is the frictional resistance of the stem in the embrace of the gland packing. This defies accurate determination since the extent to which the packing will be compressed cannot be forecast. If 'automatic' packings (see Fig. 3.8) were to be employed (and this is not usual in valves of this type), the frictional resistance could be predetermined with some degree of certainty, but in this

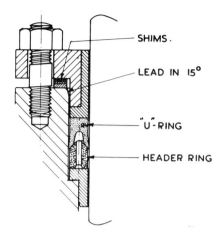

Fig. 3.8   *Typical automatic packing (Walker's Twinset packing)*

case such accuracy is scarcely warranted since the frictional resistance of such packings is so low as to be almost wholly negligible. The calculations, at best, can only yield approximate results because of the many uncertainties about the frictional properties of the materials employed, the degree of lubrication (if any) of the bearings, the lubricating effect of the working fluid on the seating faces, and to other incidental resistances of a minor nature. Allowance for these should be made instinctively in the final analysis, but some attempt to predict the effect of ordinary gland packing on the operating forces will be outlined later.

Reverting to eqn (3.11) the axial force P_s will be diminished by an amount W, the weight of the gate and its ancillaries, during the closing process with the valve arranged vertically (as in Figs 3.6 (a) and 3.6 (b)) and *increased* by the same amount in the opening process. It is conjectural, however, whether the actual force to effectively close the valve against all resistances will be comprised wholly of the two forces P and P_s acting simultaneously or whether the larger of the two will be the deciding force. It might be argued that at the instant of final closure (i.e. no fluid passing the gate) there can be no unbalanced upward force P_s to be countered. In the absence of experimental data to confirm or deny this, it is advisable to 'err' on the side of safety and to combine the two expressions:

Total axial force to effect complete closure

$$P_t = P + P_s \tag{3.12}$$

TORQUE REQUIRED TO EFFECT CLOSURE

Neglecting minor resistances, the total torque Q_T required to close the valve against the *designed* working pressure will be comprised of three separately calculated torques:

(a) that required to impart the *total* axial thrust P_T to force home the wedge-gate and to resist the unbalanced load P_s on the stem;

(b) that required to overcome the frictional resistance to rotation of the spindle collar (see Figs. 3.9 and 3.10);

(c) that required to overcome the resistance imposed by the grip of the gland packing on the stem.

These torques will be denoted by Q_a, Q_b and Q_c respectively and, for effective closure, will act in unison.

Dealing with these in the order named we have:

(a) (Considering one revolution of the handwheel)

Work done on screw = work done on handwheel

or

Total axial force on stem × pitch of screw = net manual effort
× circumference of handwheel × efficiency of screw

i.e.

$$P_T \times p_t = \tau \times \pi \times H_w \times \eta \qquad \text{(See Fig. 2.5)}$$

where P_T = total axial thrust as above,

p_t = true pitch (i.e. lead) of stem screw threads,

τ = net tangential manual effort applied to rim of handwheel,

η = efficiency of screw thread, expressed as a fraction of unity and *not* as a percentage.

Now

$$\text{Torque } Q_a = 2\left(\frac{\tau}{2} \times \frac{H_w}{2}\right) = \tau H_w/2$$

Then, by substitution and transposition,

$$P_T p_t = 2\pi Q_a \eta$$

whence

$$Q_a = P_T p_t / 2\pi\eta \qquad (3.13a)$$

If percentage values are inserted then

$$Q_a = 100 P_T p_t / 2\pi\eta \,\% \qquad (3.13b)$$

Values of η, the screw thread efficiency, may be determined from the graphs given in Appendixes P, Q, R or S or perhaps more accurately by calculation:

$$\eta = \tan\alpha / \tan(\alpha + \varphi)$$

where $\tan\alpha =$ pitch/mean circumference $= p_t / \pi d_m$
and

where d_m is the mean diameter of the screw threads.

The stem is subjected to a compressive force in the process of closing the valve down and to a tensile force during the opening process. It therefore qualifies as a strut, more especially so in the case of the larger valves where the unsupported length is appreciable, but other considerations mainly determine its diameter.

For example, it is most desirable that the screw threads conform to certain basic requirements; they should not be too steep or of too fine a pitch. If too steep, the valve will call for a far greater expenditure of manual effort (other things being equal); if too 'slow' the valve will be easier to operate but the process of opening and closing will call for too many turns of the handwheel.

The ideal relationship between *pitch* and *mean* diameter will invariably result in a stem well able to cater for the compressive forces imposed.

It is customary to adopt single start threads except in the very large valves.

(b) $Q_b = \mu_c P_T r_m$ (3.14)

where $\mu_c =$ coefficient of friction of collar materials in contact

      $r_m =$ mean radius of collar (in Fig. 3.9)

      $t_m =$ mean radius of collar (in Fig. 3.10)

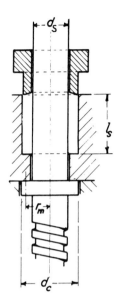

Fig. 3.9 *Inside screw valve*

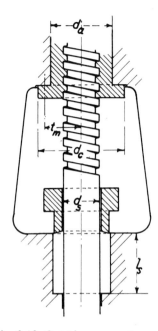

Fig. 3.10 *Outside screw valve*

Obviously

$$r_m = (d_s + d_c)/4 \qquad \text{in the case of the collar depicted in Fig. 3.9}$$

and

$$t_m = (d_a + d_c)/4 \qquad \text{in the case of the collar depicted in Fig. 3.10}$$

The two foregoing expressions for torque presuppose that certain quantities in the equations have already been established, eg the diameters of the stem, collar, etc. However, these cannot be determined precisely until the design has advanced. Certain tentative assumptions, based on experience, will need to be made at this stage, and the margin of error resulting from this will be narrowed down as and when further data is available.

For example, the diameter of the stem cannot be determined until we know what torque it will be required to transmit; the screwed portion is more or less determined through selecting the best possible compromise of mean diameter, slope and pitch of the threads rather than from the axial load it is required to carry; but almost invariably the correct combination of these three factors results in a stem whose proportions will adequately cater for the loads imposed.

Experience has shown that for square and acme threaded stems, often used on wedge-gate sluice valves, single start coarse threads are common, usually $\frac{1}{2}$ in pitch (12 mm) over a wide range of stem diameters. The lead angle a—usually about 7° in the smaller valves—becomes progressively smaller as the diameter of the stem increases.

(c) The extent of the encircling grip of the gland packing material on the stem depends almost entirely on how intensely the gland nuts are tightened down and to a lesser extent on the nature of the packing material. This material usually comprises a mixture of Indian hemp and a mineral grease in those valves destined for waterworks service. If the packing exerts a minimum pressure on the surface of the spindle, of intensity equal to that of the line pressure, the chances are that the line fluid would be just contained. It is most unlikely, however, that the extent of embrace of the packing will be constant throughout the entire length of stem in contact but we can assume the *average* minimum pressure to be equal to p at this stage. Therefore

Total grip of packing on stem = Unit pressure × Exposed area

$$= \pi d_s l_s p$$

If μ_s is the coefficient of friction between the packing and the stem then the tangential resistance to rotation of the stem is

$$T = \pi \mu_s d_s l_s p$$

and, therefore, the moment of friction is

$$Q_c = \pi \mu_s d_s l_s p d_s / 2 = (\pi/2) \mu_s l_s p d_s^2 \qquad (3.15)$$

This should be regarded as a minimal value and for purposes of design might be amended to give somewhat higher values by adopting the more empirical relationship

$$Q_c = 2 \mu_s l_s p d_s^2 \qquad (3.16)$$

For the type of packing previously mentioned and in conjunction with a polished gunmetal or steel stem, the coefficient of friction μ_s may be taken as 0·15.

We now have all the three 'ingredients' for evaluating the total torque Q_T to close the valve:

$$Q_T = Q_a + Q_b + Q_c \qquad (3.17)$$

The evaluation of Q_T now enables us to determine the size of handwheel required (or the proportions of reduction gearing in the case of geared valves) from consideration of the effort available for applying this torque. In the case of direct manually operated valves, it will be appreciated that it is essential to assume that the valve will be operated by one man only, as might easily be required should an emergency arise.

DIAMETER OF HANDWHEEL

We have seen (Fig. 2.9, p. 26) that the manual effort applied to the rim of a handwheel may be regarded as a combined push and a pull each of intensity $\tau/2$ where τ is the *net* effort applied. The common radius of application is $H_w/2$ where H_w is the effective diameter of the handwheel.

Then, the torque applied is

$$Q_T = 2\left(\frac{\tau}{2} \times \frac{H_w}{2}\right)$$
$$= \tau H_w/2$$

whence

$$H_w = 2Q_T/\tau \qquad (3.18)$$

Again, from considerations of the torque to be transmitted, we can determine the proportion of the stem termination to transmit this torque. The termination may take the form of a square, much favoured in waterworks practice as depicted at (a) in Fig. 3.11, or it may be truly cylindrical complete with key as at (b) in the same illustration. BS5163:1974 gives recommended dimensional details of squared terminations and for removable cast iron caps and socket keys for wedge-gate sluice valves 2 in to 600 mm bore inclusive.

It should be noted, however, that wedge-gate sluice valves are occasionally called for in sizes up to 1800 mm bore, in which event the size of squared termination in the larger sizes is a matter for calculation when no precedent exists.

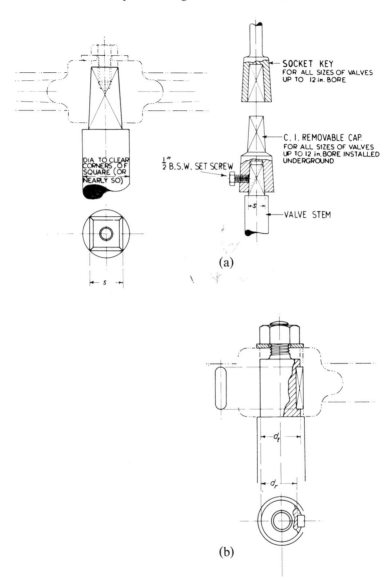

Fig. 3.11 *Square and circular stem terminations*

Now the polar modulus Z_t of a shaft of square section is given by $Z_t = 0·208s^3$ where s is the size of square (see Fig. 3.11 (a)). Taking this dimension to be that at the base of the taper since it would be more likely to shear at this point than at any other due to the abrupt change of section, and equating the moment of resistance to the torque applied, we have

$$Q_T = 0·208s^3 f_s \qquad (3.19)$$

whence

$$s = \sqrt{(Q_T/0·208 f_s)} \text{ or } s = \sqrt{(4·81 Q_T / f_s)} \qquad (3.20)$$

where f_s is the allowable shear stress in the material of the stem (see Tables J and K in the Appendix).

The polar modulus Z_t in the case of a truly cylindrical termination of diameter d_t is given by $Z_t = (\pi/16) d_t^3$ but this cannot be justifiably adopted because of the presence of the key for securing the stem to the handwheel, which produces a reduction in the value of the section modulus. This calls for some modification.

A reasonably valid approximation is to adopt a value for Z_t of $(\pi/16) d_t d_r^2$ where d_r is the distance from the bottom of the key or keyseat to the opposite edge of the stem termination (see Fig. 3.11 (b)). Then

$$Q_T = (\pi/16) d_t d_r^2 f_s \qquad (3.21)$$

whence

$$d_t = 16 Q_T / \pi d_r^2 f_s \qquad (3.22)$$

Inevitably this calls for some amount of trial and error calculations based on an assumed tentative value of d_r. Adopting BS* recommendations for the size of keys appropriate to varying shaft diameters it will be found on average that the depth of the keyseat is approximately one twelfth the diameter of the shaft, in which case d_r may be taken to be $11d_t/12$.

Substituting in eqn (3.21) we then have

$$Q_T = \frac{\pi}{16} d_t f_s \times \left(\frac{11}{12} d_t\right)^2$$
$$= \frac{\pi}{16} d_t f_s \times \frac{121}{144} d_t^2 = 0·165 f_s d_t^3$$

*BS46 Part I 1958. *Keys and Keyways*

whence

$$d_t = \sqrt[3]{(Q_T/0\cdot165f_s)} \tag{3.23}$$
$$= \sqrt[3]{(6\cdot06Q_T/f_s)} \tag{3.24}$$

It is recommended that the key securing the stem to the handwheel be of rectangular cross-section and preferably round-ended (BSK R-series), the actual section being selected from BS46 but the length is a matter for calculation having regard to the shearing force imposed.

Referring to Fig. 3.12, let F be the shearing force to be resisted by the key. Its point of application may be assumed to be at a distance $d_t/2$ from the axis of rotation (for all practical purposes).

We have seen from eqn (3.18) that the total torque $Q_T = \tau H_w/2$ where τ is the net effort applied to the handwheel and H_w is the effective diameter of the handwheel.

It follows, therefore, that

$$F = Q_T/\tfrac{1}{2}d_t = 2Q_T/d_t \tag{3.25}$$

Then equating the force applied to the moment of resistance to shear of key we have

$$F = l_k w_k f_s$$

whence the desired length is

$$l_k = F/w_k f_s = 2Q_T/d_t w_k f_s \tag{3.26}$$

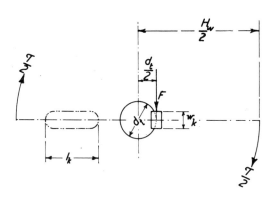

Fig. 3.12 *Force acting on key securing stem to handwheel*

BODY AND COVER CHEST THICKNESS

So far the 'dynamics' of valve design has been dealt with since we have been concerned with the behaviour and proportioning of the various moving parts.

We now turn our attention to the 'statics' of valve design, the proportioning of those elements of construction which are called upon to sustain the various stresses brought about by the fluid pressure itself and also those imposed by manipulation of the valve.

In this connection it is appropriate to deal firstly with the valve body itself and, in particular, to determine its shell thickness. The dimensions of the connecting pipe flanges are selected according to the pressure rating from the appropriate Flange Tables—British Standard, ASA or DIN as may be dictated by the customer (or determined by the manufacturer).

Now the transverse cross-sectional configurations of a sluice valve body in a plane at right angles to the longitudinal centre line of the stem are usually: roughly elliptical (there is no point in making them truly elliptical) as at (a) in Fig. 3.13; quasi-elliptical (for ease of patternmaking and dimensional economy) as at (b); or as at (c) in the larger valves operating at the higher pressures.

Types (a) and (b) enable the distance over the pipe flange facings to be kept down to a minimum but provide something of a problem in stress analysis and in the ultimate evaluation of the shell thickness appropriate to the line or test pressure imposed.

Various investigators have been intrigued by the problem, notably Swift, Timoshenko and Foster, and a wealth of formulation has emerged, but in practice somewhat thinner shells are adopted by the various manufacturers (and apparently without dire consequences) than would appear warranted by any of the mathematical analysis. There is in fact a very valid reason for this disparity between 'theory' and 'practice'. In the theoretical treatment a reasonably (if not infinitely) long non-circular cylinder is assumed (as in the case of the truly circular cylinder investigated by Lamé and others); whereas in any sluice valve, in particular, some amount of support of a relatively short cylinder is provided by the pipe flanges, the cover flanges, and in certain instances—notably in the larger valves—by the provision of judiciously proportioned and positioned stiffening ribs.

Arising out of the experience gained in the design of a wide range of sluice valves, there have emerged two important laws governing the configurations

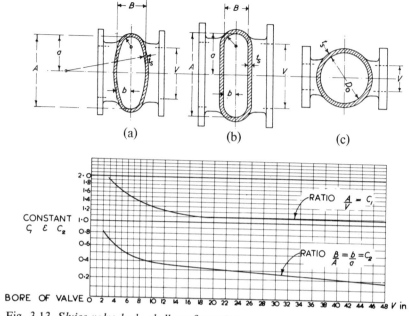

Fig. 3.13 *Sluice valve body shell configuration*

of the elliptical and/or quasi-elliptical shells and which should prove a most useful aid to those entrusted with the design of one or a range of such valves for the first time. It would appear that the ratio of the major axis A of the ellipse to the bore V of the valve body (Fig. 3.13) bears a roughly parabolic relationship, as witness the upper of the two curves; and a similar relationship exists between the major and minor axes A and B of the ellipse, as evidence in the lower.

The vertical ordinates are to a logarithmic scale in order to ensure greater accuracy for the smaller range of valves, and this results in more 'flattened' curves in this region than would otherwise obtain had the ordinates been drawn to a truly progressive scale.

Thus for any particular size of valve, as designated by the bore, the configurations of the body shell as at (c) and (b) in Fig. 3.13 may be readily established from the curves, eg major axis $A = C_1 V$ where C_1 is a constant denoted by the vertical coordinate appropriate to the valve size V taken from the upper curve. Likewise the minor axis $B = C_2 V$ where C_2 is the vertical coordinate taken from the lower curve.

Valve Design 73

In the exceptionally large sluice valves, it may be found expedient to depart from the $B = C_2 V$ relationship in order to provide for internal supplementary ribbing without encroaching on the space available for the free travel of the wedge in the process of opening or closing, and this, of course, is a matter for individual preference.

This, then, is the starting point for determining the shell thickness and, in view of previous remarks about mathematical analysis, we are compelled to fall back on precedent and, in this connection, the tabulated values for shell thicknesses given in Tables 3.1 (a) and 3.1 (b) appropriate to cast iron and to a selection of steels, and applicable for the pressure/temperature ratings given in the graphs in Appendix A to H inclusive, may be adopted with the utmost confidence.

The various curves relate to steel bodied valves destined for the higher temperatures but only three varying types of steel have been chosen in order to avoid complexity.

The black spots in each of the graphs indicate the Primary Service Pressures and appropriate temperatures.

The necks of the body, namely those portions between the pipe flanges and the shell, should be made the same thickness as the shell itself in the interests of promoting sound castings.

Table 3.1 (a) Body and bonnet shell thickness for wedge-gate sluice valves
Cast iron bodied valves

Bore of valve V	in	1	$1\frac{1}{4}$	$1\frac{1}{2}$	2	$2\frac{1}{2}$	3	4	5	6	7
	mm*	25	32	40	50	65	80	100	125	150	
Shell thickness t_s	in	$\frac{1}{4}$	$\frac{9}{32}$	$\frac{5}{16}$	$\frac{3}{8}$	$\frac{13}{32}$	$\frac{7}{16}$	$\frac{1}{2}$	$\frac{17}{32}$	$\frac{9}{16}$	$\frac{19}{32}$
	mm†	6·35	7·14	7·93	9·52	10·3	11·1	12·7	13·5	14·3	15·1

Bore of valve V	in	8	9	10	12	14	16	18	20	22	24
	mm*	200		250	300	350	400		500		600
Shell thickness t_s	in	$\frac{5}{8}$	$\frac{11}{16}$	$\frac{3}{4}$	$\frac{13}{16}$	$\frac{7}{8}$	1	$1\frac{1}{8}$	$1\frac{1}{8}$	$1\frac{3}{16}$	$1\frac{1}{4}$
	mm†	15·9	17·5	19·1	20·6	22·2	25·4	28·6	28·6	30·2	31·8

*Not an exact metric equivalent but represent continental pipe and valve sizes
†Approximate metric equivalents: for design purposes round off to nearest whole number

Table 3.1 (b) Body and bonnet shell thickness wedge-gate sluice valves
Steel bodied valves

| Bore of valve V | | Body and bonnet shell thickness t_s — Primary Service Ratings (allowable pressure varies inversely as temperature (see Appendix A (a) to (h))) | | | | | | | | | | | |
| in | mm* | 150 lb | | 300 lb | | 400 lb | | 600 lb | | 900 lb | | 1500 lb | |
		in	mm	in	mm	in	mm	in	mm	in	mm	in	mm
1	25					5/16	7·94	5/16	7·94	1/2	12·7	1/2	12·7
1¼	32					11/32	8·73	11/32	8·73	9/16	14·3	9/16	14·3
1½	40	11/32	8·73	5/16	7·94	3/8	9·53	3/8	9·53	5/8	15·9	5/8	15·9
2	50	3/8	9·53	3/8	9·53	7/16	11·11	7/16	11·11	3/4	19·1	3/4	19·1
2½	65	13/32	10·32	7/16	11·11	7/16	11·11	15/32	11·91	3/4	19·1	7/8	22·2
3	80	7/16	11·11	15/32	11·91	1/2	12·7	1/2	12·7	3/4	19·1	15/16	23·8
4	100	7/16	11·11	1/2	12·7	17/32	13·5	5/8	15·9	27/32	21·4	1 1/8	28·6
5	125	15/32	11·91	17/32	13·5	9/16	14·3	11/16	17·5	15/16	23·8	1 5/16	33·3
6	150	15/32	11·91	5/8	15·9	21/32	16·7	3/4	19·1	1 1/16	26·2	1 1/2	38·1
7		15/32	11·91	21/32	16·7	11/16	17·5	7/8	22·2	1 5/32	29·4	1 11/16	42·9
8	200	1/2	12·7	11/16	17·5	3/4	19·1	1	25·4	1 1/4	31·8	1 7/8	47·6
9		17/32	13·5	23/32	18·3	25/32	19·8	1 1/16	27·0	1 3/8	34·9	2 1/16	52·4
10	250	9/16	14·3	3/4	19·1	13/16	20·6	1 1/8	28·6	1 7/16	36·5	2 1/4	57·1
12	300	5/8	15·9	13/16	20·6	15/16	23·8	1 1/4	31·8	1 9/16	39·7	2 9/16	65·1
14	350	21/32	16·7	7/8	22·2	1 1/16	27·0	1 3/8	34·9	1 13/16	46·0	2 3/4	70·0
16	400	11/16	17·5	15/16	23·8	1 1/8	28·6	1 1/2	38·1	2 1/16	52·4	3 1/8	79·5
18	450	23/32	18·3	1	25·4	1 3/16	30·2	1 5/8	41·3	2 1/4	57·2	3 1/2	89·0
20	500	3/4	19·1	1 1/16	27·0	1 5/16	33·3	1 3/4	44·5	2 1/2	63·5	3 7/8	98·5
22		25/32	19·8	1 1/8	28·6	1 3/8	34·9	1 7/8	47·6	2 23/32	69·1	4 1/4	108·0
24	600	13/16	20·6	1 3/16	30·2	1 7/16	36·5	2	50·8	2 7/8	73·0	4 1/2	114·5

*Not a true metric equivalent but represent continental pipe and valve sizes

BONNET FLANGES AND BOLTING

The first requirement in the design of the bonnet is to establish the number and size of the securing bolts. In both the inside and outside screw pattern valves, the bolts must sustain both pressure loading and the axial force of the actuating screw *simultaneously*.

Some amount of 'trial and error' tactics may be necesary especially in regard to the number of bolts.

Assuming that the joint between the two mating flanges is of the sandwich type employing a resilient gasket, for purposes of design we may assume the line pressure to be exerted on the whole of the area bounded by the outer confines of the gasket.

It can be shown that the load to be imparted by each bolt or stud securing the bonnet of the valve against the line pressure is given by

$$P_n = \frac{p}{n}(A + a_f \eta_3) \qquad (3.27)$$

where p is the line pressure, n the number of bolts/studs, A the cross-sectional area of the opening*, a_f the contact area of the jointing face or gasket, and η_3 a factor appropriate to the nature of the gasket and its mating surfaces. In the tentative determination of n, the following rules may be adopted for the minimum chordal pitch p_m.

$p_m = 2d_b + 6$ mm ($\frac{1}{4}$ in) for ring spanners and

$2 \cdot 75 d_b$ for open jaw spanners

where d_b is the diameter of the bolt or stud.

Values of η_3 appropriate to various jointing media are given in Appendix M.

To the value of P_n thus derived must be added the load due to the axial force required to close the valve and transmitted to the bolts/studs via the thrust collar and the bonnet:

Total load per bolt/stud $P_b = P_n + P_T/n \qquad (3.28)$

The determination of A and a_f in the case of elliptical or quasi-elliptical shell openings may prove tedious, but assuming the opening to be *truly*

*This presupposes that leakage is prevented at the inner edge of the gasket if continuous to the shell opening.

elliptical, and the gasket of uniform width, the area of opening may be taken to be:

$$A = \pi ab$$

and

$$a_f = \pi(a_1 b_1 - ab) \quad \text{(see Figs. 3.13 and 3.14)}.$$

The problem of determining the requisite thickness of the bonnet flanges is not readily solved with any prospect of reasonable accuracy.

Quite a wealth of experimentation has been carried out by various authorities and individuals to investigate the behaviour of bolted flanges under varying pressure conditions in an endeavour to formulate a basis for design, but these have been mainly concerned with pipe-flanges of truly *circular* configurations.

Noteworthy among the many researchers may be cited the findings of the Pipe Flanges Research Committee sponsored by the Institution of Mechanical Engineers and supported by a large cross-section of Industry and Government Departments. Their first report was published (as a Paper to the Institution) in 1936, and their third report published in 1954* is a particularly outstanding example of the importance attached to this problem by a dedicated team of investigators.

These and subsequent findings formed the basis for revision of the British Standard Specifications for Pipe Flanges (BS 10:1962), the necessity for which had long been apparent due to the increasing upward trend in operating pressures and temperatures.

The findings of the various investigators have yielded a wealth of mathematical formulation, as may be imagined, most of which might prove unpalatable to the majority of designer-draughtsmen using this work. Instead, the less rigorous treatment which follows, although only an approximate analysis, may be more acceptable and more readily assimilated. Nevertheless it may be employed with every confidence. At least it yields results in close accord with current practice.

Consider the isometric view of the half body shown in Fig. 3.14 (a). The cover flange may be considered as a cantilever supported by the body shell and loaded by the tensile forces in the securing bolts, each of intensity P_n acting upwards as indicated.

*Pipe Flange & Research Committee. 3rd Report, *Proc. Instn mech Engrs*, 1954, **168**, 423–55

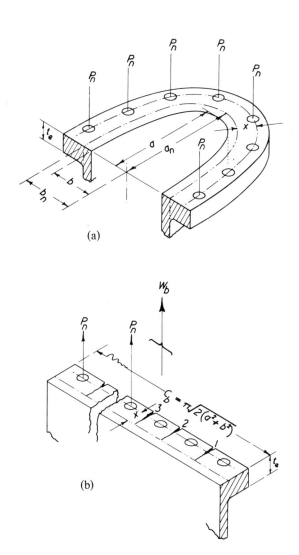

Fig. 3.14 *(a) Isometric half-section of sluice valve bonnet flange*
(b) 'Straight-line' development of sluice valve bonnet flange

Each bolt will produce a bending moment M_b of $P_n x$ where x is taken to be the distance from the bolt pitch circle to the junction of the flange with the shell, ignoring the stiffening effect of the fillet.

The collective force of the bolts may be taken as W_b where $W_b = P_n n$; then the bending moment M_b will be denoted by $W_b x$.

Now imagine the elliptical cover flange to be 'unwound' to form a dead straight wide cantilever 'beam' as at (b) in Fig. 3.14. If a_n and b_n denote the minor and major semi-axes, respectively, of the elliptical neck, then the developed perimeter C_b of that portion of the neck on which the maximum bending moment will be concentrated will be given very approximately (but near enough for all practical purposes) by

$$C_b = \pi \sqrt{\{2\ (a_n^2 + b_n^2)\}} \tag{3.29}$$

Now

$$W_b x = fZ$$

where f is the radial bending stress and Z is the modulus of the section whose perimeter is C_b.

Since

$$Z = \pi\sqrt{\{2\ (a_n^2 + b_n^2)\}} \times t_e^2/6 \tag{3.30}$$

then

$$W_b x = \frac{1}{6}\pi f t_e^2 \sqrt{\{2\ (a_n^2 + b_n^2)\}} \tag{3.31}$$

whence

$$t_e = \sqrt{\left\{\frac{6W_b x}{\pi f \sqrt{\{2\ (a_n^2 + b_n^2)\}}}\right\}} \tag{3.32}$$

which simplifies to

$$t_e = \sqrt{\left\{\frac{1\cdot 35 W_b x}{f \sqrt{(a_n^2 + b_n^2)}}\right\}} \tag{3.33}$$

Obviously, if the working pressure was zero, theoretically W_f and, therefore, t_e would be zero. To cater for the lower pressures, therefore, the values determined from the formula should be treated with reserve. In no case should the bonnet flanges be less in thickness than the pipe flanges appropriate to the working pressure.

It should be pointed out that the foregoing treatment takes no account of the circumferential stresses induced and which should bear a proportion of the bolt loading. The formula would more appropriately apply were the flange to be deliberately cut between each bolt centre as indicated by the imaginary cleavages shown at points 1, 2, 3, etc, in Fig. 3.14 (b).

It must be repeated that the foregoing is only an approximate analysis. Where any doubt exists as to the adequacy of thickness, the strength of the flange may be materially enhanced, of course, by a suitably disposed array of stiffening ribs.

For line pressures in excess of, say, 27 bar (400 psig) it is recommended that truly circular shells be adopted as in Fig. 3.15.

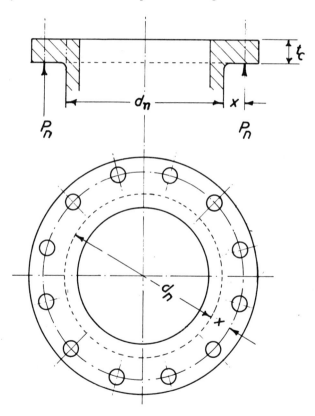

Fig. 3.15 *Section of circular bonnet flange and neck of high pressure sluice valve*

Then, applying the same reasoning as in the foregoing analysis, and denoting the perimeter of the neck at the point of maximum bending stress by C'_b, we have

$$C'_b = \pi d_n$$

where d_n = outside diameter of neck

Let t_c = the thickness of the circular flange and, again, $W_b x = fZ$ where f is the radial bending stress and Z is the section modulus of that section whose perimeter is C'_b. Now

$$Z = d_n t_c^2/6 \qquad (3.35)$$

then

$$W_b x = \pi d_n f t_c^2/6 \qquad (3.36)$$

whence

$$t_c = \sqrt{\{6 W_b x / \pi d_n f\}} \qquad (3.37)$$

(see the remarks following eqn (3.33).

STUFFING BOX AND GLAND

One common method of packing the stuffing box is that of employing square section 'rope' packing, obviously of a composition best suited to the fluid to be handled if this be known. In order to level off the contents of the box the 'lays' may be topped up with a measure of shredded packing.

Although experience might be thought the best advocate in the matter of proportioning the diameter and depth of the box, the combined recommendations of BS5150:1974 and API Standard 600 (4th edition), embodied in Appendix U are worthy of consideration and adoption, all the examples being drawn to the same scale.

The depth of the box in each case corresponds to a minimum of six rings or sections (not six turns) of the block type packing. This depth may be exceeded if desired or where circumstances dictate.

No recommendations are given in the aforementioned publications for modifying the depth of the box in line with the primary service pressure ratings but experience points to the adoption of a minimum depth equivalent to six rings for primary service pressure ratings up to $3 \cdot 5$ N/mm² (500 psig), seven from $3 \cdot 5$ to $6 \cdot 0$ N/mm² (500 to 900 psig), and eight or nine from 6 to

10 N/mm² (900 to 1500 psig). (Imperial equivalents rounded off.)

Consider the two-bolt/stud 'oval' one-piece gland. and stuffing box portrayed in Fig. 3.16.

It is suggested that the length l_g of the annular projection of the gland entering the stuffing box be made $2\frac{1}{2}$ to $3\frac{1}{2}$ times the width/depth w_s of the packing.

In order to determine the requisite size of the bolts or studs it is reasonable to assume that *at least* they could be called upon to sustain an upthrust U_p caused by the line pressure p acting on the packing annulus bounded by D_s and d_s.

In addition there would be the 'drag' of the packing on the surface of the stem. This impedance is not easily calculable but can be closely deter-

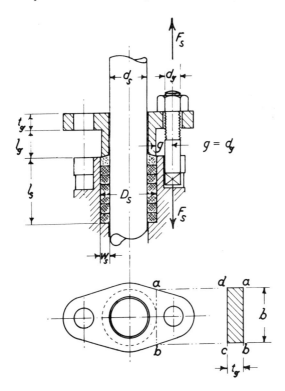

Fig. 3.16 *Two-bolt stuffing box and gland for wedge-gate sluice valves*

mined as follows. If the packing behaved as a fluid then the unit contact pressure on the surface of the stem would be equal to the line pressure but the actual extent is by no means predictable. For purposes of design, therefore, and as before, it will be assumed that the contract (or wiping) pressure will be equal to the line pressure p. Then

Total encircling grip on stem = Exposed surface × Contact pressure

$$= \pi d_s l_s p$$

and

Axial 'drag' $U_d = \pi d_s l_s p \mu_s$ (3.38)

where μ_s is the coefficient of friction between the packing and the stem, say 0·15. Thus

$$U_d = 0·15 \pi d_s l_s p$$
$$= 0·47 d_s l_s p \qquad\qquad (3.39)$$

and total load U_T to be shared by *both* studs will be given by:

$$U_T = U_p + U_d$$
$$= (\pi/4) p (D_s^2 - d_s^2) + 0·47 d_s l_s p \qquad (3.40)$$

or load per stud (for 2 studs)

$$F_s = U_T/2 = (\pi/8) p (D_s^2 - d_s^2) + 0·235 d_s l_s p$$
$$= 0·4 p (D_s^2 - d_s^2) + 0·235 d_s l_s p \text{ approx.} \qquad (3.41)$$

The foregoing it must be remembered only applies to a two-bolt or two-stud gland. If more than two fastenings are featured the formula will call for simple adjustment.

A suitable size of bolt or stud may be selected from Appendix N applicable to varying grades of steel. Appropriate adjustments will require to be made for fastenings in any other materials according to conditions of installation. In chemical works, for example, it is not only the fluids being handled by the valve which bring about rapid deterioration of the internal working parts; the atmosphere itself may be of a very highly corrosive nature and bring about similar deterioration of the external items of construction.

The thickness of the gland plate itself may now claim attention. Referring to

Fig. 3.16 the plate will be subjected to a bending moment due to the force imparted by the studs, the maximum intensity of which will occur at the plane marked abcd in the plan and in the projected view alongside.

Let M_g denote this maximum bending moment, then

$$M_g = F_s G$$

Denoting the section modulus at the plane abcd by Z_s we have

$$Z_s = b_g t_g^2/6$$

whence, since $M_g = f Z_s$ where f is the stress induced,

$$F_s g = f b_g t_g^2$$

or

$$f = 6 F_s g / b_g t_g^2 \qquad (3.42)$$

or

$$\text{Thickness } t_g = \sqrt{(6 F_s g / f b_g)} \qquad (3.43)$$

An appropriate value for f may be taken from Appendix J or K.

In the larger sizes of valves it is advisable to make the gland of cast steel (or forged steel where quantities warrant the expense of dies) in which case it is customary to fit a gunmetal bush as shown in Fig. 3.17, proportioned as indicated.

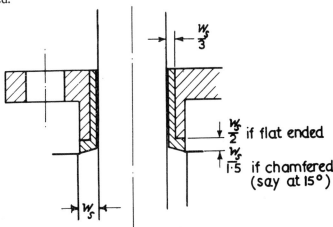

Fig. 3.17 *Bushed gland*

WORKED EXAMPLE

Determine the principal characteristics of a high-duty cast iron wedge-gate sluice valve 450 mm bore, suitable for a static pressure of 500 kN/m². The valve envisaged is of the inside-screw non-rising stem pattern manually operated, which will operate at ambient temperature. Assume the valve mounted in a horizontal pipeline with the handwheel uppermost. Take the weight of the gate as 677 N and the angle subtended by each face to the axis of the stem as $3\frac{1}{4}°$.

Solution

The working pressure $p = 500$ kN/m². It is suggested the design be based on a primary working pressure of 700 kN/m².

Axial force to be imparted by stem. (See Figs. 3.7 (a) and 3.7 (b).) From eqn (3.10)

$$P_{fw} = H\tan(a + \varphi) - W$$

Now

$$H = (\pi/4)d^2 p = 0\cdot785 \times \left(\frac{450}{1\,000}\right)^2 \times 500\text{kN}$$
$$= 79\cdot481 \text{ kN}$$

Take $\mu = 0\cdot24$ for gunmetal seating faces, then

$$\text{angle of friction } \varphi = \tan^{-1}\mu$$
$$= \tan^{-1}0\cdot24$$
$$\varphi = 13° \ 30'$$

Proceeding from eqn (3.10)

$$P_{fw} = 79\cdot481\tan(3° \ 15' + 13° \ 30') - 677/1\,000 \text{ kN}$$
$$= 79\cdot481\tan16° \ 45' - 0\cdot677$$
$$= 79\cdot481 \times 0\cdot3010 - 0\cdot677$$
$$= 23\cdot923 - 0\cdot677$$
$$= 23\cdot246 \text{ kN or } 23\ 246 \text{ N}$$

This, however, is not the total force required to effect complete closure; to this must be aded the force P_s due to the line pressure acting on the cross-sectional area of the stem (see eqns (3.11) and (3.12)).

Now $P_s = (\pi/4)pd_s^2$ (see Figs 3.9 and 3.10).

It will be necessary to assume a value for d_s at this stage, say 50 mm, and this can be checked later as calculations proceed. Then

$$P_s = 0 \cdot 785 \times 500 \left(\frac{50}{1\,000}\right)^2$$

$$= \frac{392 \cdot 7 \times 2\,500}{1\,000\,000} = 0 \cdot 982 \text{ kN or } 982 \text{ N}$$

From eqn (3.12)

$$P_T = P + P_s \quad \text{(Note: } P \text{ will become } P_{fs} \text{ in this instance)}$$

whence

$$P_T = 23 \cdot 246 + 0 \cdot 982$$
$$= 24 \cdot 228 \text{ kN or } 24\,228 \text{ N}$$

Torque to effect closure. From eqn (3.17)

Total torque $Q_T = Q_a + Q_b + Q_c$

It will be advisable to work out the three constituent torques separately. From eqn (3.13)

$$Q_a = P_T p_t / 2\pi\eta$$

Assume a single start fully square thread of pitch $p_t = 12$ mm; then mean diameter of screw $d_m = 44$ mm and the lead angle of the thread a may be determined as a preliminary to calculating the screw thread efficiency η.

$$a = \tan^{-1} p_t / \pi d_m$$
$$= \tan^{-1} 12 / (\pi \times 44)$$
$$= \tan^{-1} 0 \cdot 0868$$
$$a = 4° \, 58'$$

Now the screw thread efficiency $\eta = \tan a / \tan (a + \varphi)$

Since the screw of an inside screw valve cannot be lubricated (except by the doubtful lubricating qualities of the line fluid) a coefficient of friction $\mu = 0.24$ again may be adopted for a gunmetal spindle working in a gunmetal nut and from a previous calculation we know that in this case too the friction angle φ will be $13° 30'$.
Then

$$\eta = \tan 4° \ 58'/\tan (4° \ 58' + 13° \ 30')$$
$$= 0.0868/0.3339$$
$$= 0.26 \ (\text{or } 26\%)$$

This calculated value is confirmed by interpolation in the efficiency curves given in Appendix Q.

The busy designer will employ the curves in preference to the more tedious alternative of calculation, but it is essential for the student, for example, to be familiar with the groundwork from which the curves were prepared.

Proceeding from eqn (3.13) and substituting known values

$$Q_a = (24.228 \times 12)/(2 \times 3.142 \times 0.26 \times 1\,000) = 0.1779 \text{ kN m}$$

From eqn (3.14)

$$Q_b = \mu_c P_T r_m$$

Now for gunmetal on cast iron (unlubricated) μ_c may be taken as 0.20, then:

$$Q_b = (0.20 \times 24.228 \times 32)/1\,000 = 0.155 \text{ kN m}$$

From eqn (3.16)

$$Q_c = 2\mu_s l_s p_s d^2$$
$$= 2 \times 0.15 \, \frac{67.5}{1\,000} \times 500 \left(\frac{50}{1\,000}\right)^2 = 0.0256 \text{ kN m}$$

We now have the three 'ingredients' for determining the total torque Q_T:

$$Q_T = Q_a + Q_b + Q_c$$
$$= 0.1779 + 0.155 + 0.0256$$
$$= 0.3585 \text{ kN m}$$

Diameter of handwheel. Assume the net tangential force applied to the rim to be 350 N or 0·35 kN. Then

$$\text{Diameter } H_w = 2Q_T/\tau = (2 \times 0\cdot3585)/0\cdot35$$
$$= 2\cdot095 \text{ m}$$

which is impracticable and indicates the necessity to provide some form of reduction gearing.

Adopting machine-cut single reduction bevel gearing as depicted in Fig. 3.18 we have tangential driving force P_w, assumed concentrated at the common pitch point X, is given by

$$P_w = \text{torque/radius of application} = 0\cdot3585/R_w$$

and therefore, torque to be applied to bevel pinion (neglecting friction meanwhile) is

$$P_w r_p = 0\cdot3585 r_p / R_w$$

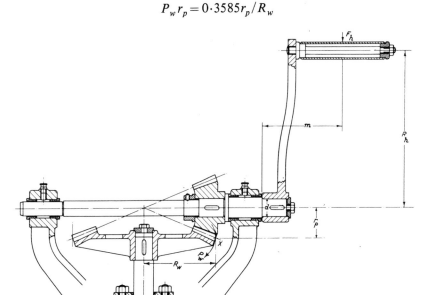

Fig. 3.18 *Manually operated wedge-gate sluice valve with bevel reduction gear*

Let F_h denote the manual effort to be imparted to the crank handle and R_h the effective radius of operation of the crank; then, still neglecting friction

$$F_h R_h = 0 \cdot 3585 r_p / R_w$$

The overall efficiency of a machine-cut bevel gear may be taken as $0 \cdot 9$ (including journal friction). Hence

$$F_h R_h = 0 \cdot 3585 r_p / 0 \cdot 9 R_w$$

Take F_h to be $0 \cdot 45$ kN (for intermittent applications).

$$0 \cdot 45 R_h = 0 \cdot 3585 r_p / 0 \cdot 9 R_w$$

Let $r_p / R_w = 1/2 \cdot 5$

then

$$R_h = 0 \cdot 3585 / (0 \cdot 9 \times 2 \cdot 5 \times 0 \cdot 45) = 0 \cdot 354 \text{ m } (13 \cdot 9 \text{ in approx., say 14 in})$$

Proportions of gear teeth. These are best designed in accordance with the well-known, well-tried and easily manipulated Lewis formula, the nomenclature of which has been modified in order to comply with that of the present text. A reversion to Imperial units is necessary if the calculations are to be meaningful.

$$P_w = f b_w p_c y \qquad (3.44)$$

where P_w = tangential driving force at the pitch point located at X in Fig. 3.18, in lbf

f = safe working stress in lbf/in^2

$$= C \left(\frac{600}{600 + V} \right) \quad \text{where}$$

V = velocity of rim in ft/min

$C = 8\,000$ lbf/in^2 for cast iron

$= 12\,000$ lbf/in^2 for bronze or gunmetal

$= 20\,000$ lbf/in^2 for steel (cast)

$= 25\,000$ lbf/in^2 for mild steel

$= 80\,000$ lbf/in^2 for heat treated nickel and chrome steels

b_w = face width of teeth in inches

P_c = circular pitch in inches

y = tooth factor depending on the number of teeth in the wheel.

For involute teeth having a pressure angle of 20°

$$y = 0 \cdot 154 - 0 \cdot 912/n$$

where n = number of teeth.

There are three variables in the Lewis formula which require to be determined: the circular pitch p_c, the face width b_w, and the number of teeth n in the wheel.

Since the circular pitch p_c would appear to be the first objective, certain related values based on speculation or insight will be needed.

If 'undercutting' is to be avoided, the smallest permitted number of teeth for 20° involute teeth is 18. For the purpose of evaluating y, therefore, let us assume the pinion will have, say, 24 teeth, then, from a previous assumption, number of teeth in the wheel is $2 \cdot 5 \times 24 = 60$.

Evaluating y we have:

$$y = 0 \cdot 154 - 0 \cdot 912/60 = 0 \cdot 139$$

It is usual to make the face width $b_w = 3p_c$ and this may be substituted for b_w in the Lewis formula.

Since the velocity V is of such a low order in manually operated gears, the expression for f the allowable working stress is virtually equal to C.

Thus, for cast iron gears (the usual material in applications such as that in this example), f may be taken as 8 000 lb/in², which would appear, incidentally, somewhat on the high side.

Proceeding, from eqn (3.44),

$$p_c = P_w/fb_w y$$

and substituting $3p_c$ for b_w

$$p_c = P_w/3p_c fy$$

whence

$$p_c = \sqrt{(P_w/3fy)} \tag{3.45}$$

Adopting a crank 14 in effective length and taking the manual effort applied to be 200 lbf (to err on the top side) in case two men should apply themselves to the handwheel,

$$P_w = (14 \times 200)/r_p$$

Assume $r_p = 2\frac{1}{2}$ in, then

$$P_w = (14 \times 200)/2\frac{1}{2} = 1\ 120\ \text{lbf.}$$

From eqn (3.45)

$$p_c = \sqrt{\{1\ 120/(3 \times 8\ 000 \times 0\cdot139)\}} = 0\cdot5\acute{7}9\ \text{in}$$

say 5/8 in circular pitch (or 6DP) if preferred.

As stated earlier, the value for f of 8 000 lbf/in² for cast iron appears to be on the high side but this value might well have been intended for those applications in which the gears were ideally housed in an enclosed gear box and provision made for their lubrication. Many sluice valves are not so ideally endowed however, some even being installed with little or no protection from the weather.

To cater for such extreme conditions a somewhat lower value of f should be adopted, say 5 000 lbf/in², when it follows that

$$P_c = \sqrt{\{1120/(3 \times 5\ 000 \times 0\cdot139)\}}$$
$$= 0\cdot733\ \text{in, say}\ \tfrac{3}{4}\ \text{in}$$

Adopting 50 teeth in the wheel and 20 in the pinion the pitch diameters would be

$$(50 \times \tfrac{3}{4})/\pi = 11\cdot936\ \text{in approx.}$$

and

$$(20 \times \tfrac{3}{4})/\pi = 4\cdot774\ \text{in}$$

If diametrical pitch is preferred then 4DP would yield pitch diameters of 15 in and 5 in exactly with the same number of teeth.

Diameter of driving shaft termination. From an examination of Fig. 3.18 it will be appreciated that the pinion shaft is not only subjected to a twisting moment but could be subjected to a bending moment *concurrently*. Design must cater at all times for the optimum possible loading; hence we must take account of a twisting moment $F_h R_h$ and a bending moment $F_h m$.

These two differing moments can be resolved into an equivalent *twisting* moment T_e by the well-known Guest formula:

$$T_e = \sqrt{(T^2 + M^2)} = (\pi/16)d_p^3 f_s$$

where $T=$ twisting moment. Take $m = 8$ in $= 0\cdot203$ m.

(Note that the effort was taken as 200 lbf in determining the proportions of the gears and, reverting to SI units, 200 lbf $= 200 \times 4\cdot448$ N $= 889\cdot6$ N.)

$M=$ bending moment

$d_p =$ diameter of pinion shaft at point of maximum bending moment

f_s = allowable shearing stress in material of shaft, say for carbon steel, 54 N/mm^2

then

$$T_e = \sqrt{\left\{\left(889\cdot6 \times \frac{14}{39\cdot37}\right)^2 + \left(889\cdot6 \times \frac{8}{39\cdot37}\right)^2\right\}}$$

$$= 364 \text{ N m or } 0\cdot364 \text{ kN m}$$

Equating to the moment of resistance and transposing:

$$d_p = \sqrt[3]{(16T_e/\pi f_s)} = \sqrt[3]{\{16 \times 384 \times 1\,000/3\cdot142 \times 54\}}$$

$$= 0\cdot0331 \text{ m or } 33\cdot1 \text{ mm}$$

This should be regarded as minimal and due allowance made for the weakening effect of the keyseat. It is suggested that this termination be made at least 40 mm diameter.

Bonnet flanges and bolting. We have seen from eqn (3.27) that the force to be imparted by each bolt (or stud) is given by

$$P_n = \frac{p}{n}(A + a_f \eta_3)$$

Now the area A of the internal neck of the shell (taken to be truly elliptical) is given by

$A = \pi ab$ (see Fig. 3.13)

Inserting known data:

$A = 3\cdot142 \times 108 \times 280 = 95\,014$ mm^2 $= 0\cdot0950$ m^2

and the contact area of the gasket, being a hollow ellipse, by

$$a_f = \pi(a_1 b_1 - ab)$$
$$= 3 \cdot 142 \ (146 \times 318 - 108 \times 280)$$
$$= 50 \ 862 \ \text{mm}^2 = 0 \cdot 050 \ 86 \ \text{m}^2$$

Take the number of bolts to be sixteen and η_3 to be $1 \cdot 75$ for vegetable fibre (millboard) sheet, then

$$P_n = \frac{500}{16} (0 \cdot 0950 + 0 \cdot 0508 \times 1 \cdot 75)$$
$$= 5 \cdot 73 \ \text{kN or 5 730 N}$$

From Appendix N, adopting a grade of bolt having an UTS of 450 N/mm^2 an M20 (20 mm dia) bolt would be just adequate.

Thickness of cover flanges. Total force exerted by *all* the bolts

$$W_b = 16 \times 5 \ 750 \ \text{N}$$
$$= 91 \ 680 \ \text{N}$$

Eqn (3.32) reads:

$$t_e = \sqrt{\left\{ \frac{6W_b x}{\pi f \sqrt{\{2 \ (a_n^2 + b_n^2)\}}} \right\}}$$

Inserting known values and taking f, the safe working stress for cast iron, as 19 000 kN/m^2, we have, taking x from drawing to be 25 mm,

$$t_e = \sqrt{\left\{ \frac{6 \times 91 \cdot 680 \times 0 \cdot 025}{3 \cdot 142 \times 19 \ 000 \sqrt{\{2(0 \cdot 108^2 + 0 \cdot 280^2)\}}} \right\}}$$
$$= 0 \cdot 000545 \ \text{m}$$
$$= 0 \cdot 02334 \ \text{m} = 23 \cdot 34 \ \text{mm}$$

Adopt a thickness not less than 35 mm in view of the remarks following eqns (3.33) and (3.37).

Chapter 4
Parallel Slide Valves

CLAIMED to have been introduced by Hopkinsons Limited (then J. Hopkinson & Co. Ltd) in 1881, this valve is a more refined member of the gate family and, as such, presents a clear uninterrupted full-bore flowpath in the fully open position, effectively a continuation of the pipeline. It derives its title from the fact that the two seatings are parallel to one another, as distinct from those of the wedge-gate valve in which they are inclined to one another.

With suitable materials of construction and careful attention to design, it is a valve admirably suited to the control of steam at the highest pressures and temperatures.

The simplest and most effective form of construction is the one employing 'spring-between-disk' mechanism as featured in Fig. 4.1. Figure 4.2 features the disk assembly adopted in the smaller sizes of valves.

The two opposed disks in telescopic assembly tend to be urged apart under the influence of a close-coiled precompressed helical spring, usually made of coils of rectangular section in the interests of saving space lengthwise. This arrangement of telescoping the two disks is restricted to the smaller size of valves. In the larger sizes the two disks are identical and are housed in a circumscribing shell, as in Fig. 4.1.

Let it be understood that the function of the spring is not to secure two pressure-tight facings as is so often presumed; a spring of very much larger proportions would be required for that, which is anyway not essential and secured only at the lower line pressures. Its function is to prevent vibration or 'chatter' and under appropriate conditions of line pressure to sweep clear, during the transition of the disks, any scale or other undesirable matter which might tend to adhere to the facings and to score them.

It is inevitable on steam lines (or in any other application where appreciable temperature variations occur) for differential expansion to take place due to the various materials and varying sections in the assembly, and this will give rise to some distortion. With the spring-between-disk

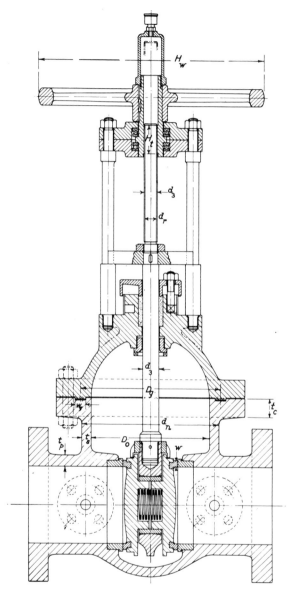

Fig. 4.1 *Typical parallel slide valve (outside screw pattern)*

GAP →||← EXAGGERATED

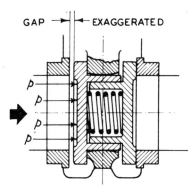

Fig. 4.2 *Behaviour of parallel slide valve seating members under pressure*

mechanism this is taken care of, the disks being free to 'breathe' as it were, the spring yielding in sympathy.

Pressure-tightness is secured on the downstream face only. If reference be directed to the closure mechanism assembly illustrated in Fig. 4.2, it will be seen that the line pressure exerted on the opposing or upstream disk forces this disk off its seating by a very small amount (shown exaggerated in the figure), and in so doing transmits the resultant force via the spring and, aided by the line pressure, to the downstream disk, the working fluid having access to the inside of the valve casing.

Simply by sliding the disks into the lowest possible position the line pressure is utilized to close the valve. This is analagous to the slide valve of a steam engine with the one difference that in this case closure is effected without the aid of a spring or any other external influence other than that of the steam pressure acting on the back of the slide valve.

Size for size and operating under the same pressure conditions, the parallel slide valve calls for less axial force to be imparted by the stem to secure positive closure than that of the screw-down stop valve. A moment's reflection should reveal why.

Neglecting all secondary resistances, the least force to be exerted in order to close down a screw-down valve is represented by the product of the line pressure and the area of the seating orifice. In the parallel slide valve, the least force is that required to *slide* the downstream disk across its facing and loaded by a force comprised of the line pressure acting on the area of the seating.

Briefly one could say that the major axial force in the case of a parallel slide valve is μ times that of a screw-down stop valve, other things being equal, where μ is the coefficient of friction between the seat contacting materials.

It will be seen from Fig. 4.1 that the design chosen by way of illustration is of the 'outside-screw rising-spindle' pattern. This is the preferred pattern since it enables a smaller stuffing box to be employed and, more important still, the actuating threads are situated remotely from the effects of high temperature steam, being virtually 'out in the cold'. Moreover, being thus located, lubrication is more readily accomplished and more lasting.

SEATING MEMBERS

In this type of valve, broad faces on the seatings themselves are essential in order to provide adequate guidance to the disks in their traverse from the open to the closed position and vice versa, the width of the facings on the disks being somewhat less. The first essential is to determine the actual contact width w (see Fig. 4.3).

We have seen in Chapter 2 that in order to ensure fluid-tightness at the seatings a clamping pressure of at least $1\frac{1}{2}$ times the line pressure is essential. This is related to a valve of the screwdown type. In the parallel slide valve (of the type portrayed in Fig. 4.1) no amount of additional torque applied to the handwheel when once the valve is closed down will secure

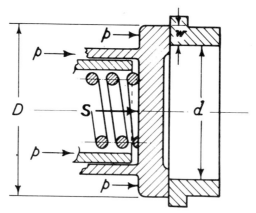

Fig. 4.3 *Forces acting on parallel slide valve downstream seating*
S = force due to precompression of spring during assembly

added tightness of the closure members.

Consequently, the motivating force for attaining pressure-tightness is the line pressure acting on the back of the disk, assisted by the thrust of the spring initially compressed in the process of assembly and remaining so throughout the life of the valve.

Ignoring the effect of the spring (the thrust of which could be regarded as bonus in the final analysis) the unit contact pressure to achieve closure tightness should vary between $2\frac{1}{2}p$ and $5p$, the lesser values for the smaller sizes and progressively increasing for the larger. The effect of the spring is more pronounced in the smaller sizes of valves than in the larger and compensates for the reduced unit pressure in these smaller sizes.

Consider by way of example the case of *any* size of parallel slide valve, and assume by way of illustration a unit contact pressure of $5p$. It is required to determine the width of contact w (see Fig. 4.3), ignoring the effect of the spring on the seating faces.

$$\text{Total thrust required on annular facing} = 5p \times \text{ area of facing}$$
$$= 5p \times (\pi/4)\{D^2 - d^2\} \quad (4.1)$$

$$\text{Available force on the disk} = p \times \text{ area of seating orifice}$$
$$= p \times (\pi/4)\,d^2 \quad (4.2)$$

Now for equilibrium these two forces are equal:

$$5p \times (\pi/4)\{D^2 - d^2\} = (\pi/4)pd^2 \quad (4.3)$$

(It will be noted that p cancels out and so the ultimate width of contact will not be a function of the line pressure.) Therefore

$$D^2 - d^2 = d^2/5$$
$$D^2 = 6d^2/5 = 1 \cdot 2d^2$$

whence

$$D = d\sqrt{1 \cdot 2}$$
$$= 1 \cdot 095d \quad (4.4)$$

$$\text{Width of contact } w = (D - d)/2$$
$$= (1 \cdot 095d - d)/2$$
$$= 0 \cdot 095d/2$$
$$= 0 \cdot 0475d \quad (4 \cdot 5)$$

We might infer, therefore, that the width of contact is given by $w = kd$ (where k is equal to $0 \cdot 0475$ in the foregoing example) but k will be a variable quantity depending upon the chosen ratio of the unit contact pressure to the line pressure since we have elected to adopt a progressively increasing value ranging from $2\frac{1}{2}p$ to $5p$.

To spare repetitive calculation, values of k appropriate to the range of sizes 40 mm ($1\frac{1}{2}$ in) to 600 mm (24 in) bore, together with the corresponding values of w, are tabulated in Table 4.1(a) and (b) and these yield results which are in accord with average practice.

AXIAL FORCES TO EFFECT CLOSURE

The *maximum* axial force required to be imparted by the stem to effect complete closure is in the final sequence—that is to say at the precise instant that flow is positively arrested—and this is compounded of five factors:

$$\text{Total axial force } P_A = P_1 + P_2 + P_3 + P_4 - W \qquad (4.6)$$

where $P_1 = $ axial force to overcome frictional resistance of downstream disk to sliding under the influence of the line pressure exerted on back of disk;

$P_2 = $ axial force required to overcome frictional resistance (drag) of the stem in the gland packing;

$P_3 = $ axial force required to oppose unbalanced upthrust of stem occasioned by line pressure exerted on cross-sectional area of stem;

$P_4 = $ axial force required to overcome frictional resistance of downstream disk on its seating occasioned by thrust of spring due to the precompression;

$W = $ weight of moving parts.

Note that the valve is assumed installed with the handwheel uppermost, in which event the weight of the moving parts assists in the closing process and resists in the opening process. It is customary to ignore W excepting in the very large valves since, at best, all calculations to determine the axial force appropriate to a given line pressure cannot be expected to yield anything but an approximate result.

It is suggested that the values of P_1, P_2, P_3 and P_4 be separately calculated.

Table 4.1 Parallel slide valve seating face data

(a) Inch units

Bore of valve (in)	$1\frac{1}{2}$	2	3	4	6	8	10	12	14	16	18	20	24
Factor k	0·093	0·092	0·089	0·087	0·084	0·079	0·075	0·071	0·067	0·063	0·059	0·055	0·047
Width of contact w (in)	0·139	0·184	0·267	0·438	0·504	0·632	0·75	0·85	0·94	1·00	1·06	1·10	1·13
Suggested fractional size (in)	$\frac{9}{64}$	$\frac{3}{16}$	$\frac{17}{64}$	$\frac{11}{32}$	$\frac{1}{2}$	$\frac{5}{8}$	$\frac{3}{4}$	$\frac{27}{32}$	$\frac{15}{16}$	1	$1\frac{1}{16}$	$1\frac{3}{32}$	$1\frac{1}{8}$

(b) Metric units

Bore of valve (mm)	40	50	80	100	150	200	250	300	350	400	450	500	600
Factor k	0·093	0·092	0·088	0·087	0·083	0·079	0·075	0·071	0·067	0·063	0·059	0·055	0·047
Width of contact w (mm)	3·72	4·6	7·04	8·7	12·45	15·8	18·75	21·3	23·45	25·2	26·55	27·5	28·2

(1) $$P_1 = (\pi/4)pd^2\mu_1$$ (4.7)

where μ_1 is the coefficient of friction of the seating materials in contact and 'lubricated'—however ineffectively—by the line fluid itself, other symbols as previously indicated.

(2)   The frictional resistance imposed by the gland packing on the stem is difficult to assess since so much depends on how tightly the gland studs or bolts may have been tightened down.

It must be assumed that no undue restriction has been imposed in the process of tightening down, the extent of which should be that which is sufficient just to prevent leakage. After a period of service the nuts can then be 'followed up'.

It will be assumed, therefore, for purposes of design that a uniform pressure p equal to the line pressure will be exerted on the surface of the stem for the entire length of the packing. Actually, the contact pressure will be greater at the top of the box due to the tightening down of the gland bolts and diminish appreciably towards the bottom (as has been proved experimentally). We may resonably assume, therefore, an average value of p for the embracing effect of the packing on the stem, as in previous Chapters:

$$P_2 = \pi\mu_s d_s l_s p$$ (4.8)

This expression presupposes that the length l_s is known. Details enabling the stuffing box and gland to be proportioned to suit the prevailing pressure may be obtained from Appendix U and from previous Chapters.

(3)   This force can be determined with reasonable arithmetical exactitude:

$$P_3 = (\pi/4)d_s^2 p$$ (4.9)

(4)   Force P_4 is based on prior knowledge of the rating of the spring adopted and its initial compression on assembly between the disks; and also on an assumed value for the coefficient of friction (under working conditions) for the seating materials in contact.

The former factor may be determined with reasonable accuracy, the latter merely being a conjecture based on experience. Fig. 4.4 gives details of a variety of springs from which a suitable spring may be selected. Thus

$$P_4 = \mu_1 S$$ (4.10)

where μ_1 is the coefficient of friction and S is the thrust of the spring due to its initial compression and determined appropriately from Fig. 4.4.

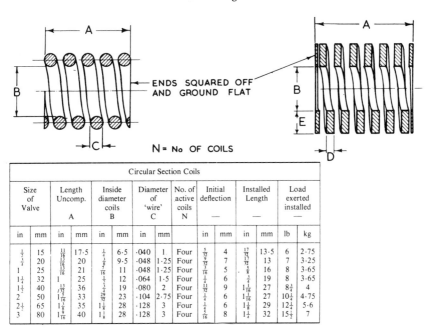

ENDS SQUARED OFF AND GROUND FLAT

N = No OF COILS

		Circular Section Coils												
Size of Valve		Length Uncomp. A		Inside diameter coils B		Diameter of 'wire' C		No. of active coils N	Initial deflection —		Installed Length —		Load exerted installed —	
in	mm	in	mm	in	mm	in	mm		in	mm	in	mm	lb	kg
$\frac{1}{2}$	15	$\frac{11}{16}$	17·5	$\frac{1}{4}$	6·5	·040	1	Four	$\frac{5}{32}$	4	$\frac{17}{32}$	13·5	6	2·75
$\frac{3}{4}$	20	$\frac{13}{16}$	20	$\frac{3}{8}$	9·5	·048	1·25	Four	$\frac{9}{32}$	7	$\frac{17}{32}$	13	7	3·25
1	25	$\frac{13}{16}$	21	$\frac{7}{16}$	11	·048	1·25	Four	$\frac{3}{16}$	5	$\frac{5}{8}$	16	8	3·65
$1\frac{1}{4}$	32	1	25	$\frac{1}{2}$	12	·064	1·5	Four	$\frac{1}{4}$	6	$\frac{3}{4}$	19	8	3·65
$1\frac{1}{2}$	40	$1\frac{13}{32}$	36	$\frac{3}{4}$	19	·080	2	Four	$\frac{11}{32}$	9	$1\frac{1}{16}$	27	$8\frac{3}{4}$	4
2	50	$1\frac{5}{16}$	33	$\frac{29}{32}$	23	·104	2·75	Four	$\frac{1}{4}$	6	$1\frac{1}{16}$	27	$10\frac{1}{4}$	4·75
$2\frac{1}{2}$	65	$1\frac{3}{8}$	35	$1\frac{1}{8}$	28	·128	3	Four	$\frac{1}{4}$	6	$1\frac{1}{8}$	29	$12\frac{1}{4}$	5·6
3	80	$1\frac{9}{16}$	40	$1\frac{1}{8}$	28	·128	3	Four	$\frac{5}{16}$	8	$1\frac{1}{4}$	32	$15\frac{1}{2}$	7

		Rectangular Section Coils														
Size of Valve		Length Uncomp. A		Inside diameter coils B		Thickness of section D		Breadth of section E		No. of active coils N	Initial deflection —		Installed length —		Load exerted installed (each spring) —	
in	mm	in	mm	in	mm	in	mm	in	mm		in	mm	in	mm	lb	kg	
4	100	2	51	$1\frac{1}{2}$	38	$\frac{3}{32}$	2·5	$\frac{9}{32}$	7	Six	$\frac{5}{8}$	16	$1\frac{3}{8}$	35	$16\frac{1}{4}$	7·5	
5	125	$2\frac{5}{16}$	59	$1\frac{1}{2}$	40	$\frac{1}{8}$	3	$\frac{3}{8}$	9	Nine	$\frac{5}{8}$	16	$1\frac{11}{16}$	43	25	11·4	
6	150	$2\frac{5}{8}$	66	$1\frac{5}{8}$	40	$\frac{1}{8}$	3	$\frac{3}{8}$	9	Eight	$\frac{5}{8}$	16	2	50	$27\frac{1}{2}$	12·5	
7	175	$3\frac{1}{4}$	83	$1\frac{11}{16}$	43	$\frac{1}{16}$	4·7	$\frac{1}{2}$	12	Eight	$\frac{1}{4}$	22	$2\frac{1}{2}$	64	62	28	
8	200	$3\frac{1}{2}$	95	$1\frac{1}{4}$	44	$\frac{3}{16}$	5	$\frac{9}{16}$	15	Eight	$\frac{7}{8}$	22	$2\frac{7}{8}$	73	126	57	
9	225	4	102	$1\frac{7}{8}$	48	$\frac{3}{16}$	4·7	$\frac{9}{16}$	15	Eight	$1\frac{1}{8}$	28	$2\frac{7}{8}$	73	139	63	
10	250	$4\frac{1}{4}$	108	2	50	$\frac{3}{16}$	5		15	Seven	$1\frac{1}{4}$	32	3	76	140	63·4	
12	300	$4\frac{1}{2}$	114	3	76	$\frac{1}{4}$	6	$\frac{1}{2}$	18	Seven	$1\frac{1}{4}$	32	$3\frac{1}{4}$	82	154	70	
14	350	$4\frac{1}{2}$	114	$3\frac{1}{2}$	89	$\frac{5}{16}$	8	$\frac{15}{16}$	24	Seven	$1\frac{1}{4}$	32	$3\frac{1}{4}$	82	224	102	
16	400	$4\frac{1}{4}$	108	2	50	$\frac{3}{16}$	5	$\frac{9}{16}$	15	Seven	$1\frac{1}{4}$	32	3	76		68	Three springs
18	450	$4\frac{1}{4}$	108	$2\frac{5}{16}$	58	$\frac{3}{16}$	5	$\frac{9}{16}$	15	Five	$1\frac{1}{4}$	32	3	76		68	per valve
20	500	$4\frac{1}{4}$	108	$2\frac{5}{16}$	58	$\frac{3}{16}$	5	$\frac{9}{16}$	15	Five	$1\frac{3}{8}$	35	$3\frac{1}{16}$	78	162	73·5	in this range
22		$4\frac{1}{4}$		$2\frac{5}{16}$	58	$\frac{1}{4}$	5	$\frac{9}{16}$	15	Five	$1\frac{3}{8}$	35	$3\frac{1}{16}$	78	162	73·5	
24	600	$4\frac{1}{2}$	114	$3\frac{1}{2}$	89	$\frac{1}{4}$	6	$\frac{1}{4}$	19	Six	$\frac{1}{4}$	32	$3\frac{1}{4}$	83	175	79·4	

Fig. 4.4 *Disk separating helical compression springs; parallel slide valve*

(5)   Regarding W, the weight of the moving parts (i.e. disks, spring, banjo) its determination is a matter for estimation when the design has proceeded sufficiently to enable this to be attempted. The effect of W will be more significant in the larger sizes of valves, of course.

The total axial force P_T is a matter of simple addition of the five components.

STEM PROPORTIONS

The axial force to be countered by the stem tends to produce buckling in the manner of a strut since there is a far greater extent of unsupported length in the case of a parallel slide valve stem than in the case of a lift valve, amounting to something in excess of the bore of the valve. It will be recalled that the lift in the case of a screw-down stop valve is near enough one quarter the bore with perhaps a little in hand to compensate for any intrusions on the area presented to flow.

The mere ability to resist buckling, however decisive a factor that may be, is not the sole criterion of design. It is essential that a diameter be chosen that will permit the ideal relationship between mean diameter and pitch and slope of screw threads to be achieved. It is customary to adopt two-start threads of square, acme or stub-acme form in this type of valve, sometimes three-start in the case of the very large valves. In this connection it is recommended that the lead angle a (note: $\tan a =$ lead or *true* pitch/pitch circumference) should lie somewhere between $12°$ in the case of the lower range of valves and $6°$ in the larger. The angle diminishes as the bore increases, which is natural since an increased mechanical advantage is required in order to match the greater forces imposed. An examination of one range of parallel slide valves, in sizes ranging from 1 in up to 16 in in the 250 lb/in² steam range and of the form illustrated in Fig. 4.1, embodied stems having full depth square threads whose lead angles plotted against the bore as in Fig. 4.5 appear to indicate that almost a straight line relationship exists between the two. This graph may serve as a guide to the designer. Obviously, it is too much to expect a rigorous adherence to the lead angles read off the graph as this would inevitably yield a non-standard (or non-producible) pitch and an awkward stem diameter, or both.

When the screw thread relationship has been settled the stem diameter may be checked to see if it is of adequate strength to satisfy the requirements of a strut, and the values for the allowable working stresses for

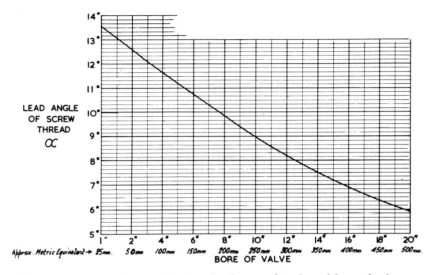

Fig. 4.5 *Relationship between lead angle of screw threads and bore of valve*

various materials and ratios of *unsupported length* to *minimum diameter* given in Appendix T will be found useful. The values given are based on *unit cross-sectional area.*

Denoting the *minimum diameter* of loaded plain stem (*root* diameter in the case of screwed stems) by d_r and the allowable unit stress by f'_c, then:

$$f'_c = \text{load/area}$$
$$= P_A/(\pi/4)d_r^2$$
$$= 4P_A/\pi d_r^2 \qquad (4.11)$$

The value of f'_c thus derived may then be checked from Appendix T and any adjustments to the diameter of the stem made accordingly, if deemed necessary.

TORQUE REQUIRED TO EFFECT CLOSURE

The total torque (in the case of the design featured in Fig. 4.1) will be compounded of two torques: (*a*) that required to produce the necessary axial force P_A through the agency of the screwed stem and (*b*) that to overcome the frictional resistance to rotation of the collar on the screwed sleeve bearing (see Fig. 4.6) against the crosshead and subjected to the axial force P_A. Since the stem is non-rotating there will be no frictional *torque* at the gland packing to be overcome. The frictional resistance to *axial* motion has been taken into account in determining the total axial force P_T. Denoting these torques by Q_a and Q_b respectively

Total torque $Q_T = Q_a + Q_b$ (4.12)

Now consider one revolution of the handwheel.

work expended on handwheel = work done by screw

or

$$2\pi Q_a \eta = P_A p_t$$

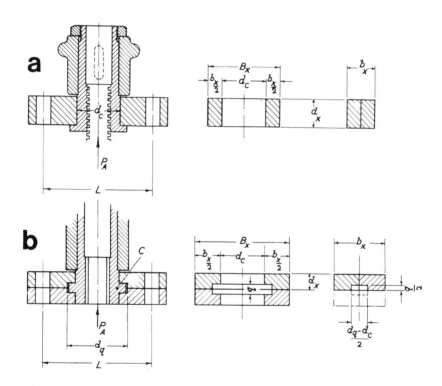

Fig. 4.6 *Forms of parallel slide valve crossheads*
(a) *One-piece* (b) *Laminated*

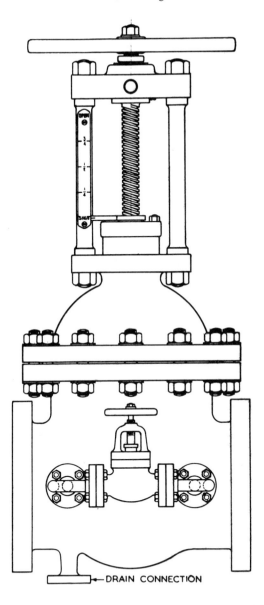

Fig. 4.7 *Typical bypass valve applied to a high pressure parallel slide valve*

where η = efficiency of screw thread (see appropriate graph in Appendix
        P, Q, R or S)

   P_A = maximum axial force

   p_t = true pitch (i.e. lead) of screw thread

Hence

$$Q_a = P_A p_t / 2 \pi \eta \qquad (4.13)$$

Referring now to Figs 4.6 and 4.7 it can be shown that the moment of
friction (or torque) is

$$Q_b = \frac{1}{2} \mu_3 P_A \frac{1}{2} (D_c + d_c)$$

$$= \frac{1}{4} \mu_3 P_A (D_c + d_c) \qquad (4.14)$$

where μ_3 = the static coefficient of friction of the materials of the actuating
        sleeve and the crosshead (having regard to the extent of lubrica-
        tion, if any),

   D_c, d_c = the outside and inside diameters respectively of the sleeve collar

   P_A = the total axial force imposed.

The evaluation of eqn (4.13) presupposes that D_c and d_c have been
established. At this stage, values for D_c and d_c will need to be assumed and
later checked for validity.

DIAMETER OF HANDWHEEL

We have already seen in Chapters 2 and 3 that

   diameter $H_w = 2 Q_T / \tau$ \qquad (4.15)

where τ is the *net* manual effort applied to the rim of the handwheel,
normally taken to be 0·35 kN (80 lbf) or 0·45 kN (100 lbf) for intermittent operation. Before passing to the next aspect of design, it is as well to
remember that the axial load to be carried by the stem, in the case of valves
of moderate size and working at the higher steam pressures, can be somewhat appreciable. In these cases this thrust warrants the substitution of a ball
thrust washer for the simple metal-to-metal frictional collar featured in Figs
4.6 and 4.8 in which event the frictional resistance to rotation, previously

denoted by Q_b, may be almost discounted from our calculations, so slight is the extent of the resistance.

For guidance in the design of the handwheel see Appendix X and Y.

ACTUATING SLEEVE

The top portion of the sleeve whose outer and inner diameters are denoted by d_1 and d_2 respectively (Fig. 4.8) transmits the full torque Q_T. Whilst the *inner* diameter is readily determined, being slightly in excess of the stem diameter d_s (usually $d_s + 0.8$ mm or 1/32 in), the *outer* diameter will require to be calculated, bearing in mind that the weakening effect due to the intrusion of the key complicates the issue somewhat and due compensation must be made. To offset the weakening effect of the keyseat, rectangular section keys involving shallower keyseats are to be preferred to keys of square section.

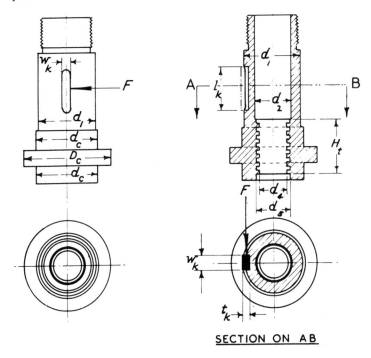

Fig. 4.8 *Details of actuating sleeve, parallel slide valve*

In order to avoid lengthy calculations it is best to calculate on the basis of a hollow shaft devoid of intrusion and then to make due allowance for it when the actual dimensions of the key have been settled.

Now the torsional moment of resistance of a hollow shaft is given by:

$$M_t = (\pi/16)f_s \left(\frac{d_1^4 - d_2^4}{d_1} \right)$$

where f_s = allowable shearing stress.

Equating the twisting moment to the moment of resistance:

$$Q_T = M_t = (\pi/16)f_s \left(\frac{d_1^4 - d_2^4}{d_1} \right) \tag{4.16}$$

The most suitable way to determine the outer diameter d_1 is to assume a tentative value (and the experienced designer should have some idea, with the value of d_2 already known) and then to see if the resulting shear stress falls within the permissible value from the following transposition of eqn (4.16):

$$f_s = 16 Q_T d_1 / \pi (d_1^4 - d_2^4) \tag{4.17}$$

Having satisfied ourselves that the chosen value of d_1 is satisfactory in all respects, it only remains to compensate for the weakening effect of the keyseat but before this can be done we shall have to determine the size of the key. Having done this the tentatively accepted value of d_1 should be increased to some value d_1' such that

$$d_1' = d_1 + t_k/3 \tag{4.18}$$

This expression is purely empirical, based on practical experience, since there is no analytical means of determining the weakening effect of a keyway or keyseat. One authority suggests that the weakening effect be compensated by adopting an allowable shear stress of only 75% of that which would normally be employed for a solid shaft (or an uncut sleeve in our case).

SIZE OF KEY

We saw in Chapter 3 (wedge-gate sluice valves, eqn (3.25)) that the shearing force F acting on the key was given by

$$F = 2Q_T / d_t$$

In the present treatment the diameter of the sleeve previously denoted by d_t in Chapter 3 is now denoted by d_1 (see Fig. 4.8).

If the effective length and width of the key are again denoted by l_k and w_k respectively, then

$$F = l_k w_k f_s$$

where f_s is the allowable shear stress in the material of the key, then

$$l_k = F / w_k f_s = 2Q_t / d_1 w_k f_s \qquad (4.19)$$

It is recommended, as before, that round-ended keys (BSK R-series) be adopted*.

Since the key is of steel and the sleeve almost invariably of gunmetal, the shear strength of the key *per se* is not the sole criterion of design. The sleeve usually being comprised of softer material than that of the key may be more prone to shear than the key but in a somewhat more irregular manner due to the end restraints provided by the closing in of the keyseat at the two ends, but as the exact line of rupture is unpredictable it is advisable to adopt a 'long by narrow' key rather than a short wide one. The ideal would be a Woodruff key, but the shell-like nature of the sleeve rules out this type, the keyseat for which intrudes appreciably on the 'shaft'.

PILLARS

These are proportioned at the ends only to resist the *tensile* forces imposed in *closing down* the valve. Whilst they are just as often subjected to *compressive* forces in the opening process, the relatively robust proportions of the midsection is sufficient to offset the buckling tendencies induced in *opening* the valve.

The upper extremities as well as the lower will take the brunt of the total axial force P_A previously determined, but since the lower extremities will also be subjected to some bending due to the pull on the handwheel, they will be larger than the upper extremities as we shall see.

Consider first the upper extremities:

Tensile force in each pillar $= P_A / n_p$

where $n_p =$ number of pillars (generally *two* but in the larger size valves working at high pressures *four* are sometimes essential).

*BS46:1958 Part 1: *Keys and Keyways*

If d_{r0} = the *root* diameter of the upper extremity and

f_t = the allowable tensile stress

then

$$d_{r0} = \sqrt{(4P_A / \pi n_p f_t)} \tag{4.20}$$

A suitable standard size of screwed terminations appropriate to the calculated root diameter may then be determined from appropriate tables, noting that $\frac{1}{2}$ in BSW or 12 mm should be regarded as minimal, whatever the working pressure.

Regarding the lower extremities, the next standard size *above* that adopted for the upper extremity represents customary practice; this will cater for the bending stress inevitably imposed in pulling on the handwheel.

STOP-MEMBER

Parallel slide valves featuring the 'spring-between-disk' seating mechanism normally incorporate a stop-member for arresting the downward travel of the disks. Thus, no amount of additional force applied to the handwheel will affect closure-tightness. The line pressure, assisted by the precompressed spring, is the sole agent for securing closure-tightness.

Consequently, the full extent of the axial force P_A could be transmitted to the stop member, and this would induce bending, but it could be argued that this would occur only if the valve were closed down hard under conditions of zero line pressure. The alert operator, finding that the disks were approaching their final position as indicated by the position of the stop member, would relax his efforts at the approach to full closure. (It is recommended that the stem be eased back slightly after bottoming in order to mitigate the possible binding effects of differential expansion.)

Were the stop member to be designed to resist fully the total axial force P_A, then it would assume proportions approximating to those of the crosshead which, of course, cannot escape the full impact of this force.

CROSSHEAD

In the simpler form of parallel slide valve employing two pillars only, the crosshead is effectively a beam, more or less centrally loaded by the axial force P_A and supported at the ends by the pillars. The actual degree of support is open to question; in terms of beam theory, the crosshead is neither *encastré* (built-in) nor simply supported (resting on knife edges). For a centrally applied load P_A and a 'span' L, the bending moment at the centre of the span would be $P_A L/6$ for an *encastré* beam and $P_A L/4$ for a beam simply supported, but again P_A is by no means a point load but is uniformly distributed over an annular area around the centre of the span.

As the degree of fixity and loading as both uncertain, experience suggests a compromise bending moment of

$$P_A L/5$$

Then since the bending moment $M = FI/y = fZ$ where f is the allowable stress, I the moment of inertia (better described as the 'second moment of area'), y the distance from the neutral axis to the remote 'fibres', and Z the section modulus for a crosshead of perfectly rectangular cross-section, we have

$$P_A L/5 = fb_x d_x^2/6 \qquad (4.21)$$

whence

$$b_x = 6P_A L/5 d_x^2 f \qquad (4.22)$$

$$d_x = \sqrt{(6P_A L/5b_x f)} \qquad (4.23)$$

where b_x is the effective breadth of the crosshead at the centre and d_x the depth. By *effective* breadth is meant the actual measured breadth B_x *minus* the diameter of the central hole d_c for containing the actuating sleeve (see Fig. 4.6 (a)).

The crossheads of parallel slide valves (or any other manually operated valves with pillars) may be of two kinds: the one-piece pattern depicted at (a) in Fig. 4.6 or the two-piece—or laminated—pattern depicted at (b).

In this latter form a collar C formed integrally with the sleeve and trapped between the two crosshead laminations—with appropriate running clearances—has the added advantage of providing some degree of resilience, much in the manner of a carriage spring, and is thus able to some extent to cater for any axial expansion of the stem.

It must not be overlooked, however, that in calculating the depth d_x this will be the depth of *either* lamination since each will behave alternately as a single entity under each reversal of loading and *not* as a combined unit. This is the result of the integral thrust collar being located *between* and not under the two laminations.

In the case of the laminated crosshead, the mid-section is not simply comprised of two rectangles (as in the transverse section in Fig. 4.6(a)), because of the recess for accommodating the collar on the actuating sleeve. If the two adjacent portions of the mid-section be slid towards each other, the result would be the 'massed-up' figure shown in Fig. 4.6(b) of width b_x and depth d_x. This would have the same moment of inertia (second moment of area) and section modulus as that of the true section of width B_x.

The effect of the recess is to alter the position of the neutral axis of the section, which will now be displaced upwards slightly, and the determination of the moment of inertia (I) or of the section modulus (Z) is made less simple.

However, since the expression for the bending moment ($P_A L /5$) is at best only a compromise, and since the intrusion of the recess in the massed-up figure is so small, we can ignore these complications. Consequently, for all practical purposes, the cross-section of one lamination of the compound crosshead depicted in Fig. 4.6(b) may be taken as a solid section of breadth b_x and depth d_x (see massed-up figure) when eqns (4.21), (4.22) and (4.23) will apply equally for both forms of crosshead.

Where it is expedient to incorporate ball thrust washers in the crosshead to resist the axial load and to reduce the operating torque, the section is more complicated and these simplified equations will not apply. In such cases it will be advisable to determine the second moment of area (I) with precision and this provides an interesting problem which is featured in the worked example with which this chapter ends.

LENGTH OF THREAD ENGAGEMENT

Proceeding as in the case of the screw-down valve (Chapter 2) where a_b denotes the required bearing area, d_3 and d_4 the outside and root diameters respectively of the stem, H_t the length of thread engagement, p_s the pitch of the threads, n the total number of turns contained in the desired length H_t, p_b the allowable intensity of bearing pressure on the engaging surfaces of the screw threads, and P_A (in this case) the maximum axial load to be sustained, then

Bearing area per pitch of screw $= \pi /4 (d_3^2 - d_4^2)$

very approximately.

Required bearing area $= P_A /p_b$

Therefore

$$n = a_b / (\pi/4)\{d_3^2 - d_4^2\}$$
$$= 4P_A / \pi p_b \{d_3^2 - d_4^2\}$$

and

$$H_T = n p_s \qquad (4.24)$$

A value of p_b of 1 000 lbf/in² or 7 N/mm² is recommended for gunmetal on carbon steel or on stainless steel. Any value of H_T less than $1\frac{1}{2}d_3$ should be rejected.

BYPASS VALVES

In the larger sizes of valves, and especially with high pressures, it is essential to incorporate a bypass valve (see Fig. 4.7) whereby both sides of the main valve may be placed in equilibrium—or nearly so—prior to opening the main valve.

This has the effect of reducing the pressure loading on the downstream seating face, which means that a smaller axial force is needed to manipulate the main valve. Moreover, the inclusion of a bypass valve has the added advantage of permitting the ancillary pipework and the equipment beyond to be warmed up slowly, instead of violently as happens when the main valve is opened up to its fullest extent (in the matter of a few seconds in some instances).

There would appear to be no fixed rule correlating size of bypass with size of main valve but the relationship given in Table 4.2 is representative of average current practice.

Table 4.2 Size of bypass valves for parallel slide valves

Size of main valve		Size of bypass recommended	
Inch	Nearest metric running size in mm	inch	mm
4	100	$\frac{1}{2}$	12
5, 6, 7	125–150	$\frac{3}{4}$	20
8 to 14	200–350	1	25
15, 16	400	$1\frac{1}{4}$	32
18 to 20	500	$1\frac{1}{2}$	40
22 to 24	600	2	50

CHEST THICKNESS

The bodies of parallel slide valves are of three kinds: the lower pressure valves generally favour the 'box' section shown at (a) in Fig. 4.9; medium pressure valves sometimes favour the 'quasi-elliptical' section shown at (b); whilst the ultra high pressure valves should have truly cylindrical configuration as at (c).

Table 4.3 gives an approximate outline of the recommended working conditions appropriate to the three kinds, but is not to be interpreted as rigidly conforming to any makers' standard practice or to be in strict accord with any ruling specification. In this latter respect, however, the reader would be well-advised to study Tables A1 and A2 of BS4504:1969 giving temperature/pressure ratings appropriate to various flange materials since what applies to the flanges must equally apply to the body of which they form an integral part. The designer should be alerted to the fact that, in valve work, pressure and temperature should be regarded as being in inverse ratio; as the temperature *increases* the allowable working pressure *decreases*. In any calculation the figures adopted for the safe working stress should take account of the anticipated working temperature. The values given in Tables A and B of the Appendix are those at 'room' temperature.

For any pressure vessel, the 'box' section featured in (a) is inherently bad 'pressure vessel' design, but in the lower range of pressures and temperatures it is acceptable since it permits the smallest possible length over the connecting flanges. The 'quasi-elliptical' section is a distinct improvement on the box section since it is approaching the 'cylindrical' form, but the truly cylindrical section is ideal and is the only logical section in the realms of high pressure combined with temperature.

The determination of the chest thickness in the case of the box section body by mathematical analysis is beset with complexity and there is no simple rule. This particular problem has intrigued many investigators, noteworthy among these being P. Field Foster. To those with only a moderate grasp of mathematics Mr Foster's analysis may prove 'heavy going'.

Table 4.3 gives chest thicknesses appropriate to various valve sizes and materials of construction, the thicknesses given being representative of the author's own findings.

The aim at all times should be to maintain a uniform chest thickness throughout the entire body and to avoid sudden changes in contour (wellnigh impossible in the case of the box section pattern). An exception is sometimes desirable in the case of the neck portion adjacent to the pipe

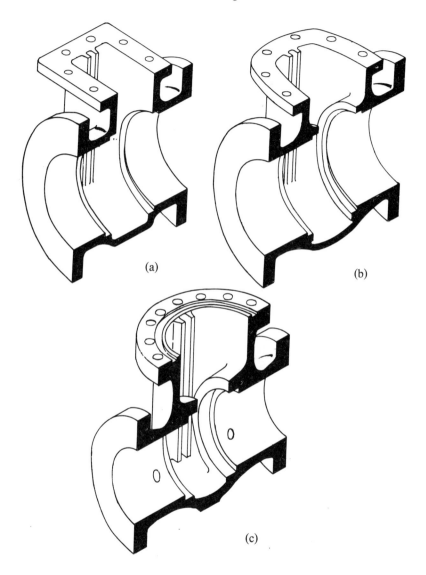

Fig. 4.9 (a) *Typical parallel slide valve body—rectangular or 'box' section*
(b) *Typical parallel slide valve body—quasi-elliptical section*
(c) *Typical parallel slide valve body—circular section*

Table 4.3 Recommended chest thicknesses for parallel slide valve bodies and bonnets
Appropriate to various primary service pressure ratings

Size of valve mm	Recommended minimum chest thickness mm						Size of valve mm
	Rectangular 'box' section	Quasi-elliptical section	Circular section	Circular section	Circular section	Circular section	
	Grey cast iron	Cast carbon steel (up to 350°C) or Carbon molybdenum steel			Cast chromium molybdenum steel		
	1 N/mm²	2 N/mm²	2·75 N/mm²	3·5 N/mm²	6 N/mm²	10 N/mm²	
25	*	*	*	8	9	12	25
32	*	*	*	9	11	14	32
40	*	8	9	10	12	15	40
50	8	9	10	11	14	19	50
65	9	11	12	13	16	22	65
80	10	12	13	14	19	24	80
100	11	13	14	16	21	29	100
125	12	16	18	19	26	37	125
200	13	17	19	25	31	47	200
250	14	19	21	28	36	57	250
300	15	21	24	31	40	66	300
350	16	22	27	35	46	70	350
400	17	24	28	37	53	79	400
450	18	25	30	41	57	89	450
500	19	27	33	44	63	98	500
600	21	30	36	50	73	114	600

Size of valve in	Rectangular 'box' section — Grey cast iron — 150 psig	Quasi-elliptical section — Cast carbon steel (up to 650°F) or Carbon molybdenum steel — 300 psig	Circular section — 400 psig	Circular section — 500 psig	Circular section — Cast chromium molybdenum steel — 900 psig	Circular section — 1500 psig
1	*	*	*	$\frac{5}{16}$	$\frac{3}{8}$	$\frac{1}{2}$
$1\frac{1}{4}$	*	*	*	$\frac{11}{32}$	$\frac{7}{16}$	$\frac{9}{16}$
$1\frac{1}{2}$	*	$\frac{5}{16}$	$\frac{11}{32}$	$\frac{3}{8}$	$\frac{1}{2}$	$\frac{19}{32}$
2	$\frac{11}{32}$	$\frac{3}{8}$	$\frac{13}{32}$	$\frac{7}{16}$	$\frac{9}{16}$	$\frac{3}{4}$
$2\frac{1}{2}$	$\frac{3}{8}$	$\frac{7}{16}$	$\frac{15}{32}$	$\frac{15}{32}$	$\frac{5}{8}$	$\frac{7}{8}$
3	$\frac{13}{32}$	$\frac{15}{32}$	$\frac{1}{2}$	$\frac{1}{2}$	$\frac{3}{4}$	$\frac{15}{16}$
4	$\frac{7}{16}$	$\frac{1}{2}$	$\frac{9}{16}$	$\frac{5}{8}$	$\frac{27}{32}$	$1\frac{1}{8}$
6	$\frac{15}{32}$	$\frac{5}{8}$	$\frac{11}{16}$	$\frac{3}{4}$	$1\frac{1}{32}$	$1\frac{1}{2}$
8	$\frac{1}{2}$	$\frac{11}{16}$	$\frac{3}{4}$	1	$1\frac{1}{4}$	$1\frac{7}{8}$
10	$\frac{9}{16}$	$\frac{3}{4}$	$\frac{27}{32}$	$1\frac{1}{8}$	$1\frac{7}{16}$	$2\frac{1}{4}$
12	$\frac{5}{8}$	$\frac{13}{16}$	$\frac{15}{16}$	$1\frac{1}{4}$	$1\frac{9}{16}$	$2\frac{5}{8}$
14	$\frac{21}{32}$	$\frac{7}{8}$	$1\frac{1}{16}$	$1\frac{3}{8}$	$1\frac{13}{16}$	$2\frac{3}{4}$
16	$\frac{11}{16}$	$\frac{15}{16}$	$1\frac{1}{8}$	$1\frac{1}{2}$	$2\frac{1}{16}$	$3\frac{1}{8}$
18	$\frac{23}{32}$	1	$1\frac{3}{16}$	$1\frac{5}{8}$	$2\frac{1}{4}$	$3\frac{1}{2}$
20	$\frac{3}{4}$	$1\frac{1}{16}$	$1\frac{5}{16}$	$1\frac{3}{4}$	$2\frac{1}{2}$	$3\frac{7}{8}$
24	$\frac{13}{16}$	$1\frac{3}{16}$	$1\frac{7}{16}$	2	$2\frac{7}{8}$	$4\frac{1}{2}$

Recommended minimum chest thickness in

*Castings not recommended in these sizes and ratings.

connecting flanges by increasing the wall thickness at these two points to cater for the endwise crushing forces which could result from expansion of the connecting pipework.

BONNET FLANGES AND BOLTING

The same procedure as that adopted in the case of the wedge-gate sluice valve should apply equally well in the case of the parallel slide valve, but bearing in mind that in the latter type of valve we have to contend with very much higher working temperatures in most applications. This calls for more discrimination in the choice of material for the bolts securing the bonnet to the body. In the severest cases, creep-resisting steel is indicated and in this connection attention is directed to Tables A1 and A2 of BS4504:1969.

In Chapter 3, eqn (3.27), it was stated that the load to be imparted by *each* cover bolt or stud may be determined from the relation

$$P_n = \frac{p}{n}(A + a_f \eta_3) \tag{4.25}$$

where p is the line pressure, n the number of bolts or studs, A the cross-sectional area of the neck of the body casing based on the mean diameter D_g of the gasket, a_f the contact area of the jointing face or gasket, and η_3 a factor appropriate to the nature of the gasket and its mating surfaces. Values of η_3 appropriate to various jointing media are given in Appendix M.

To the value of P_n must be added the load due to the axial force required to close the valve, this being transmitted to the bolts/studs via the thrust collar and the bonnet, i.e.

Total load per bolt/stud $P_b = P_n + P_T/n$ $\hspace{2cm}$ (4.26)

With elliptical and quasi-elliptical necked bodies (Figs. 4.10 (a) and (b)) it is customary to employ graphited asbestos sheet gaskets between the mating flanges of the body and bonnet, the gasket arranged to be confined by the inner surfaces of the bolts or studs. For all practical purposes the cross-sectional area of the shell opening may be taken as

$$A = \pi a b$$

where a and b are the semi-major and semi-minor axes respectively and the surface area of the entrained gasket as

$$a_f = \pi(a_1 b_1 - ab)$$

where a_1 and b_1 are semi-major and semi-minor external axes of the gasket.

THICKNESS OF BODY AND BONNET FLANGES

We saw in Chapter 3, eqn (3.33), that the thickness in the case of an elliptical or quasi-elliptical necked body may be determined from the approximate relationship

$$t_c = \sqrt{\left\{ \frac{1 \cdot 35 W_b x}{f\sqrt{(a^2 + b^2)}} \right\}} \qquad (4.27)$$

where W_b = collective force in bolts/studs

x = distance from centre of bolt/stud to junction of neck with flange (i.e. leverage)

f = allowable working stress in flange

a = semi-major axis of shell opening

b = semi-minor axis of shell opening

and in the case of a circular necked body (eqn 3.37) the thickness is given by

$$t_c = \sqrt{(6W_b x / \pi d_n f)} \qquad (4.28)$$

where d_n = outside diameter of neck, other symbols as above.

The derivation of the foregoing formulae is fully outlined in Chapter 3.

STUFFING BOX AND GLAND

Appendix U gives recommendations for the width w_s of the packing annulus or size of square block packing appropriate to various stem diameters, and stipulates that the minimum depth of the box l_s shall be such as to accomodate six rings or sections of packing. For high pressure superheated steam service, this minimum proviso is seldom implemented and the number of sections is increased in accordance with the conditions prevailing or anticipated.

The three-bolt shrouded gland is recommended for the intermediate and larger sizes of valves (sometimes four bolts are preferred), design following

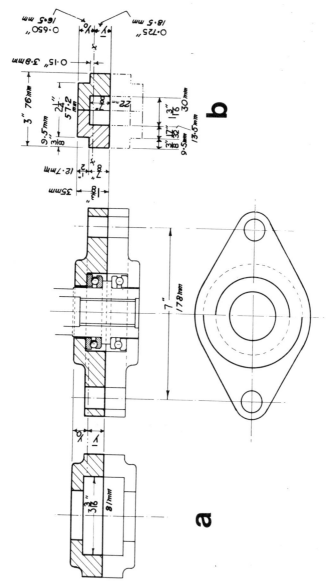

Fig. 4.10 *Laminated crosshead details, 6 in parallel slide valve, working pressure 450 lbf/in²*

the lines previously advocated in Chapter 2 (Fig. 2.5 (b)). For example, the length of penetration l_g may be made $2\frac{1}{2}$ to $3\frac{1}{2}$ times the width w_s of the packing annulus.

It has been shown (eqn 3.40) that the total force U_T to be resisted by the full complement of gland bolts or studs—two, three or four—is given by:

$$U_T = U_p + U_d$$
$$= (\pi/4)p\{D_s^2 - d_s^2\} + 0\cdot47d_s l_s p \qquad (4.29)$$

where $p =$ the working pressure, $D_s =$ diameter of stuffing box, $U_p =$ upthrust due to line pressure, $U_d =$ upthrust due to 'drag' of packing, $d_s =$ diameter of stem passing through and $l_s =$ length of packing space.

Then load per bolt or stud

$$F_S = U_T / n \qquad (4.30)$$

where $n =$ number of bolts or studs adopted.

The requisite size of bolt or stud may then be selected from Appendix N and other proportions from Fig. 2.5 (b).

WORKED EXAMPLE

Determine the essential requirements of a 150 mm diameter parallel slide valve of the type employing 'spring-between-disk' closure mechanism, suitable for a maximum working steam pressure of 3 100 kN/m², the steam being superheated to a total temperature of 425°C.

Assume the spring separating the disks exerts an installed thrust of 125 N. Ignore the balancing effect of any bypass valve which, although expedient, might not be opened prior to the main valve, especially in an emergency.

Solution

For these conditions a truly circular body as illustrated in Fig. 4.9 (c) is advised, the material of both body and cover being cast steel. The pipe connecting flanges may conform to Table 40.1 of BS4504:1969 although this might depend upon the customer's preference according to the eventual geographical location of the valve.

Naturally, the valve will require to be of the outside screw pattern, the actuating screw mechanism being best located well away from the high temperature zone.

Seating members. These will be comprised of rings, preferably of heat-resisting nickel alloy, pressed into the body and into the cast (or forged) steel disks respectively. The actual contact width w may be selected from Table 4.1 which in our case is $\frac{1}{2}$ in (12·45 mm, to be precise).

Axial force to effect closure. We have seen from eqn (4.6) that the *total* axial force P_A is compounded of a number of separate resistances, all of which will require to be overcome simultaneously in the very final instant of closure.

Dealing with these in turn we have, from eqn (4.7), the axial force to overcome frictional resistance of downstream disk to sliding is

$$P_1 = (\pi/4)pd^2\mu_1$$

Take μ_1 at the temperature of 425°C to be 0·20, then

$$P_1 = 0·785 \times 3\,100 \times 0·150^2 \times 0·20 = 10·96\ \text{kN}$$

From eqn (4.8) the axial force to overcome the frictional resistance (or drag) of the stem in the gland packing:

$$P_2 = \pi\mu_s d_s l_s p$$

Take μ_s as 0·15 and d_s will require tentatively to be assumed (and later checked for accuracy of forecasting) say 35 mm, when, from Appendix V, the width of the packing annulus w_s may be interpreted as 8 mm, whence the *minimum* depth $l_s = 6w_s = 48$ mm.

Under the conditions stated in the example a depth l_s of 64 mm would be more in line with practical requirements and this will be adopted, then substituting known data:

$$P_2 = 3·142 \times 0·15 \times \frac{35}{1\,000} \times \frac{64}{1\,000} \times 3\,100$$

$$= 3·272\ \text{kN}$$

From eqn (4.9) the axial force to oppose the upthrust due to the line pressure exerted on the cross-sectional area of the stem of diameter d_3 (assumed 35 mm diameter at this point) is

$$P_3 = (\pi/4)d_s^2 p$$

$$= 0·785\ \left(\frac{35}{1\,000}\right)^2 \times 3\,100 = 2·981\ \text{kN}$$

From eqn (4.10) the force to overcome the frictional resistance of the downstream disk on its seating due to the thrust exerted by the spring initially compressed on assembly is

$$P_4 = \mu_1 S$$

Again μ_1 is 0·20 and S was given in the example as 125 N. Then

$$P_4 = 0·20 \times 125 = 25·0 \text{ N or } 0·025 \text{ kN}$$

The last remaining consideration is the mass effect of the moving parts but we have seen that it is usual to ignore this in the case of the smaller valves as being insignificant compared with the other forces to be overcome. At all events, the weight of the moving parts *assists* the closing process in a valve appropriately installed with the handwheel uppermost.

We now have all the 'ingredients' for assessing the *total* axial force required:

$$P_A = P_1 + P_2 + P_3 + P_4 - W$$
$$= 10·96 + 3·272 + 2·981 + 0·025 - 0$$
$$= 17·24 \text{ kN}$$

Stem proportions. Tentatively assume a stem screwed 30 mm diameter at its upper extremity with square threads of 6 mm pitch, 12 mm lead (i.e. two start thread), the mean diameter of which will be 27 mm if cut the full depth of half the pitch. The lead angle a of this thread may be readily determined, viz:

$$\tan a = \text{lead/pitch circumference}$$
$$= 12/(\pi \times 27) = 0·1415$$

whence from trigonometrical tables $a = 8°3'$ which is within the slope range recommended in the text.

The unsupported length of stem when the valve is in the final closure stage will be 180 mm so that the ratio of unsupported length to the minimum diameter will be $180/24 = 7·5$, and from Appendix T the allowable stress for a stainless steel stem (see column headed 'hard steel') of this diameter and ratio will lie between 109 N/mm² and 138 N/mm². This figure may be checked from eqn (4.11):

$$f'_c = 4P_A / \pi d_r^2 = (4 \times 17·24)/(3·142 \times 24^2)$$
$$= 0·038 \text{ kN/mm}^2 \text{ or } 38 \text{ N/mm}^2$$

clearly indicating that the stem is strong enough to resist the buckling force imposed, but it must be remembered that this is not the only criterion of design; an advantageous slope of actuating screw thread determines the diameter in this case. In the larger sizes of valves where the ratio of length to diameter is greater, the calculated value of the stress and that given in the table might prove to be in closer agreement.

Torque to effect closure. We have seen that the *total* torque is compounded of two separate and distinct torques: (*a*) that to produce the axial force P_A and (*b*) that to overcome the frictional resistance to rotation of the collar on the actuating sleeve bearing on the crosshead with an axial thrust of intensity P_A.

Taking these in turn, from eqn (4.13),

$$Q_a = P_A p_t / 2 \pi \eta = (17 \cdot 24 \times 12)/(2 \times 3 \cdot 142 \times \eta)$$

This expression contains one unknown, namely η, the mechanical efficiency of the screw thread. This may be determined from the fundamental relationship

$$\eta = \tan a / \tan (a + \varphi)$$

where a = the lead angle = $8° \ 3'$ (previously determined)

φ = the friction angle where $\tan \varphi = \mu$ = the coefficient of friction of the mating materials, lubricated or otherwise.

Assume the threads in our case are perfectly dry; then μ may be taken as $0 \cdot 20$ for stainless steel (stem) on gunmetal (sleeve). One would expect some provision to be made for lubrication of the threads but we must base our design on the worst expectation, then:

$\tan \varphi = \mu = 0 \cdot 20$

$\varphi = 11° \ 21'$

Therefore

$\eta = 0 \cdot 1415/\tan(8° \ 3' + 11° \ 21')$

$= 0 \cdot 1415/0 \cdot 3522$

$= 0 \cdot 4018$ (or $40 \cdot 18\%$)

(This figure may be established from the efficiency curve given in Appendix P.)

Inserting in eqn (4.13), we have

$$Q_a = (17 \cdot 24 \times 12)/(2 \times 3 \cdot 142 \times 0 \cdot 4018)$$
$$= 81 \cdot 946 \text{ kN mm or } 81 \cdot 946 \text{ N mm}$$

and $Q_b = \frac{1}{4}\mu_3 P_A (D_c + d_c)$

Tentatively take $d_c = 50$ mm, $D_c = 66$ mm (to be checked later) and $\mu_3 = 0 \cdot 15$, the contacting surfaces assumed perfectly dry, then:

$$Q_b = \frac{1}{4} \times 0 \cdot 15 \times 17 \cdot 24 \, (66 + 50)$$

$$= 75 \text{ kN mm or } 75\,000 \text{ N mm}$$

Then, from eqn (4.12),

Total torque $Q_T = Q_a + Q_b = 81\,946 + 75\,000$
$$= 156\,946 \text{ N mm}$$

Diameter of handwheel. From eqn (4.15),

Diameter of handwheel $H_w = 2Q_T / \tau$

Taking $\tau = 360$ N for intermittent operation,

$$H_w = (2 \times 156\,946)/360 = 872 \text{ mm } (34 \cdot 3 \text{ in})$$

which is absurdly high, yet it is the size appropriate to a badly conceived design to operate under the conditions stated, wherein no provision has been made for lubricating the essential accessible working surfaces or a bypass valve provided for balancing out—partially or wholly—the load on the downstream disk.

Let us now see what can be done to bring the diameter of the handwheel down to more reasonable proportions, bypass apart.

In the first place we cannot lubricate the valve disks and seatings and so P_A—and consequently Q_A—remain unchanged. Supposing, however, we could eliminate entirely the frictional torque Q_b (an impossibility, of course) then the diameter of handwheel H_w would be equal to

$$2Q_a/360 = (2 \times 81\,946)/360 = 455 \text{ mm (approx.)}$$

The ideal diameter, therefore, would appear to lie somewhere between 455mm and 871 mm. Let us, therefore, reduce the frictional torque Q_b either by arranging grease lubrication of the sleeve within the crosshead (a Stauffer lubricator would suffice) or, better still, by providing a ball thrust washer to take the axial thrust. Let us examine both expedients in turn. Firstly, by adopting grease lubrication, the coefficient of friction μ'_3 may be assigned a value of 0·035, when

$$Q'_b = \frac{1}{4} \times 0·035 \times 17·24 \, (66 + 50)$$

$$= 17·5 \text{ kN mm or } 17\,500 \text{ N mm}$$

The diameter of the handwheel becomes

$$H'_w = (2/360) \, \{81\,946 + 17\,500\} = 552 \text{ mm } (21·73 \text{ in})$$

representing a considerable reduction.

Now let us consider the effect of introducing a ball thrust washer. According to Goodman the coefficient of friction of a ball bearing may vary from 0·0010 to 0·0015. Taking the larger of these values and the pitch diameter of the race to be 63·5 mm,

$$Q'_b = P_A \mu d_b / 2 = (17·24 \times 0·0015 \times 63·5)/2 = 0·821 \quad \text{kN} \quad \text{mm} \quad \text{or}$$
$$= 821 \text{ N mm}$$

an almost insignificant figure and one pointing to the wisdom of employing ball thrust washers.

Again

$$H'_w = 2 \, (81\,946 + 821)/360$$
$$= 460 \text{ mm } (18 \text{ in}), \text{ a more reasonable size.}$$

One manufacturer actually employs an $18\frac{1}{4}$ in (465 mm) diameter handwheel on a valve of this size and intended for the same working conditions as those cited in the example.

Larger valves for the same working conditions and suitably lubricated or employing ball thrust washers would necessitate some form of reduction gearing when the handwheel diameter would otherwise work out inordinately large. The foregoing calculations further emphasize the wisdom of incorporating a bypass valve for equalizing the pressure on the seatings and thereby appreciably reducing the axial force required to close (or open) the valve. Calculations, however, must be based on the assumption that the bypass may be overlooked in an emergency. Two forms of handwheels are given in Appendix X and Y.

Stuffing box and gland. We have now sufficient data to enable us to determine the proportions of the stuffing box and gland. Since these items are based to a great extent on the lower diameter of the stem and the size of the packing annulus the data given in Appendix U should be considered.

Actuating sleeve. We have seen (eqn 4.17) that, to establish the diameter d_1 (see Fig. 4.8) of the sleeve termination, firstly assume a value for d_2, the inner diameter (which is slightly in excess of that of the screwed portion of the stem), and then determine the shear stress f_s imposed, disregarding meantime the weakening effect of the loss of metal due to the intrusion of the keyseat.

Proceeding on these lines, take $d_2 = 30$ mm and assume $d_1 = 50$ mm. Then, from eqn (4.17),

$$\text{Shear stress induced} f_s = 16 Q_T d_1 / \pi (d_1^4 - d_2^4)$$
$$= (16 \times 156\ 946 \times 50)/3 \cdot 142\ (50^4 - 30^4)$$
$$= 7 \cdot 341\ \text{N/mm}^2$$

which is reasonably low, but we must compensate for the weakening effect of the keyseat. Moreover, the sleeve may be subject to some amount of bending concurrently with the torque imposed. Let us hold this figure meanwhile and determine the size of key to be adopted.

Size of key. Taking the width of the key $w_k = d_1/8$ then

$$w_k = 50/8 = 6 \cdot 25\ \text{mm (say 6 mm)}$$

Adopt a key of rectangular section, then from eqn (4.19), taking $f_s = 46$ N/mm²,

$$\text{Length } l_k = 2 Q_T / d_1 w_k f_s = (2 \times 156\ 946)/(50 \times 6 \times 46) = 22 \cdot 75\ \text{mm}$$

Adopt the nearest standard length (25 mm).

The weakening effect due to the intrusion of this particular key would not cause any appreciable increase in the shear stress; therefore, the originally assumed value of 50 mm for d_1 should be accepted.

Pillars. First consider the upper screwed extremities.

From eqn (4.20),

$$\text{root diameter } d_{ro} = \sqrt{(4 P_A / \pi n_p f_t)}$$

Take n_p the number of pillars to be two and f_t the permissible tensile stress for mild steel (the usual material) to be 70 N/mm². Then,

$$d_{r0} = \sqrt{\{(4 \times 17{\cdot}24 \times 1\ 000)/(3{\cdot}142 \times 2 \times 70)\}} = 12{\cdot}52\ \text{mm}$$

$$(0{\cdot}49\ \text{in approx.})$$

Since 12·52 mm is the theoretical root diameter the upper screwed termination should conform to the metric standard M16, i.e. 16 mm diameter at the top of the thread. The lower extremities may be made one size larger, say M20, so as to compensate for any bending stresses incurred by tugging on the handwheel.

Crosshead. Before we can determine the essential scantlings of the crosshead, we shall require to form some idea of the space taken up by the gland in order to establish the smallest possible centre distance of the pillars and the precise configurations of the actuating sleeve, together with the space taken up by the ball thrust washers which will also have an influence on the design of the crosshead.

It would be advisable, therefore, at this stage to finalize the stuffing box and gland dimensions in so far as these affect the disportation of the pillars and the crosshead.

First determine the size of the gland bolts/studs required. Adopt three in number, then from eqn (4.29), the total force to be imparted by gland bolts/studs is

$$U_T = (\pi/4)p\{D_s^2 - d_s^2\} + 0{\cdot}47 d_s l_s p$$

$$= 0{\cdot}785 \times 3\ 100\ \left\{\left(\frac{50}{1\ 000}\right)^2 - \left(\frac{35}{1\ 000}\right)^2\right\}$$

$$+ \frac{0{\cdot}47 \times 35 \times 64 \times 3\ 100}{1\ 000 \times 1\ 000}$$

$$= 3{\cdot}104 + 3{\cdot}26 = 6{\cdot}364\ \text{kN or } 6364\ \text{N}$$

Then

force per bolt $= 6364/3 = 212$ N

From Appendix N M16 bolts are indicated if of 430 N/mm² steel and although this table is primarily intended for the bolts securing the cover plates of pressure vessels it could apply equally in this case.

From the design so far completed the outside diameter of the gland would approximate to 125 mm when the centres of the pillars, two in number be it remembered, could be made 178 mm.

The split crosshead is shown to better advantage in the sub-assembly outlined in Fig. 4.10.

Since the particular diameter of the sleeve denoted by d_c, in Fig. 4.8 more or less determines the bore of the ball thrust washers, this almost invariably results in the adoption of washers strong enough to sustain the maximum axial load ever to be imposed in the manipulation of the valve. In the present case the axial load P_A is 17 240 N and the ball thrust washers adopted are each capable of sustaining a steady load of approximately 30 kN (3 tonf) according to one well-known bearing manufacturer, provided the rotation is relatively slow, as in the case of our valve.

The proportions of the ball thrust washers, and that of the collar on the actuating sleeve separating them, also decide to some extent the mid-proportions of the split crosshead, so the best procedure to adopt in this case is to decide on a convenient section and then test it for adequacy of strength to resist the somewhat speculative bending moment imposed by the centrally applied axial load P_A.

This involves prior knowledge of the moment of inertia I of the section concerned or of Z, the section modulus. For the section adopted, namely that of a 'bossed up' flat plate, the determination of I is somewhat involved.

The first step is to determine the area of the transverse cross-section of the *upper* portion of the split or laminated crosshead. It must be remembered that only one laminate at a time resists the axial forces, the *top* laminate when the valve is being *closed*, the *bottom* one when the valve is being *opened.* Each laminate is virtually a single crosshead; the two cannot share the load with this arrangement. The true transverse cross-section is shown to the left of the sectional arrangement, i.e. at (a) in Fig. 4.10. To the right of the sectional arrangement (at (b)) is shown the 'bossed up' figure resulting from the simple process of sliding each half of the section towards the other, the resulting figure presenting the same area of material and having the same moment of inertia (about a horizontal axis yet to be determined) as would obtain in the case of the true cross-section shown at (a).

Note that in order to avoid unnecessary complication, radiused corners are ignored.

Let A_C = cross-sectional area of figure, then

$$A_C = 57 \cdot 2 \times 35 + 22 \times 19 - 22 \times 30$$
$$= 1\ 758\ \text{mm}^2$$

Now determine the position of the neutral axis, distant $\bar{y}$ from the lower face:

$\bar{y}$ = sum of moments of area about lower face/area of figure

$= \{19 \times 22 \times 11 + 57 \cdot 2 \times 35 \times 17 \cdot 5 - 30 \times 22 \times 11\}/1\ 758$

$= 18 \cdot 5$ mm

The neutral axis xx (Fig. 4.10 (b)) may now be drawn in.

We now require to determine the moment of inertia I (or the section modulus Z) of the section. Consider the section to be comprised of two separate sections, each sharing a common base line xx, then I_{base} of any rectangle $= bd^3/3$ where b and d are the breath and depth respectively. Then,

$I_{xx} = \{76 \times 18 \cdot 5^3 - 30 \times 18 \cdot 5^3 + 57 \cdot 2 \times 16 \cdot 5^3 - 30 \times 3 \cdot 8^3 +$
$$19 \times 3 \cdot 8^3\}/3$$
$= \{481\ 203 - 189\ 948 + 256\ 949 - 1\ 646 + 1\ 042\}/3$

$= 182\ 533$ mm^4 units

Now $M/I = f/y_0$ where M is the bending moment, y_0 is the vertical distance from the neutral axis xx to the remote 'fibres' under consideration, in our case the top, or tension, side when $y_0 = 35 - 18 \cdot 5$ mm $= 16 \cdot 5$ mm.

From the treatment proceding eqn (4.21) it was decided to adopt a compromise bending moment M of $P_A L/5$, then substituting in the above expression:

$$P_A L/5I_{xx} = f/y_0$$

Inserting known values and transposing:

$f = (17 \cdot 24 \times 178 \times 16 \cdot 5)/(5 \times 182\ 533)$

$= 0 \cdot 05547$ kN/mm$^2 = 55 \cdot 47$ N/mm^2

$= 55\ 470$ kN/m^2

which is reasonably low for cast steel but not so low as to justify revising the original dimensions.

Length of thread engagement. From eqn (4.24),

Number of pitches $n = 4P_A / \pi p_b(d_3^2 - d_4^2)$

Adopt a value for p_b of 7 N/mm² or 0·007 kN/mm² for stainless steel on gunmetal,

$$n = (4 \times 17·24)/\{3·142 \times 0·007\ (32^2 - 25^2)\}$$

$$= 7·86, \text{ say } 8 \text{ turns}$$

Now

$$H_T = np_s = 8 \times 6 \text{ mm} = 48 \text{ mm} \ (1·9 \text{ in})$$

Body shell configurations. We have seen that for the working conditions stated the cylindrical form of body featured in Fig. 4.9 (c) should be adopted, the inside diameter of which is readily determined once a plan view has progressed sufficiently to ensure that the disks will not foul the enveloping circle denoted by the inner diameter of the neck of the body.

The thickness of the shell appropriate to the working conditions may be selected from Table 4.3 but the wall thickness adjacent to the pipe connecting flanges should be thicker, bearing in mind that sufficient clearance should be provided for the nuts or bolt heads of the joint bolts. In the design under consideration the inside diameter works out at 248 mm ($9\frac{3}{4}$ in) and its thickness 19 mm ($\frac{3}{4}$ in).

The thickness t_p of the 'pipe' portions may be made larger, say 22 to 24 mm.

Bonnet flanges and bolting. The first essential is to determine the size of the bolts to be employed. We saw in Chapter 3, eqn (3.27), that the load to be imparted by *each* bolt to secure the bonnet or cover against the line pressure is

$$P_n = \frac{p}{n}(A + a_f \eta_3)$$

where p = the line pressure, n = the number of bolts, A = the cross-sectional area of the shell opening (in this case the cross-sectional area of a circle denoting the mean diameter of the joint ring), a_f = the contact area of the jointing face or gasket, and η_3 = a factor appropriate to the nature of the gasket and taken from Appendix M.

Now this force P_n due to the pressure loading is not the only force to be sustained by each individual bonnet-securing bolt. In the case of the parallel slide valve design in which the pillars are screwed directly into the bonnet (see Fig. 4.11) the axial force P_A required to effectively close the valve and

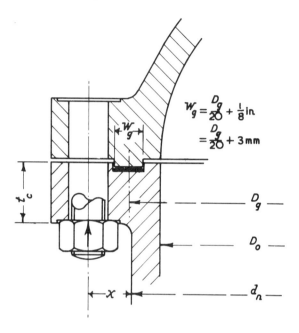

Fig. 4.11 *Detail of parallel slide valve body and bonnet joint flanges*

previously calculated will be transmitted to the bolts, hence:

Total load per bolt $P_b = P_n + P_A / n$

Let us take the number of bolts n to be sixteen; from the design so far completed this would appear to be the ideal number, the bolts neatly pitched, and the following 'key' dimensions then emerge (see Fig. 4.11):

Inside diameter of body casing $D_o = 248$ mm ($9\frac{3}{4}$ in)

Inside diameter of bonnet joint ring spigot $D_g = 290$ mm ($11\frac{3}{8}$ in)

Width of joint ring $w_g = (D_g/20) + 3$ mm

$$= (290/20) + 3 = 17.5 \text{ mm}$$

Evaluating further:

$$A = (\pi/4) D_g^2 = 0.785 \times 290^2 = 66\,052 \text{ mm}^2$$

and

$a_f = \pi D_g w_g$ very approx.

$\quad = 3 \cdot 142 \times 290 \times 17 \cdot 5 = 15\ 944\ \text{mm}^2$

Adopting a serrated 'Monel' joint ring as shown at (c) in Appendix M we see that the gasket factor η_3 is given as $3 \cdot 75$, then we have:

$$P_b = P_n + P_A / n$$

$$= \frac{p}{n}(A + a_f \eta_3) + \frac{P_A}{n}$$

Substituting previously determined values:

$$P_b = \frac{3100}{16}\left(\frac{66\ 052}{1000^2} + \frac{15\ 944 \times 3 \cdot 75}{1000^2}\right)$$

$$= 24 \cdot 38\ \text{kN or } 24\ 380\ \text{N}$$

Referring to Appendix N sixteen M22 bolts would be sufficient if of 1000 N/mm² UTS heat-resisting steel (65 tonf/in²).

From eqn (4.28) the thickness t_c of the bonnet flanges may be determined:

$$t_c = \sqrt{(6W_b x / \pi d_n f)}$$

where d_n = outside diameter of neck, W_b = collective force in bolts (stud-bolts in our case), x = distance from centre of studs to junction of the neck with the flange. Note:

$$x = \{345 - (248 + 2 \times 19)\}/2 = 29 \cdot 5\ \text{mm}$$

and f = allowable working stress for flange material (cast steel). A working temperature of 425°C (800°F) indicates that f should be assigned a value of 50 000 kN/m², then inserting known values:

$$t_c = \sqrt{\{(6 \times 16 \times 24 \cdot 38 \times 29 \cdot 5)/(3 \cdot 142 \times 286 \times 50\ 000)\}}$$

$$= 0 \cdot 0392\ \text{m} = 39 \cdot 2\ \text{mm}\ (1 \cdot 54\ \text{in})$$

This value should be increased to make allowance for the weakening effect due to the encroachment of the joint recess, and a thickness of 45 mm ($1\frac{3}{4}$ in) is suggested for the body bonnet flange although for the sake of appearance both flanges should be of identical thickness.

Bypass valve. The foregoing calculations have taken no account of the advantages which could come from a bypass valve, the opening up of which

BYPASS VALVE CONNECTIONS

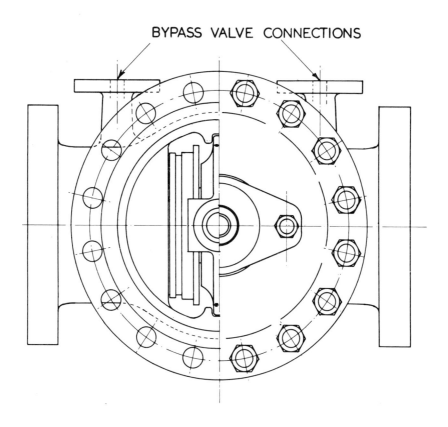

Fig. 4.12 *6 in high pressure parallel slide valve*
Working pressure 450 lbf/in² (3·1 N/mm²)
Working temperature 800°F (427°C)

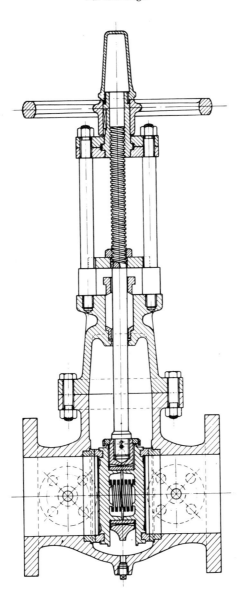

Table 4.4 Parallel slide valve body forms appropriate to optimum working conditions

Type of body	Body and bonnet material	Optimum working Steam Pressure with Temp.
(a). Rectangular 'box' (Fig. 4.11 (a))	Copper alloy e.g. Gunmetal	16 bar at 200°C (max. size 200 mm)
	Grey cast iron	10 bar at 200°C (max. size 350 mm) No superheat
(b) Quasi-elliptical (Fig. 4.11 (b))	Cast carbon steel (up to 350°C) or Carbon molybdenum	24 bar at 425°C (max. size 500 mm)
(c) Circular (Fig. 4.11 (c))	Cast carbon steel (up to 350°C) or Carbon molybdenum	30 bar at 425°C (max. size 400 mm)
	Cast chromium molybdenum steel For temps. >425°C	170 bar at 500°C (max. size 300 mm)

Type of body	Body and bonnet material	Optimum working Steam Pressure with Temp.
(a) Rectangular 'box' (Fig. 4.11 (a))	Copper alloy e.g. Gunmetal	250 psig at 400°F (max. size 8″)
	Grey cast iron	150 psig at 400°F (max. size 14″) No superheat
(b) Quasi-elliptical (Fig. 4.11 (b))	Cast carbon steel (up to 650°F) or Carbon molybdenum	350 psig at 800°F (max. size 20″)
(c) Circular (Fig. 4.11 (c))	Cast carbon steel (up to 650°F) or Carbon molybdenum	450 psig at 800°F (max. size 16″)
	Cast chromium molybdenum steel For temps. >800°F	2500 psig at 950°F (max. size 12″)

conditions	Recommended Flange Designation BS4504:1969	
Water		
Pressure with Temp.		
28 bar at 200°C (max. size 200 mm)	Table 16/11	
16 bar at 120°C (max. size 350 mm)	Table 10/11	Valves destined for the petroleum industry should be flanged in accordance with BS1560:1958, *steel pipe flanges and flanged fittings (nominal sizes ½ in to 24 in) for the petroleum industry*, and BS1560:1970 (part 2) (Metric dimensions).
30 bar at 250°C (max. size 500 mm)	Table 25/1	
40 bar at 250°C (max. size 400 mm)	Table 40/1	
280 bar at 350°C (max. size 350 mm)	Table 250/1	

conditions	Recommended Flange Designation BS4504:1969	
Water		
Pressure with Temp.		
410 psig at 400°F (max. size 8")	Table 16/11	
250 psig at 250°F (max. size 14")	Table 10/11	Valves destined for the petroleum industry should be flanged in accordance with BS1560:1958, *steel pipe flanges and flanged fittings (nominal sizes ½ in to 24 in) for the petroleum industry*, and BS1560:1970 (part 2) (Metric dimensions).
450 psig at 450°F (max. size 20")	Table 25/1	
600 psig at 450°F (max. size 16")	Table 40/1	
4000 psig at 650°F (max. size 14")	Table 250/1	

reduces the effort required to manipulate the main valve.

In the present worked example the design illustrated in Fig. 4.12 features flanged connections for a $\frac{3}{4}$ in (20 mm) bypass valve (not shown) which could take the form of a screw-down stop valve or of a parallel slide valve, according to individual preference.

Whatever the type selected, the same care, of course, must be lavished on its design and choice of materials of construction as with the main valve of which it is a most important and essential adjunct for high pressure/temperature service (see Table 4.4).

Chapter Five
Non-Return Valves

SUCH valves are variously styled *check, back pressure, reflux* or *retention* valves according to their differing duties, but all may be classified under the simple descriptive title 'non-return valves' since their function is to permit of only unidirectional flow.

Of necessity all check valves must be automatic in their action, opening and closing 'of their own free will' to permit unidirectional flow only, closing promptly (in theory) at the slightest suggestion of flow reversal (reflux).

Figure 5.1 illustrates a simple valve of this type intended for use in a vertical pipeline. Horizontal pipelines can also be catered for by an alternative design.

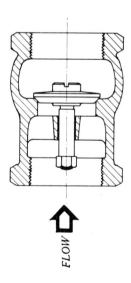

Fig. 5.1 *Simple lift check valve for vertical pipelines*

Now such a valve is prone to derangement resulting from repeated hammer blows of the clack (valve member) on its seating if provision is not made for dampening the inevitable pulsating movement of the clack under the influence of fluctuating flow surges. Some makers attempt to achieve some amelioration of this hammering tendency simply by curtailing the lift of the clack. This ill-conceived practice savours of misrepresentation since restricting the lift is tantamount to supplying an undersize valve. The theoretical lift to give an edge area equivalent to that of the bore is one quarter the diameter of the bore, as can be readily calculated and is perhaps generally known. The lift necessitated in the larger valves is, therefore, somewhat excessive and engenders large inertia forces if means are not provided to dampen the pulsations. This can be achieved in a variety of ways, as will be shown.

Pounding of the seating is caused by the clack being forced hard against the boss of the cover plate and then bouncing back to deal the delicate seating edges a severe blow. This most undesirable propensity may be mitigated by forming the head of the clack with a close—but not too

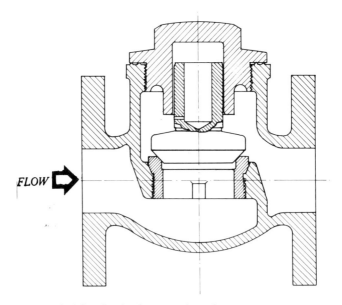

FLOW

Fig. 5.2 *Simple lift valve for horizontal pipelines*

close—fitting piston, arranged to slide freely in a cylinder formed in the
cover. Such a valve embodying this feature is illustrated in Fig. 5.2; the fluid
temporarily trapped above the piston serves to cushion the blow otherwise
occasioned. A small vent hole permits entrained 'fluid' to escape or return
slowly, a feature most desirable when handling incompressible fluids i.e.
liquids.

In another design, still employing the piston and cylinder device, further
dampening is provided by the interposition of a spring (see Fig. 5.3) but the
one selected should not be of proportions more readily associated with a
high pressure safety valve or the lift will be grossly restricted and might not
even result at all, except when the build up of pressure decrees that it should
do so.

As may be appreciated the detail design of small bore non-return valves
for relatively low and medium pressure service calls for little or no
mathematical scrutiny, but larger valves call for some display of stress
analysis. In this regard much helpful data may be gleaned and adapted from
Chapter 2, eg, the design aspects of cover plates, etc.

One form of vertical non-return valve which is an essential prerequisite of
every pumping application involving a suctionhose (e.g. fire-fighting pumps)

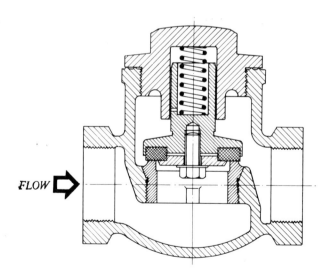

Fig. 5.3 *Horizontal check valve—lift type with spring damping device*

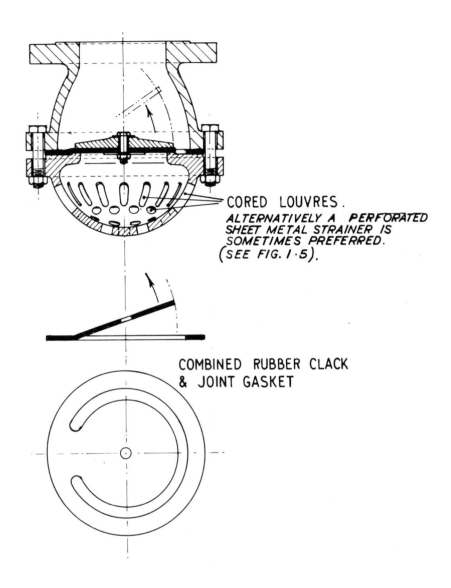

CORED LOUVRES.
ALTERNATIVELY A PERFORATED
SHEET METAL STRAINER IS
SOMETIMES PREFERRED.
(SEE FIG. I·5).

COMBINED RUBBER CLACK
& JOINT GASKET

Fig. 5.4 *Typical foot valve and strainer*

is the 'foot-valve' depicted in Fig. 5.4 and advisedly complete with a strainer for preventing the ingress of alien material likely to jamb the valve clack and cause the pump to lose its prime, when any entrained water would then simply fall back into the pond or tank from which it was drawn.

It is recommended that strainers of the 'in-line' pattern (Fig. 5.5) be fitted on the upstream side of any non-return valve for the same reason, but the

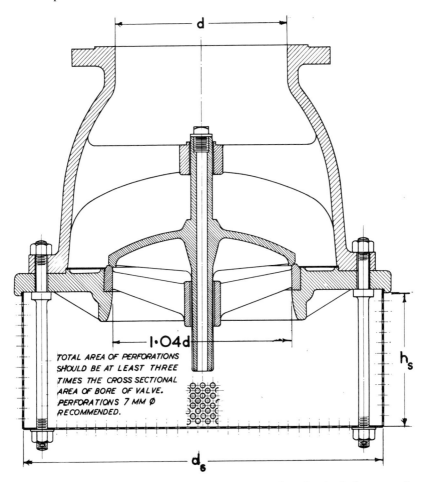

TOTAL AREA OF PERFORATIONS SHOULD BE AT LEAST THREE TIMES THE CROSS SECTIONAL AREA OF BORE OF VALVE. PERFORATIONS 7 MM Ø RECOMMENDED.

Fig. 5.5 *Typical long bore poppet-type foot valve with galvanized sheet metal strainer*

strainer element itself must be taken out periodically for the removal of any accumulations of foreign matter and for cleansing generally.

ISOLATING (NON-RETURN) VALVES

Where two or more boilers discharge into one common steam main it is obligatory to provide a particular form of non-return valve on the downstream side of each boiler stop valve as a precaution against steam passing from a live boiler into one drained and laid up for examination or repair (and in which men may be working) should the stop valve on that boiler be inadvisedly left open, opened accidentally by someone unaware of men working in the boiler or even apparently closed but possibly leaking imperceptibly. Not every stop valve can be relied upon to be one hundred per cent steam tight so the provision of a non-return valve of the type described should provide that degree of safety so patently desired, the seatings of which should be kept in good condition at all times.

Such a non-return valve is illustrated in Fig. 5.6 and is universally termed an *isolating* valve. It is a somewhat refined member of the non-return valve family in that the clack is doubly guided throughout its lift and cushioned against the previously mentioned battering action by means of a close fitting (but not too close fitting) superimposed piston working in its mating cylinder, the piston being devoid of piston rings which might easily become

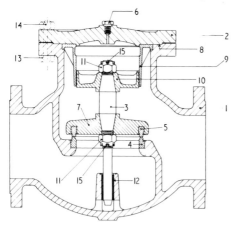

REF NO	DESCRIPTION	MATERIAL
I	BODY	
2	COVER PLATE	CAST STEEL
3	SPINDLE	MILD STEEL
4	SEAT	NI CU ZN ALLOY
5	VALVE FACING	NI CU ZN ALLOY
6	PLUG	MILD STEEL
7	VALVE PLATE	MILD STEEL
8	COVER JOINT RING	NICKEL ALLOY
9	DASHPOT	NI CU ZN ALLOY
10	PISTON	NI CU ZN ALLOY
11	CASTLE NUT	MILD STEEL
12	BUSH	G M OR NI ALLOY
13	BOLT	STEEL
14	NUT	STEEL
15	SPLIT PIN	MILD STEEL

Fig. 5.6 *Boiler isolating valve*

'ironed-in' and thus prevent free movement of the piston. The illustration may give rise to some misconception in this respect; the corrugations are merely grooves cut into the piston in an endeavour to reduce frictional resistance and to impound any small particles of scale or other alien material tending to impede the free movement of the piston.

Apart from the safeguarding propensities of the isolating valve it tends to promote equal steaming of all the boilers in a range, since steam generated at a higher pressure in one particular boiler cannot flow into an adjacent boiler steaming at a lower pressure, its attempt to flow into that boiler being baulked by its isolating valves. Thus the shortcomings of any boiler in the range (or its stoker—human or otherwise) cannot be obscured by the superior performance of any of its neighbours.

The non-return valves so far described and illustrated have all been of the vertical lift pattern, that is to say, the valve member or clack in each case is ordained to rise or fall in a truly vertical path, whether the valve be arranged for installation in either a horizontal or a vertical pipeline. Other forms of non-return valves favour the swinging disk construction, a simple example of a relatively small bore pattern being illustrated in Fig. 5.7.

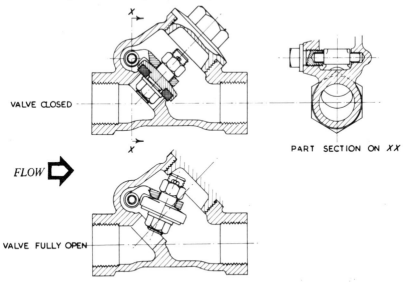

Fig. 5.7 *Non-return or check valve—hinged disk type. Sometimes styled back-pressure valve*

This is a very neat form of non-return valve, care being taken in design to see that the complete assembly of disk (valve member), hinge and attendant parts may be readily passed through the upper screwed hole for receiving the sealing cap.

Where any doubt exists in this regard these may be allayed somewhat by making a cardboard template representing the complete internals assembly and passing same without hindrance through a hole of diameter corresponding to the root diameter of the threaded hole in question.

The hinge should be arranged a slack fit on the pin and the disk itself permitted some amount of 'lost motion' in order that it may sit squarely on the seating face.

REFLUX OR RETENTION VALVES

More elaborate non-return valves of the swinging or door type are exemplified in the reflux or retention valve, mainly employed in waterworks practice, a sectional arrangement of a typical example being illustrated in Fig. 5.8. A commendable feature of this design is the

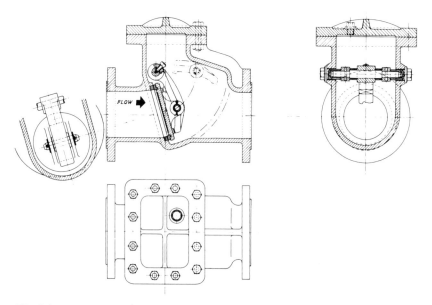

Fig. 5.8 *Reflux or retention valve*

articulated arrangement of hinge and door which again ensures the latter will sit squarely on the seating as in the former more elementary example.

Inordinately large reflux valves, say 400 mm or 16 in bore upwards, incorporate a number of relatively small doors or flaps rather than a single one of most pretentious proportions, the slamming effect of which occasioned by a sudden reflux might well be imagined. Even in single door valves, say up to 200 or 230 mm (8 in or 9 in) bore, the slamming effect and consequent damage to the seating faces may be offset to a great extent by the provision of a simple counterpoise device to balance the door.

Figure 5.9 shows some such device. Instead of the door being free to swing about the hinge pin, or the pin to rotate in its bearing, it is keyed or otherwise secured to the pin (or shaft) which now passes out of the body through a stuffing box and gland to carry a weight-loaded lever, the weight preferably being slidably located on the lever so as to provide some measure of adjustment.

The extent of the hammer blow on the seating face of a reflux valve resulting from a sudden flow reversal is incalculable, as may be appreciated, and it is for this reason that fairly wide seating faces are to be advocated. The inclusion of a somewhat robust longitudinal rib connecting the outlet flange to the body-cover flange will play its part in resisting the hammer blow imparted to the inside of the body casing.

Special designs of reflux valves are available for reducing the effects of shock-loading but these are outside the scope of this particular volume.

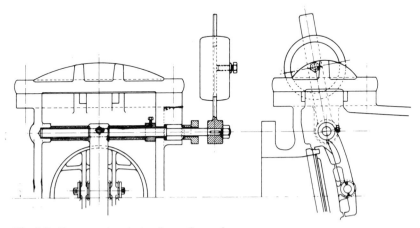

Fig. 5.9 *Counterpoise device for reflux valve*

It is customary in the larger sizes of reflux valves to feature a liberal display of ribbing in view of the fact that the stresses imposed in what at best is a somewhat awkward shape are virtually incalculable; experience more than any other ploy must be the guiding factor.

In another arrangement (Fig. 5.10) again the door is secured to the hinge pin or shaft which passes out of the body through a stuffing box and gland to carry a bell crank lever pinned to the rod of a piston ordained to travel up and down in sympathy with the swing of the door. This piston is housed in a cylinder containing a liberal quantity of light mineral oil which is in communication with both sides of the piston by the inclusion of a vertical cavity having apertures at both top and bottom, the upper one featuring a needle regulating valve whereby the flow to and from each side of the piston can be controlled to a nicety.

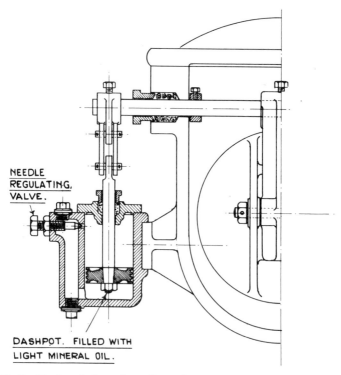

Fig. 5.10 *Cushioning dashpot for reflux valve*

FEED CHECK VALVES

One form of non-return valve essential to the working of all steam boilers (and some other pressure vessels) is the feed check valve, a particular example of the design favoured for both shell type and water-tube boilers being illustrated in Fig. 5.11. The valve permits feed water to be pumped into the boiler against the steam pressure, return flow being prevented by the check valve housed in the branch elbow shown.

This is really a combination of a screw down *manually* operated valve and an entirely *automatic* valve, the screw-down feature enabling the valve either to be screwed down hard to give complete closure for purposes of overhauling the boiler itself or enabling the check portions to be examined or repaired, or to be partially closed, thus controlling the lift and so regulating the rate of feed.

This will be apparent from the illustration (Fig. 5.11).

The valve is very versatile; it may be converted to a 'left hand' valve simply by removing the blank flange on the boiler branch and attaching it to the opposite end of the branch pipe and the inlet elbow may be orientated as desired.

It will be seen that the lower extremity of the manually controlled valve member is in the form of a somewhat robust peg which serves to control the lift of the lower valve member or clack. When the stop valve member is screwed down hard on to its seating the clack should still be permitted a small amount of lift, say 3 mm ($\frac{1}{8}$ in), thus ensuring that the stop valve positively seats at all times without hindrance from the check valve clack whenever the valve is required to be shut down. In the event of this proviso being overlooked it would be impossible to remove the elbow when the boiler was under steam. Even when idle, yet with a goodly supply of water still remaining in the boiler, removal of the elbow could be accompanied by a deluge.

It is most desirable that any feed check valve can be operated satisfactorily from the boiler-house floor (see Clause 35 of BS 759) without recourse to the use of a ladder or similar aid, any of which might well be found to be missing in an emergency.

Where the installation is such that the handwheel would be disadvantageously positioned it is imperative that an extension shaft and gearing be incorporated so as to bring the handwheel within easy reach of even the most diminutive boilerman.

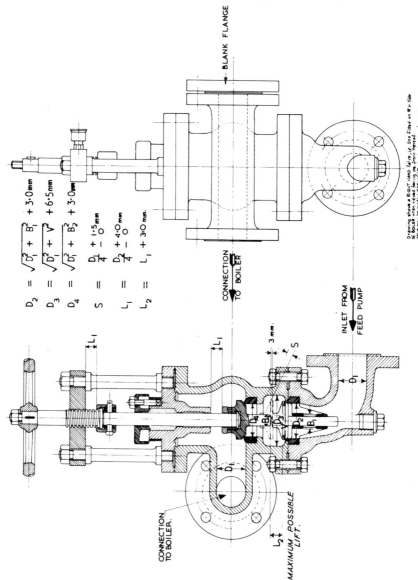

Fig. 5.11 *Accessible type boiler feed check valve*

In boiler design the problem inevitably arises of determining the size of feed valve to employ (especially where no precedent exists to guide selection) appropriate to the evaporative capacity of the boiler. Based solely on the ideal velocity of flow of water in pipes and on the evaporation, the problem is virtually one of simple arithmetic. However, from experience the size of valve so determined almost invariably works out smaller than that chosen by the boiler-maker, pointing to the fact that the purely theoretical aspects of the problem are mellowed somewhat by a certain element of empiricism.

Basing calculations on the evaporative capacity, and dealing first with only the purely arithmetical aspects;

let

E = evaporation (kg/hr or lb/hr)

d = diameter of feed pipe or valve (mm or in)

S = density of feed water (kg/litre or lb/ft³)

v = velocity of flow (m/s or ft/sec)

then

$$E = 3.6 \times \pi/4d^2 \times S \times v \,(\text{kg/hr})$$

or

$$E = 3600 \times \pi/4 \times (d/12)^2 \times S \times v \,(\text{lb/hr})$$

(5.1)

Now, if velocity of flow $(v) = 1.5$ m/s (or 5 ft/sec) and the feed water density $(S) = 1$ kg/litre (or 62.5 lb/ft³) then the above equations will simplify to give

$$d = 0.4856 \sqrt{E} \text{ mm (or } d = 0.01277 \sqrt{E} \text{ in)} \qquad (5.2)$$

At higher temperatures the water density will be somewhat less than the above values, although the difference is so slight as to be inconsequential in calculations of this order. Indeed when it is remembered that there is no particular virtue in flow velocities of *exactly* 1.5 m/s (or 5 ft/sec), and that the final value will be a round figure dimension anyway, then it will be appreciated that for most practical purposes the above expressions can be regarded as:

$$d\,(\text{mm}) = \sqrt{\frac{\text{Evaporative capacity}}{2}}\;(\text{kg/hr})$$

or

$$d\,(\text{in}) = \sqrt{\frac{\text{Evaporative capacity}}{80}}\;(\text{lb/hr})$$

$$(5.3)$$

The above formulation takes no account of the restrictions imposed by any irregular configurations of the valve thoroughfares, the presence of valve guide webs or pegs and other incidental resistances; consequently, the purely theoretical findings require some modification to bring them into line with practical expediency. As another example of such restriction may be cited the case where a feed pump of the reciprocating type is employed, the check valve of which is repeatedly opening and closing with each stroke of the ram, and this of itself has the effect of reducing the output (or input) of the feed valve.

Table 5.1 Correction factors for calculations to determine the size of boiler feed check valves

Evaporation (E)		Correction factor
(kg/hr)	(lb/hr)*	(k_1)
500	1000	2·50
1000	2000	2·45
1500	3000	2·40
2000	4000	2·35
2500	6000	2·25
3000	7000	2·18
3500	8000	2·15
4000	9000	2·05
4500	10 000	2·00
5000	11 000	1·95
6000	13 000	1·85
8000	17 000	1·67
10 000	22 000	1·65
12 000	26 000	1·50
15 000	33 000	1·45
20 000	44 000	1·40
25 000	55 000	1·28
30 000	66 000	1·23
35 000	77 000	1·17
40 000	88 000	1·13
50 000	110 000	1·08

*Corresponding approximate imperial figures

From the collated evidence provided by a prodigious number of boiler specifications relating to boilers of various types and evaporative capacities we are able to devise a relationship between the theoretically derived diameter, as previously determined, and that dictated by practical requirements. From such evidence it would appear desirable to multiply the value of d as derived from eqns (5.2) and (5.3) by some correction factor, k_1, whose value varies from 2·5 for low evaporations to 1·25 for high evaporations (limits 500 to 50 000 kg/hr, or say 1000 to 100 000 lb/hr).

Table 5.1 gives appropriate values of k_1.

Accordingly, eqn (5.2) may be modified in the light of the foregoing to read

$$d\,(\text{mm}) = 0\cdot4856\,k_1\,\sqrt{E}\,(\text{kg/hr}) \text{ or } d\,(\text{in}) =$$
$$0\cdot01277\,k_1\,\sqrt{E}\,(\text{lb/hr}) \tag{5.4}$$

and from eqn (5.3)

$$d\,(\text{mm}) = (k_1\,\sqrt{E})/2\,(\text{kg/hr}) \text{ or } d\,(\text{in}) = (k_1\,\sqrt{E})/80\,(\text{lb/hr}) \tag{5.5}$$

Feed check valves less than 25 mm (1 in) nominal diameter should never be employed, even where the evaporation is so low as to suggest that a smaller valve would appear sufficient.

The size of valve as determined from the modified expression denoted in eqn (5.5) relates, of course, to a single valve. Large boilers are generally fitted with two valves, in which case d, as calculated above, may be termed the 'referred' diameter and the combined areas of the two valves may be made equal to that of a single valve of 'referred' diameter d.

Thus where two feed valves are employed conjointly the diameter of each *individual* valve may be calculated from the relation

$$d\,(\text{mm}) = \frac{k_1\sqrt{E}}{2\cdot9}\,(\text{kg/hr})$$

or

$$d\,(\text{in}) = \frac{k_1\sqrt{E}}{110}\,(\text{lb/hr}) \tag{5.6}$$

The detail design of the various components of a feed check valve follows closely the general principles outlined in Chapter 2 relating to screw-down stop valves, with, perhaps one outstanding difference in that feed check valves are more often subjected to shock loading, the intensity of which defies precise investigation. Shock may be due to water-hammer or to erratic behaviour of the feed pump. Consequently, design should make allowance for these effects by arranging liberal chest thicknesses and by the avoidance of sudden changes in section. The fracture of a feed check valve body in service could have disastrous consequences.

A worked example will illustrate the foregoing.

WORKED EXAMPLE

Determine the size of a feed check valve required for an economic boiler of 5000 kg/hr [or 10 000 lb/hr] evaporative capacity. If two feed check valves of idential size were preferred, determine the diameter of each valve.

Solution

From eqn (5.5) the size of one valve would be

$$k_1 (\sqrt{5000/2}) \text{ mm [or } k_1 (\sqrt{10\ 000/80}) \text{ in]}$$

now, from Table 5.1 the values of k_1 corresponding to this evaporative capacity is 1·95 [2·00].

Hence, the size for one valve should be

$$1\cdot95 (\sqrt{5000/2}) \text{ mm [or } 2 (\sqrt{10\ 000/80}) \text{ in]}$$
$$= 68\cdot93 \text{ mm } [= 2\tfrac{1}{2} \text{ in]}$$

If two valves are to be used, then from eqn (5.6) the size of each ought to be

$$1\cdot95 (\sqrt{500/2\cdot9}) \text{ mm [or } 2 (\sqrt{10\ 000/110}) \text{ in]}$$

which is 48·76 mm [or 1·818 in]

to the nearest standard size this would be 50 mm bore [or 2 in bore]

Chapter Six
Safety and Relief Valves

THE function of any safety valve or relief valve is to prevent an undue rise in pressure in the vessel to which it is fitted as, for example, a steam boiler or air receiver. There are countless other pressure vessels all calling for such protection.

The terms *safety* and *relief* are really synonymous although the former appellation is generally applied to valves protecting any vessel which could explode and endanger life and limb whereas the latter appellation is more applicable to the valve protecting those vessels from over-pressure where the contents contain a non-expansible fluid, a burst occasioning no violent explosion. For example, the valve intended to prevent undue over-pressure in a cold water main would be termed a relief valve.

The underlying principles of design of such valves are virtually the same irrespective of their titles. Such valves must operate independently of human agency (although in some designs a test lever is featured whereby the valve member may be eased off its seating in order to test its effectiveness or to blow off any trapped scale); in short, the valve must operate automatically, opening promptly at the approach of an impending undue rise in pressure and promptly closing when the normal pressure is restored due to discharge. Prompt closing is not always achieved but this may be due to a variety of circumstances.

Safety or relief valves may be classified into four *basic* types (five if we include the spring-balance type, long since obsolescent). Other more exotic types have made their debüt within recent years but these are outside the scope of this work. The four types are:

(a) Lever and weight type (Fig. 6.1);
(b) Deadweight type (Fig. 6.2);
(c) Direct spring-loaded type (Fig. 6.3);
(d) Torsion-bar type (Fig. 6.4).

As the latter is somewhat of a proprietary fitting recently introduced

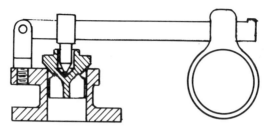

Fig. 6.1 *Lever safety or relief valve*

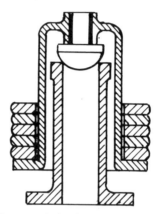

Fig. 6.2 *Dead-weight safety or relief valve*

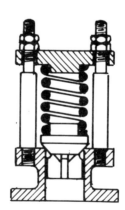

Fig. 6.3 *Spring safety or relief valve*

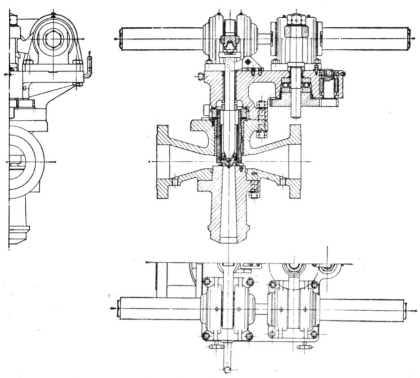

Fig. 6.4 *Hopkinson torsion bar safety valve*
(Courtesy of Hopkinsons Ltd, Huddersfield)

(relatively) only the first three types will receive detailed consideration.

Figures 6.1, 6.2, 6.3 and 6.4 are but elementary concepts of their respective types merely illustrating their *modus operandi.* More detailed designs representative of current practice—but devoid of over-embellishment—will illustrate the treatment which follows.

The direct-acting spring type is the one most commonly employed although there are some applications wherein the lever and weight and the deadweight patterns are preferred for reasons best known to their advocates.

SAFETY-VALVE SEATINGS

As in other types of valves the seating is the heart of the valve and is the starting point in any valve design. Indifferent performance of a safety valve is mainly due to a lack of appreciation of one fundamental essential requirement, one so often overlooked by designers, that of ensuring that the point of thrust of the valve stem should be located somewhat below the seating faces.

Failure to observe this requirement will inevitably result in a valve that is 'chatter-prone' since the valve member will lack self-righting tendencies inherent in a correctly designed assembly of these two components.

Figures 6.5 (a) and (b) show correct and incorrect methods, respectively, of arranging the point of thrust.

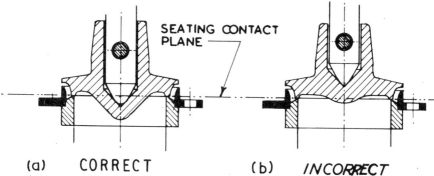

(a)   CORRECT   (b)   *INCORRECT*

Fig. 6.5 *Correct and incorrect methods of arranging point of thrust in safety and other similar valves*

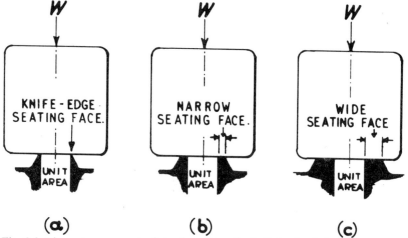

(a)   (b)   (c)

Fig. 6.6 *Elementary concept of dead-weight safety/relief valve behaviour*

CONDITIONS AFFECTING PRESSURE LOADING

Consider the imaginary elementary deadweight safety valve illustrated diagrammatically in Figs 6.6 (a), (b) and (c), wherein leakage from the vertical thoroughfare is supposedly prevented by the superimposed mass of metal resting thereon. Assume the underside of this mass to be ground and lapped to present a dead flat, smooth, seating surface.

Also assume the cross-sectional area of the valve seating to be 1000 mm² precisely, and the pressure within each thoroughfare to be exactly 1 MPa.

It is natural to suppose that if the superimposed mass of metal weighed exactly 1 MN, then each of the three valves would blow off at a pressure of 1 MPa exactly. Such is by no means the case. (Similarly a valve of 1 in² area loaded with a 10 lb weight will not blow off at exactly 10 psi).

In the arrangement shown at (a) the seating edges are assumed to be knife-edged, i.e. with no measurable width, razor sharp. A valve so arranged would be the one most likely to blow off at precisely 1 MPa but such an arrangement would be impracticable due to the vulnerability of the seating face.

At (b) we have a somewhat definable seating face, admittedly narrow but not knife-edged. With this arrangement the valve would blow off at some pressure less than 1 MPa.

At (c) we have an inordinately wide seating face and the valve would blow off (if it ever held at all) at a pressure considerably lower than 1 MPa.

One could be excused for asking why there should be any diversity of blowing-off pressure in these three examples having *bores* of identical dimensions.

The explanation is as follows. In any safety or relief valve not only must there by a *downward* force W opposing the *upward* force ap due to the line pressures exerted on the effective area of the seating but there must also be an additional *downward* force sufficient to produce a *clamping* pressure between the seating faces of intensity sufficient to prevent leakage across these faces.

Anyone doubting this statement should try the experiment of carefully weighing the apparent total deadweight required to suit a given accurately machined bore and the required blow-off pressure in the case of a deadweight safety valve and noting the *exact* pressure at which blow-off occurs. It will be found that the valve lifts prematurely showing extra deadweight is required. This discrepancy would pass unnoticed in a spring-loaded safety valve, corrected unconsciously by a further turn (or less) of the compression screw.

Accordingly, the actual deadweight required (or downward thrust) in any safety valve, however secured may be denoted by

$$W = ap + k_2 \qquad (6.1)$$

We have seen that k_2 would vanish from the above equation if perfectly knife-edged seatings were adopted but this is impracticable since the concentration of loading at the knife edges would be enormous, quite apart from their inherent vulnerability. Moreover such seatings would soon be rendered ineffective by erosion, the inevitable outcome of high velocity fluid (especially steam) passing through the confines of the narrow gap presented by a valve member lifting a very small amount at blow-off in all but the more 'exotic' types of safety valves, i.e. 'high lift' and 'full-bore' patterns. These will be described later.

If knife-edged seatings were feasible the actual discharge in a valve so fitted would be prompt and decisive and, after discharging, would settle down promptly without 'feathering'. Few, if any, steam safety valves will settle down after discharge until the pressure has dropped appreciably below the set pressure. This drop in pressure is appropriately termed 'drop' in the test-shop or 'blow-down' in more sophisticated language.

BS 759:1975 limits the blow-down to a figure varying from 5 to 10 per cent of the blowing-off pressure, depending upon the type of safety valve.

WIDTH OF SEATING ANNULUS

We have seen that the determination of the requisite downward thrust to be imparted to the valve member—either by deadweight or spring—calls for something more than merely striking a balance between pressure upthrust (see eqn (6.1)) and downthrust.

At the precise point of blow-off there would be virtually no metallic contact between the two seating faces and very little more as the valve progressively settled down; but it is essential to aim at closure tightness as soon after blowing-off as possible. Consequently, there must be some point dictated by the permissible *blown-down* at which fluid-tightness at the seatings is obtained. Provided these have been effectively lapped to a fine degree of surface finish, fluid-tightness may be rightly expected at all pressures ranging from zero to at least the *blow-down* pressure (not the *blow-off* pressure) by the deadweight obviously remaining constant throughout and the seat contact pressure progressively decreasing at all stages leading up to blow-off.

This would appear to suggest we may correlate permissible blow-down pressure, blowing-off pressure and that most desirable objective, width of seating annulus, viz:

Let d = effective diameter of the seating, taken as the *inside* diameter (bore) for the sake of simplification (We cannot establish with any degree of certainly the pressure boundary at which fluid-tightness across the annulus is achieved.)

w = the radial width of the seating contacting surface.

p_b = the blowing-off pressure.

F_d = the downwardly acting thrust to be exerted on the valve member/seating to counter the upthrust due to the line pressure at blow-off.

then $F_d = \dfrac{\pi}{4} d^2 p_b$

If we accept a blow-down factor of, say, 5 per cent (see BS 759:1975) then the pressure at which the valve should achieve positive tightness will be $0 \cdot 95 p_b$, giving an upthrust, say F_u denoted by $F_u = 0 \cdot 95 p_b \times \dfrac{\pi}{4} d^2$.

Therefore, there will be an excess of *downthrust* over *upthrust* tending to re-seat the valve member, or:

Excess thrust $F_e = F_d - F_u$

$$= \frac{\pi}{4} d^2 p_b - 0 \cdot 95 p_b \times \frac{\pi}{4} d^2$$

$$= \frac{\pi}{4} d^2 p_b (1 - 0 \cdot 95)$$

$$= 0 \cdot 05 p_b \times \frac{\pi}{4} d^2$$

Since the width w of the seating annulus is relatively small the area of the annulus may be taken to be $\pi d w$.

Then the unit contact pressure $u = \dfrac{\text{load}}{\text{area}}$

$$= \frac{F_e}{\pi\,d\,w}$$

$$= \frac{0\!\cdot\!05\,\pi\,p_b\,d^2}{4\,\pi\,d\,w} = \frac{0\!\cdot\!0125\,p_b\,d}{w} \tag{6.2}$$

In order to secure a pressure tight joint between accurately lapped metallic seating surfaces (as are exemplified in the case of safety valves) it has been found that a unit contact pressure of about $1\frac{1}{4}$ times the line pressure is invariably required.

Adopting this figure:

$$u = 1\!\cdot\!25\,p_b$$

or $\dfrac{0\!\cdot\!0125\,p_b\,d}{w} = 1\!\cdot\!25\,p_b$

whence $w = \dfrac{0\!\cdot\!0125\,p_b\,d}{1\!\cdot\!25\,p_b}$

$$= 0\!\cdot\!01\,d \tag{6.3}$$

It will be noted that the width is independent of the blowing-off pressure. It will be apparent, however, that strict compliance with the foregoing relationship would invariably yield an inordinately narrow annulus, vulnerable in the extreme, and from practical considerations the width must be increased substantially if reasonable working life is to be expected. Naturally this could increase the blow-down somewhat on a valve of the *most ordinary construction.*

Practical requirements demand that the values as derived by eqn (6.3) be multiplied by a factor which varies from approximately 6 in the case of the very small valves diminishing to approximately 4 in the case of the larger valves. The graphs over Fig. 6.7 will simplify selection and serve to demonstrate the disparity between the practical and purely theoretical findings.

We shall see, however, that the working pressure *has* to be taken into account when faced with adopting a suitable value for the width w. As the pressure rises and more closely approaches the blowing-off pressure the seat contacting pressure will proportionately relax until—at the point of blow-off—the seating members will 'float', neither touching nor separating! It is this lack of contact or mere contact that causes 'feathering' and 'drop' close to the blowing-off pressure and which calls for some *additional* downward force to be applied to the valve member, additional to that merely to counter the upthrust occasioned by the pressure at blow-off. We will denote this *total* force by F_T hence $F_T > F_a$. This additional force required defies accurate determination but experience suggests that a force of approximately $2\frac{1}{2}$ per cent of the blowing-off pressure meets most applications.

We may therefore adopt the following relationship:

$$\text{total force } F_T = 1 \cdot 025\, F_a \tag{6.4}$$

Consider the conditions prevailing when the line pressure is zero, say during a shut-down. The full force F_T imposed on the valve member, through the agency of deadweight or spring, will be wholly transmitted to the seating annulus and it behoves the designer to see if the seating area is adequate to sustain such loading, having regard to the load bearing propensities of the materials chosen for the seating members and then:

$$\text{area } a_s \text{ of annulus} = \pi d w \text{ (very approximately)}$$

$$\text{then intensity of surface stress } u_s = \frac{F_T}{\pi d w} \tag{6.5}$$

This should not exceed the appropriate values given in Table 6.1. If it does, then w may be determined by transposition,

$$w = \frac{F_T}{\pi d\, u_s} \tag{6.6}$$

$$\text{Now} \quad F_T = \frac{1 \cdot 025\, \pi d^2 p_b}{4}$$

$$\text{whence } w = \frac{1 \cdot 025\, \pi d^2 p_b}{4 \pi d\, u_s}$$

$$= \frac{0 \cdot 256\, d p_b}{u_s} \tag{6.7}$$

Similarly eqn (6.5) becomes:

$$u = \frac{0 \cdot 256\, d p_b}{w}$$

[When using the foregoing equations care must be taken to employ wholly consistent units throughout. The most convenient procedure is to

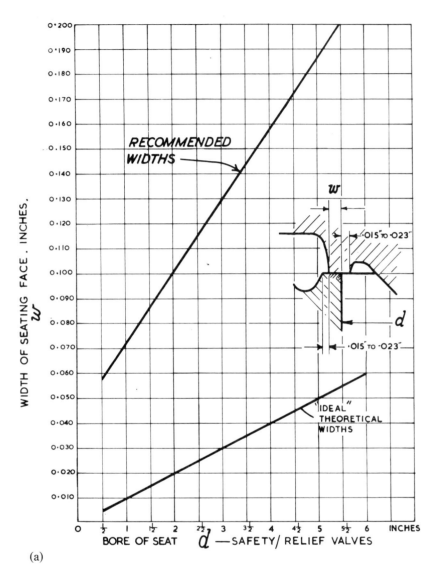

(a)

Fig. 6.7 *Width of seating annulus (theoretical and recommended)*
(a) Imperial; (b) Metric

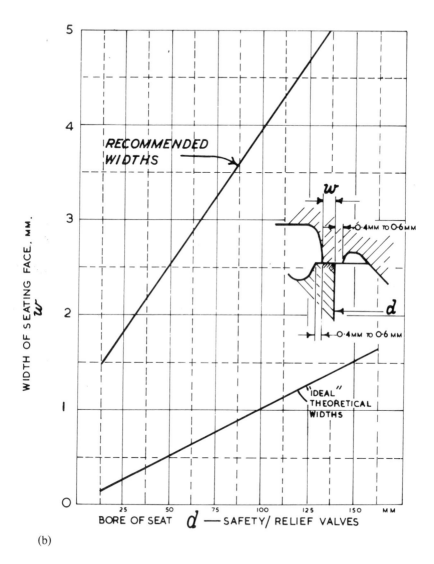

(b)

Table 6.1 Permissible unit surface stress on safety valve seatings

Metals in contact	Approximate Brinell Hardness No. (3000 kg)	Applications	Permissible unit surface stress (u_s)	
			MPa	lbf/in²
Cast iron	180	Somewhat unreliable Essential in certain chemical applications	7	1000
Gunmetal	75 to 78	Used mainly on low pressure saturated steam, water, oil and some gases at 'medium' temperatures	14	2000
'Monel' metal*	270	Favoured for high pressure and superheated steam, on valves for marine applications and for acidic and salt waters	31	4500
Nickel bronze (sand cast)	240	Suitable for medium pressure steam applications and certain chemical applications	24	3500
Nickel–copper–tin alloy (sand cast)	260	Largely preferred for superheated steam and hot gases. (There are numerous proprietary alloys in the valve industry.)	28	4000
Phosphor bronze	100	Suitable for medium pressure saturated steam, high pressure hot water, oils and certain gases	21	3000
Stainless steel (various grades)†	175 to 400 according to heat treatment	Sometimes the preferred choice for high pressure superheated steam. To some extent imperative on certain corrosive liquids and gases	40–62	6000–9000

*'Monel' (Registered Trade Mark) is a proprietary alloy of approximately two thirds nickel, one third copper.
†preferably dissimilar grades in contact.

express all dimensions as millimetres, all loads as newton and all pressures as MPa. Since 1 MPa = 1 N/mm² this procedure ensures that all answers come out with the decimal point in the right place, thus avoiding a frequent source of error.]

It will be noted that flat-faced seatings are featured on all the illustrations so far, displayed (with the exception of the one diagrammatic example shown in Fig. 6.2). There is no particular virtue in any other form, flat-faced seatings being the more logical and commendable form for at least two sound reasons.

(a) Flat-faced seatings are readily ground and lapped-in to a grinding plate to give that fine degree of surface finish so essential to securing fluid-tightness at all pressures up to blow-off. Note that the two mating components, the seating and the valve member (sometimes called the 'lid') should not be lapped-in, the one to the other; this tends to accentuate the low spots. Each should be lapped-in to a grinding plate separately.

(b) When the valve member expands—as it will with rising

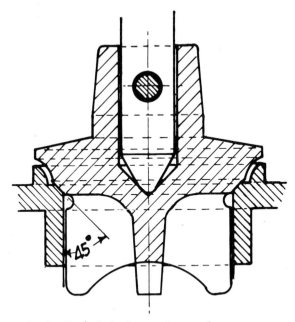

Fig. 6.8 *Mitre faced safety/relief valve seating members*

temperature—it can slide unhindered across the surface of its mating seating without jamming, as would definitely occur with a mitred face valve member (Fig. 6.8) if its expansible qualities differed from that of the seating. Moreover, the latter form invariably calls for guide wings and these are generally frowned upon by survey authorities. Not only do such wings restrict the area presented to flow through the seating but they tend to promote distortion of the valve member under the influence of heat due to their irregular configurations. In certain cases, however, where there is no other positive restraint, e.g. the simple low-pressure lever safety valve, the winged pattern valve member would appear desirable.

The lapping-in of a mitred valve member is an appreciably more difficult operation than that presented by the simpler, yet more practical, flat faced pattern.

At this point it is pertinent to point out that certain rules governing the design and expected performance are laid down by the British Standards Institution and (in this country) by the Board of Trade, and the designer is advised to familiarise himself with their respective publications, viz:

(a) BS 759:1975, 'Valves, gauges and other safety fittings for application to boilers and to piping installations, for and in connection with boilers'.

(b) Board of Trade Rules: 'Instructions as to the Survey of Passenger Steamships'.

The former is obtainable from the Sales Department, British Standards Institution, Newton House, 101, Pentonville Road, London, N1 9WD and the latter from HMSO, York House, Kingsway, London, WC2 and certain provincial centres.

BS 759:1975 defines six classes of safety valves, viz:

(1) *Ordinary lift safety valves.* One in which the valve member lifts automatically a distance of *at least one twenty-fourth* of the bore of the seating member with an overpressure not exceeding 10 per cent of the set pressure.

(2) *High lift safety valve.* One in which the valve member lifts automatically a distance of *at least one twelfth* of the bore of the seating member with an overpressure not exceeding 10 per cent of the set pressure.

(3) *Full lift safety valve.* One in which the valve member lifts automatically a distance such that the area of discharge which limits the flow through the valve is between 100 and 80 per cent of the minimum area at any section at or below the body seating. The lift is to be achieved by a rapid

opening with an overpressure not exceeding 5 per cent of the set pressure.

(4) *Assisted safety valve.* A safety valve which, by means of an extraneously powered assistance mechanism, will lift at a predetermined pressure below its unassisted set pressure and will, in the event of failure of the assistance mechanism, comply with all the requirements for safety valves given in BS 759:1975.

(5) *Supplementary loaded safety valve.* A safety valve which has, until the pressure at the inlet to the safety valve reaches the set pressure, an additional force which increases the sealing force. This additional force (supplementary load), which may be provided by means of an extraneous power source, shall be released reliably when the pressure at the inlet of the safety valves reaches the set pressure. The amount of supplementary loading shall be so arranged that if such supplementary loading is not released the safety valve shall attain its rated capacity with a pressure at the inlet of the safety valve not greater than 115 per cent of the design pressure of the pressure vessel on which the safety valve is mounted.

(6) *Pilot operated safety valve* (indirect operated safety valve). A safety valve, the operation of which is initiated and controlled by the steam discharge from a pilot valve which is itself a direct operated safety valve subject to the requirements laid down regarding the precautions to be taken against the possibility of obstructions due to failure of any component, and bearing in mind that *two* independent pilot device systems shall be provided for each main safety valve. The lift of the main valve shall be achieved with an overpressure not exceeding 5 per cent of the set pressure.

In a work of this kind, mainly intended for technical students, we shall only concern ourselves with the three basic types of safety/relief valves, namely the lever and weight, the deadweight and the spring safety valve, with worked examples of each type.

Reference is directed to BS 759: 1975, giving various formulae for calculating the rated discharge capacity appropriate to the various basic types of safety valves and operating conditions and some of these will now be considered.

SATURATED STEAM

From equation (21.6.2) of BS 759:1975 the following relationship emerges

$$E = C_m AP \qquad (6.9)$$

where E is the rated discharge capacity of saturated steam (kg/h [lb/h]*.

P is the highest set pressure of any safety valve mounted on the boiler (bar absolute [psi absolute]).

A is the area (mm² [in²]). For ordinary lift and high lift safety valves A is the area of the minimum bore of the body seating. For full lift safety valves A is defined in BS 759:1975 under the heading Full Lift Safety Valves, and its value can only be obtained by the manufacturer.

C_m is a constant appropriate to the type of valve taken from the following table or as established by tests carried out in accordance with Appendix A of BS 759:1975.

Table 6.2 Constants appropriate to evaporative capacities

Type of valve	Value of constant C_m
Ordinary lift	0·05 [5]*
High lift	0·10 [10]
Full lift	0·24 [24]

SUPERHEATED STEAM

E_s, the rated discharge capacity of a safety valve which discharges super-heated steam may be calculated from the following equation

$$E_s = 31 \cdot 6 E \sqrt{(1000 + 2 \cdot 7 T_s)} \qquad (6.10)$$

where E is the rated discharge capacity of saturated steam, calculated using eqn (6.9) above

T_s is the degree of superheat (°C)

The three basic patterns will now be considered in turn.

LEVER AND WEIGHT SAFETY VALVES

This is one of the simplest of all safety valves, the downward thrust on the stem to counter the pressure upthrust being affected by the deadweight effect of a cheeseweight—pendulously or slidably mounted on a lever—whose weight effect is magnified by the leverage provided. This arrangement is shown diagrammatically in Fig. 6.9 to which reference is now directed.

---

*The units/values given in square brackets are not the strict imperial equivalents of the metric units used, but rather the imperial units/values which should be used. This style is followed throughout the remainder of the book.

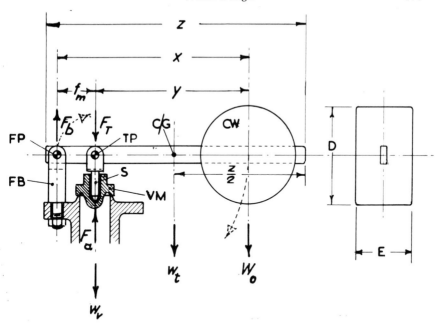

Fig. 6.9 *Diagrammatic arrangement of lever safety/relief valve*

The upthrust F_a due to the fluid pressure acting on the underside of the valve member VM will tend to produce anti-clockwise rotation of the lever and weight about the fulcrum pin FP and the downthrust of the cheese-weight CW will tend to produce clockwise rotation about the same pin. (See dotted arrows.)

Since the system is in static equilibrium the algebraic sum of these moments is zero; then, ignoring meanwhile the weight of the lever and other moving parts and also the frictional resistance of the pins, we have:

$$F_T f_m - W_o x = 0 \qquad (6.11)$$

whence $F_T = \dfrac{W_o x}{f_m}$ \qquad (6.12)

and we have seen that $F_T = 1 \cdot 025 F_a$ when $F_a = (\pi/4) d_m^2 p_b$, where d_m is the mean diameter of the seating face and p_b is the blowing-off pressure. The effect of the weight of the lever itself cannot justifiably be ignored especially when the operating pressure is low, but the exploitation of eqn

Weight lb	D	E	F	G	H	J	K	L	M	N	P	R	S	T	U	V	W	X	Pinching Screw		
																			A	B	W
	in	in	in	in	in	in	in	in	in	in	in	in	in	in	in	in	in	in	in	in	in
5	5	1 1/2	4 1/2	1	5/8	1 3/4	1 3/16	4	1 3/8	5/8	13/16	1/4	none		3/8	1 1/2	3/8	7/16	2	1 3/4	3/8
10	5 5/8	1 3/4	5 1/8	1 1/4	5/8	1 3/4	1 5/16	4 5/8	1 1/2	5/8	13/16	1/4	none		3/8	1 1/2	3/8	7/16	2 3/8	1 7/8	3/8
15	5 3/4	2	5 1/4	1 1/2	5/8	1 3/4	1 7/16	4 3/4	1 5/8	5/8	13/16	1/4	none		3/8	1 1/2	3/8	7/16	2 3/8	2	3/8
20	7	2 1/2	6 3/8	1 7/8	5/8	2	1 5/8	6	1 3/4	11/16	1 1/32	5/16	6	3/32	3/8	1 3/4	1/2	9/16	2 7/8	2	1/2
25	8	2 1/2	7 1/4	1 7/8	3/4	2 1/4	1 5/8	6 3/4	1 7/8	11/16	1 1/32	3/8	6 3/4	3/32	1/2	2	1/2	9/16	3 1/4	2 1/8	1/2
30	8 1/2	2 1/2	7 3/4	1 7/8	3/4	2 1/4	1 5/8	7 1/4	1 7/8	11/16	1 1/32	1/2	7	3/32	1/2	2	1/2	9/16	3 1/2	2 1/8	1/2
35	9	2 5/8	8 1/8	1 7/8	3/4	2 1/4	1 11/16	7 5/8	1 7/8	11/16	1 1/32	1/2	7 5/8	3/32	1/2	2	1/2	9/16	3 3/4	2 1/4	1/2
40	9 5/8	2 5/8	8 1/2	1 7/8	7/8	2 3/4	1 13/16	8	2 1/4	13/16	1 1/4	5/8	8	3/32	5/8	2 1/2	5/8	11/16	3 3/4	2 1/4	5/8
45	10 1/4	2 5/8	9 1/4	2	7/8	2 3/4	2	8 3/4	2 1/4	13/16	1 1/4	5/8	8 1/2	1/8	5/8	2 1/2	5/8	11/16	4 1/8	2 1/4	5/8
50	10 3/4	2 5/8	9 3/4	2	7/8	2 3/4	2	9 1/4	2 1/4	13/16	1 1/4	5/8	9	1/8	5/8	2 1/2	5/8	11/16	4 3/8	2 1/4	5/8
55	11 1/4	2 5/8	10	2	7/8	2 3/4	2	9 1/2	2 1/4	13/16	1 1/4	13/16	9 1/4	1/8	5/8	2 1/2	5/8	11/16	4 5/8	2 1/4	5/8
60	12	2 5/8	10 3/4	2	7/8	2 3/4	2	10 1/4	2 1/4	13/16	1 1/4	13/16	10	3/16	5/8	2 1/2	5/8	11/16	5	2 1/4	5/8
65	12 3/8	2 5/8	11	2	1	2 3/4	2	10 1/2	2 1/4	13/16	1 1/4	13/16	10 1/4	3/16	5/8	2 1/2	5/8	11/16	5 3/8	2 1/4	5/8
70	13	2 5/8	11 3/4	2	1	2 3/4	2	11 1/4	2 1/4	13/16	1 1/4	13/16	11	3/16	3/4	2 1/2	5/8	11/16	5 1/2	2 1/4	5/8
75	13	2 3/4	11 3/4	2 1/8	1	2 3/4	2 3/16	11 1/4	2 3/8	15/16	1 7/16	13/16	11	3/16	3/4	2 1/2	3/4	7/8	5 1/2	2 5/8	3/4
80	13	2 7/8	11 3/4	2 1/4	1	2 3/4	2 3/16	11 1/4	2 3/8	15/16	1 7/16	7/8	11	3/16	3/4	2 1/2	3/4	7/8	5 1/2	2 5/8	3/4
90	14	3	12 1/2	2 1/4	1	3 1/4	2 1/4	12	2 5/8	15/16	1 7/16	1	11 3/4	1/4	3/4	3	3/4	7/8	5 3/4	2 5/8	3/4
100	14 3/4	3	13	2 1/4	1 1/4	3 1/2	2 1/4	12 1/2	2 3/4	15/16	1 7/16	1 1/2	12 1/4	1/4	7/8	3	3/4	7/8	6 1/8	2 3/4	3/4
120	15	3 1/2	13 1/2	2 5/8	1 1/4	3 1/2	2 1/2	13	2 3/4	15/16	1 7/16	1	12 3/4	1/4	7/8	3	3/4	7/8	6 1/4	2 3/4	3/4

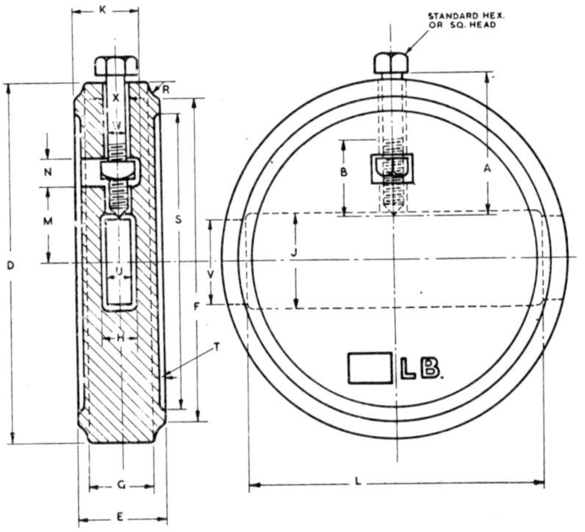

(a).

Fig. 6.10 *(a) Slidably and (b) pendulously mounted cheeseweights for safety/relief valves (values in Imperial units)*

Weight	D	E	F	G	R	r	P	Q	S	T	U	V	W	X	Y
	in	in	in	in	in	in	in	in	in	in	in	in	in	in	in
5	4 1/4	1 7/8	3	1/8	2	1/8	5/16	1/2	1 1/8	1 3/4	7/8	5/16	7/16	1	1/4
6	4 3/8	2	3	1/8	2 3/16	1/8	5/16	1/2	1 1/8	1 3/4	7/8	5/16	7/16	1	1/4
7	4 1/2	2	3	1/8	2 1/4	1/8	5/16	1/2	1 1/8	1 3/4	7/8	5/16	7/16	1	1/4
8	4 3/4	2 1/8	3 1/4	1/8	2 3/8	1/8	5/16	1/2	1 1/8	1 3/4	7/8	5/16	7/16	1	1/4
9	5	2 1/8	3 1/2	1/8	2 1/2	1/8	5/16	1/2	1 1/8	1 3/4	7/8	5/16	7/16	1	1/4
10	5 1/8	2 3/8	3 3/4	1/8	2 9/16	1/8	7/16	5/8	1 3/8	2 1/8	1 1/8	3/8	9/16	1 3/8	3/8
12	5 3/8	2 1/2	3 7/8	1/8	2 11/16	1/8	7/16	5/8	1 3/8	2 1/8	1 1/8	3/8	9/16	1 3/8	3/8
14	5 3/4	2 1/2	4	1/8	2 7/8	1/8	7/16	5/8	1 3/8	2 1/8	1 1/8	3/8	9/16	1 3/8	3/8
16	6	2 5/8	4	1/8	3	1/8	1/2	11/16	1 1/2	2 1/2	1 3/8	1/2	11/16	1 1/2	3/8
18	6	3	4	1/8	3	3/16	1/2	11/16	1 1/2	2 1/2	1 3/8	1/2	11/16	1 1/2	3/8
20	6 1/4	3	4 1/8	1/8	3 1/8	3/16	1/2	11/16	1 1/2	2 1/2	1 3/8	1/2	11/16	1 1/2	3/8
25	7 1/8	3	4 5/8	3/16	3 1/2	3/16	1/2	11/16	1 1/2	2 1/2	1 3/8	1/2	11/16	1 1/2	3/8
30	7 3/8	3 1/4	5	3/16	3 3/4	3/16	1/2	11/16	1 1/2	2 1/2	1 3/8	1/2	11/16	1 1/2	3/8
35	8	3 1/4	5 1/2	3/16	4	3/16	1/2	11/16	1 1/2	2 1/2	1 3/8	1/2	11/16	1 1/2	3/8
40	8 3/8	3 1/2	6	3/16	4 1/8	1/4	1/2	11/16	1 1/2	2 1/2	1 3/8	1/2	11/16	1 1/2	3/8
45	8 3/4	3 1/2	6 3/8	3/16	4 3/8	1/4	5/8	7/8	1 3/4	3	1 5/8	5/8	7/8	2	7/16
50	9	3 3/4	6 1/2	3/16	4 1/2	1/4	5/8	7/8	1 3/4	3	1 5/8	5/8	7/8	2	7/16
55	9 1/4	3 7/8	6 3/4	3/16	4 5/8	1/4	5/8	7/8	1 3/4	3	1 5/8	5/8	7/8	2	7/16
60	9 1/2	3 7/8	7	3/16	4 3/4	1/4	7/8	1 1/16	1 7/8	3 1/4	2	3/4	1	2 1/4	1/2
65	9 3/4	3 7/8	7 1/4	3/16	4 7/8	1/4	7/8	1 1/16	1 7/8	3 1/4	2	3/4	1	2 1/4	1/2
70	9 7/8	4	7 1/2	3/16	4 15/16	1/4	7/8	1 1/16	1 7/8	3 1/4	2	3/4	1	2 1/4	1/2
75	10	4	7 1/2	3/16	5	1/4	7/8	1 1/16	1 7/8	3 1/4	2	3/4	1	2 1/4	1/2
80	11	3 7/8	8	3/16	5 1/2	1/4	7/8	1 1/16	1 7/8	3 1/4	2	3/4	1	2 1/4	1/2
90	11 1/2	4	8 1/2	1/4	5 3/4	1/4	1	1 1/8	2 1/8	3 1/2	2	3/4	1	2 1/2	1/2
100	12	4	9	1/4	7	1/4	1	1 1/8	2 1/8	3 1/2	2	3/4	1	2 1/2	1/2
125	12	5	9	1/4	10	3/8	1	1 1/8	2 1/8	3 1/2	2	3/4	1	2 1/2	1/2
150	12	6	9	1/4	12	1/2	1 1/8	1 3/8	2 7/8	4 3/4	2 1/2	1	1 1/4	2 7/8	5/8
175	13 1/8	6	10	5/16	13	1/2	1 1/8	1 3/8	2 7/8	4 3/4	2 1/2	1	1 1/4	2 7/8	5/8
200	14	6	11	3/8	14	1/2	1 1/8	1 3/8	2 7/8	4 3/4	2 1/2	1	1 1/4	2 7/8	5/8

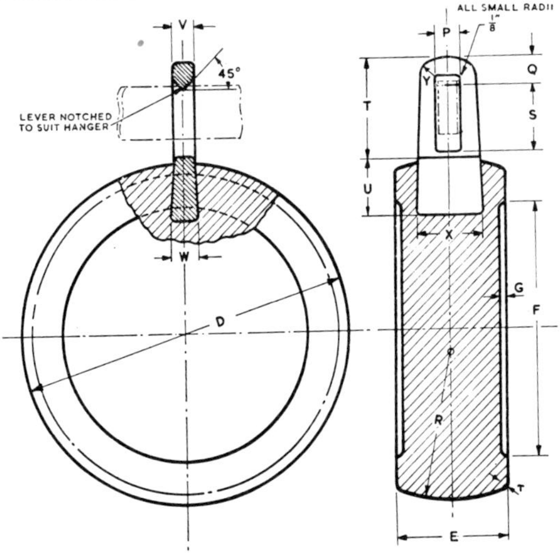

(b)

(6.12) will give a preliminary indication of the general outline of the valve, enabling adjustments to be made later. Some trial and error calculations are inevitable, for example, deciding upon a tentative length and size of lever. Its weight may be readily calculated, and this will be denoted by w_l. (The actual section should be subsequently checked for strength by means to be described later).

The combined weight of the valve member VM and stem S denoted by w_v may be estimated by geometrical means and suitably accounted for in the following more precise expression (again taking moments about FP):

$$F_T f_m - W_o x - w_l z / 2 - w_v f_m = 0 \qquad (6.13)$$

(Note that in the third expression the length of lever has been taken as that measured from the centre of the fulcrum pin FP to avoid complexity; the resulting error is somewhat inconsequential.)

$$\text{whence } W_o = \frac{F_T f_m - w_l z/2 - w_v f_m}{x} \qquad (6.14)$$

The determination of the relevant dimensions of a cheeseweight to provide a desired mass is a tedious involvement. To save the designer much time a comprehensive list of cheeseweights is featured in Figs 10 (a) and 10 (b), depicting the slidably and pendulously mounted patterns respectively.

BS 759:1967 states: 'The weights on lever safety valves shall be so secured on the lever as to prevent unauthorized interference'. This would appear to rule out the pendulous form of cheeseweight which could be lifted off its lever: a pin passing through the cheeseweight and the lever and fitted with a padlock would comply with the above requirement but would restrict any ultimate adjustment should the blowing-off pressure ever need to be altered. The revised version, BS 759:1975 makes no mention of lever safety valves, evidently with the intention of them being abandoned in favour of the more compact spring safety valve, less prone to derangement and unauthorised interference. It would be a pity to see them abandoned entirely, especially in locations with restricted access.

Quite apart from the necessity of providing adequacy of area to meet the requisite discharge capacity, the size of valve to a great extent is limited by the size and weight of the cheeseweight and this can assume prodigious proportions.

Whilst lever safety valves of 8 in (approximately 200 mm) bore have been known, this size would appear to be the maximum and it is in the range

25–100 mm (approximately 1 in to 4 in) that this type of valve is generally found.

When the size becomes prohibitive, and the lever type safety valve is the preferred type, then the requisite area of discharge can generally be met by employing such valves in tandem, mounted on a 'breeches' or 'Y' pipe.

Lever and pins

Both the fulcrum pin FP and thrust pin TP (Fig. 6.9) will be subjected to shearing and bending forces imposed by the cheeseweight. The shear stress imposed will be greater than the bending stress and only this will be considered. The requisite diameters of these two pins will need to be determined before the dimensions of the lever can be established since the presence of the holes in the lever to receive the pins will have a marked weakening effect which must be taken into account.

First consider the fulcrum pin FP.

The deadweight effect of the cheeseweight will tend to stretch the fulcrum bolt FB since the lever is endeavouring (unsuccessfully) to rotate about the

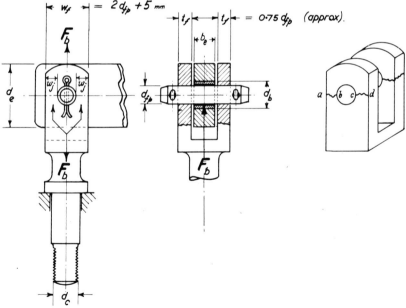

Fig. 6.11 *Fulcrum bolt—lever safety/relief valves*

thrust pin TP, see-saw fashion. The fulcrum bolt, therefore, will be subjected to a maximum tensile force, say F_b and the pin to a shearing force of the same magnitude, whether the valve is under pressure or not.

Taking moments about TP (Fig. 6.9) and neglecting the weight of the lever:

$$W_o y = F_b f_m \text{ but } y = x - f_m$$

therefore $W_0 (x - f_m) = F_b f_m$ \hfill (6.15)

whence $F_b = \dfrac{W_o}{f_m}(x - f_m)$ \hfill (6.16)

Let d_{fp} = the diameter of the fulcrum pin FP (Figs 6.9 and 6.11). Since the pin passes through the two jaws of the fulcrum bolt (Fig. 6.11) it will be in double shear under the influence of the force F_b. It is customary to consider a pin in double shear to be only $1\frac{3}{4}$ times as resistant as one in single shear, not twice as strong as might appear. Then, equating the shear resistance to the load applied, we have:

$$1\cdot 75 \frac{\pi}{4} d^2_{fp} f_s = F_b$$

where f_s is the allowable shear stress, whence:

$$d_{fp} = \sqrt{\left(\frac{4 F_f}{1 \cdot 75 \, \pi f_s}\right)} = \sqrt{\left(\frac{0 \cdot 728 \, F_b}{f_s}\right)} \hfill (6.17)$$

The value of d_{fp} may work out inordinately small on valves designed for the lower pressure range so it is advisable from considerations of safety and practical requirements to cater for such cases by adopting a low stress value (see Worked Example) and by introducing a constant in the foregoing formula. It is suggested, therefore, that this be amended to read:

$$d_{fp} = \sqrt{\left(\frac{0 \cdot 728 \, F_b}{f_s}\right)} + 6 \text{ mm } [0 \cdot 25 \text{ in}] \hfill (6.18)$$

The increased diameter will also provide for greater wearing surface and compensate for any bending stresses, however slight in extent these may be.

Similarly the diameter of the thrust pin TP may be determined from the relation

$$d_{tp} = \sqrt{\left(\frac{0 \cdot 728 \, F_T}{f_s}\right)} + 6 \text{ mm } [0 \cdot 25 \text{ in}] \hfill (6.19)$$

Now consider the screwed termination of the fulcrum bolt. Let d_c denote the *core* diameter; then equating the resistance in tension to the load applied, we have:

$$\frac{\pi}{4}d_c^2 f_t = F_b$$

where f_t is the allowable tensile stress, whence:

$$d_c = \sqrt{\left(\frac{4F_b}{\pi f_t}\right)} = \sqrt{\left(\frac{1\cdot273\,F_b}{f_t}\right)} \qquad (6.20)$$

Note that the result is the *core* diameter of the screwed termination, *not* the actual outside diameter which can be readily selected from appropriate tables.

Again it is recommended that a low working stress be adopted since failure of this component could have disastrous consequences; the cheese-weight would lose no time in obeying the laws of gravity.

It is recommended therefore that the foregoing formula be amended, as in the previous case, by the addition of a constant to read:

$$d_c = \sqrt{\frac{1\cdot273\,F_b}{f_t}} + 6\text{ mm }[0\cdot25\text{ in}] \qquad (6.21)$$

For f_t, the safe tensile stress, a factor of safety of not less than six is recommended.

The low stress value will compensate for initial tightening stresses, the constant to guard against inordinately small screwed terminations.

Jaw portion

Referring to Fig. 6.11 it is recommended that the width w_f be made equal to $2d_{fp} + 6$ mm [0·25 in]. The jaw would tend to tear across the *four* sections ab and cd (only the foremost flank being shown) containing the fulcrum pin; then the area a_j subject to the tensile force F_b will be given by:

$$a_j = 2t_f(w_f - d_{fp}) \qquad (6.22)$$

Equating the resistance to the load:

$$2t_f f_t(w_f - d_{fp}) = F_b$$

whence

$$t_f = \frac{F_b}{2f_t(w_f - d_{fp})} \tag{6.23}$$

Any values less than $0.625\,d_{fp}$ should be rejected as failing to provide the required degree of *lateral* stiffness.

Lever

The lever is usually made of rectangular section mild steel bar and it is thus advisable to fit brass bushes in the two holes in the lever to receive the thrust and fulcrum pins, especially if steel (even stainless) pins are employed. The pins may be a close fit in the jaws of the fulcrum bolt, but the lever and the valve stem must have reasonable freedom of movement. The bushes should

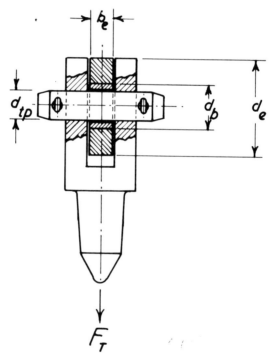

Fig. 6.12 *Valve stem—lever safety/relief valves*

be a press fit in the lever and of nominal diameter

$$d_b = d_{tp} + 5 \text{ mm } (0 \cdot 1875 \text{ in}) \text{ or } d_{fp} + 5 \text{ mm } (0 \cdot 1875 \text{ in})$$

The lever will be subjected to a bending moment under the influence of the cheeseweight through the leverage y (Fig. 6.9) and this will be a maximum at the section containing the thrust pin TP.

If M denotes the maximum bending moment, then

$$M = W_o y$$

Equating M to the moment of resistance

$$M = fZ$$

where Z is the section modulus and equal to

$$\frac{b_e}{6}(d_e^2 - d_b^2)$$

b_e being the width of the lever and f the allowable stress, tensile or compressive, then

$$W_o y = \frac{b_e}{6}f(d_e^2 - d_b^2)$$

One should assume a value for b_e tentatively and calculate d_e, viz:

$$d_e = \sqrt{\left(\frac{6 W_o y}{b_e f} + d_b^2\right)} \qquad (6.24)$$

The nearest commercially available section should be adopted.

The lever, being flat, is relatively weak laterally but as it could only be deflected in this plane by accidental (or intentional) blows there is little more that could be done to cater for such exigencies other than that provided by the guide bracket (Fig. 6.9) whose main function is to maintain the lever in its ordained position relative to the valve member.

This guide should be open topped for preference; otherwise it would be an easy matter for one malignantly inclined to wedge the lever in the guide and thus render the valve inoperative.

One argument in favour of the closed top guide is that it prevents the valve from being blown out of its seating but this is a very remote possibility. It could possibly be lifted out, wholly or partially, by anyone bent on tampering with the valve, however.

It is appropriate to conclude this aspect of safety valve design with a worked example.

WORKED EXAMPLE

Determine the essential details of a 75 mm (3 in) lever safety valve to operate on saturated steam and required to blow-off at a pressure of 0·45 MPa [65 lb/in²].

Solution

For the conditions stated a cast iron bodied valve with gunmetal seating members will suffice.

Seating details. The first essential is to determine the width *w* of the seating annulus.

From eqn (6.3) the theoretical width $w = 0·01d = 0·01 \times 75 = 0·75$ mm [$0·01 \times 3 = 0·03$ in] but from practical considerations the width should be taken from the upper 'curve' of the graph over Fig. 6.7 from which it will be seen that a width of 3·3mm [0·130 in] is advocated; then the *outside* diameter of the seating annulus will be $75 + (2 \times 3·3) = 81·6$ mm [$3 + (2 \times 0·130) = 3·26$ in] and the mean diameter will be $75 + 3·3 = 78·3$ mm [$3 + 0·130) = 3·13$ in].

We have seen that it is on the area corresponding to the *mean* diameter that the pressure at blow-off is assumed to be exerted since it will be recalled we cannot but hazard a guess at the position of the precise boundary at which leakage across the seating is arrested; then pressure upthrust at blow-off

$$F_a = \frac{\pi}{4} d_m^2 p_b$$

where $d_m = $ *mean* diameter of seating $= 78·3$ mm [3·13 in]

and p_b = blowing off pressure $= 0·45$ MPa [65 lb/in²]

then pressure upthrust at blow-off

$$F_a = \frac{\pi}{4} \times 78·3^2 \times 0·45 = 2167N \left[\frac{\pi}{4} \times 3·13^2 \times 65 = 500 \text{ lb} \right] \text{ approximately}$$

but we have seen from eqn (6.4) that the total deadweight to be applied, namely

$$F_T = 1.025 F_a = 1.025 \times 2167N \ [1.025 \times 500 \ \text{lb}]$$
$$= 2221N \ [512.5 \ \text{lb}]$$
$$\text{say} \quad 2225N \ [513 \ \text{lb}]*$$

At this stage we should check from eqn (6.7) to ascertain if the permissible unit contact pressure for the chosen seating materials falls within the prescribed limiting values, then unit contact pressure, taking the effective diameter of the seating as the mean diameter d_m in this instance,

$$u_s = \frac{0.256 d_m P_b}{w} = \frac{0.256 \times 78.3 \times 0.45}{3.3} \left[= \frac{0.256 \times 3.13 \times 65}{0.130} \right]$$
$$= 2.73 \ \text{MPa} \quad [= 401 \ \text{lb/in}^2]$$

which is decidedly on the safe side.

Cheeseweight. From eqn (6.11) (neglecting the weight of the lever and other 'moving' parts until other dimensions have been more closely established) we have:

$$\text{weight } W_o = \frac{F_T f_m}{x}$$

Now we know F_T but not f_m or x. The fulcrum distance f_m may be estimated with reasonable accuracy but as design proceeds this may be definitely established. We will forecast that f_m is 75 mm [3 in] tentatively and x is 600 mm [24 in].

$$\text{Proceeding: } W_o = \frac{2225 \times 75}{600} = 278N, \text{ a mass of } \frac{278}{9.81} = 28.35 \ \text{kg}$$
$$\left[= \frac{513 \times 3}{24} = 64.12 \ \text{lb} \right]$$

To gain some idea of the proportions of the cheeseweight it may be assumed to be perfectly cylindrical and solid throughout; solid it would be in the case of the suspensory type (Fig. 6.10 (b)) and virtually so in the case of the slidably mounted version (Fig. 6.10 (a)) due to it containing a portion of the lever.

*It should be noted that these are not exact equivalents.

Let D denote the diameter of such a cylinder and E its thickness. Take cast iron to weight $7 \cdot 2$ mg/mm³ [$0 \cdot 26$ lb/in³] then assuming E to be 125 mm [5 in] we have:

$$125 \times 7 \cdot 2 \ \pi/4 \times D^2 = 28\,350\,000 \text{ mg} \quad [5 \times 0 \cdot 26 \times \pi/4 \ D^2 = 64 \cdot 12 \text{ lb}]$$

or $\quad D^2 = \dfrac{28\,350\,000 \times 4}{125 \times 7 \cdot 2 \times \pi} \qquad \left[D^2 = \dfrac{64 \cdot 12 \times 4}{5 \times 0 \cdot 26 \times \pi} \right]$

whence $\qquad D = \sqrt{40107} \qquad\quad [D = \sqrt{62 \cdot 8}]$

$\qquad\qquad\quad = 200 \cdot 27 \qquad\qquad [\quad = 7 \cdot 92]$

$\qquad\qquad\quad$ say 200 mm $\qquad$ [say 8 in]

This latter calculation, simple as it may be, could be avoided—whenever the design of a range of weight-loaded valves is contemplated—by selecting a suitable cheeseweight appropriate to the calculated 'avoirdupoid' from one or other of the Tables given in Figs 10 (a) or 10 (b).

Fulcrum pin. From eqn (6.16) the upward force tending to shear the pin is denoted by F_b, and in the present case

$$F_b = \frac{9 \cdot 81 \times 28 \cdot 35}{75}(600 - 75) \qquad \left[F_b = \frac{64 \cdot 12}{3}(24 - 3) \right]$$

$\qquad = 1948$ N approximately $\qquad$ [$\quad = 449$ lb approximately]

From eqn (6.17) the diameter of the fulcrum pin is given by:

$$d_{fp} = \sqrt{\left(\frac{0 \cdot 728 \ F_b}{f_s} \right)} + 6 \text{ mm } [0 \cdot 25 \text{ in}]$$

For the gunmetal pin the allowable sheer stress f_s may be taken as 55 MPa or 8000 lb/in².

Then $d_{fp} = \sqrt{\left(\dfrac{0 \cdot 728 \times 1948}{55} \right)} + 6 \text{ mm} \left[d_{fp} = \sqrt{\left(\dfrac{0 \cdot 726 \times 449}{8000} \right)} + 0 \cdot 25 \text{ in} \right]$

$\qquad = \sqrt{25 \cdot 8} + 6 \text{ mm} \quad [= \sqrt{0 \cdot 0409} + 0 \cdot 25 \text{ in}]$

$\qquad = 5 \cdot 07 + 6 \text{ mm} \qquad [= 0 \cdot 202 + 0 \cdot 25 \text{ in}]$

$\qquad = 11 \cdot 07 \text{ (say 12) mm} \quad [= 0 \cdot 452 \text{ (say } 0 \cdot 5) \text{ in}]$

Similarly from eqn (6.19) the diameter of the thrust pin (TP) will be given by

$$d_{tp} = \sqrt{\left(\frac{0 \cdot 728 \times F_T}{f_s}\right)} + 6 \text{ mm } [0 \cdot 25 \text{ in}]$$

$$= \sqrt{\left(\frac{0 \cdot 728 \times 2225}{55}\right)} + 6 \text{ mm } \left[= \sqrt{\left(\frac{0 \cdot 728 \times 513}{8000}\right)} + 0 \cdot 25 \text{ in}\right]$$

$$= \sqrt{29 \cdot 37} + 6 \text{ mm } [= \sqrt{0 \cdot 0467} + 0 \cdot 25 \text{ in}]$$

$$= 5 \cdot 42 + 6 \text{ mm } [= 0 \cdot 216 + 0 \cdot 25 \text{ in}]$$

$$= 11 \cdot 42 \text{ (say 12) mm } [= 0 \cdot 460 \text{ (say } 0 \cdot 5) \text{ in}]$$

Fulcrum bolt threaded termination. From eqn (6.20) the *core* diameter of the screwed termination is given by

$$d_c = \sqrt{\left(\frac{1 \cdot 273 \, F_b}{f_t}\right)} + 6 \text{ mm } [0 \cdot 25 \text{ in}]$$

Take $f_t + 35$ MPa or 5000 lb/in^2 as the allowable tensile stress for this item, then:

$$\text{core diameter } d_c = \sqrt{\left(\frac{1 \cdot 273 \times 1948}{35}\right)} + 6\text{mm}$$

$$\left[d_c = \sqrt{\left(\frac{1 \cdot 273 \times 449}{5000}\right)} + 0 \cdot 25\text{in}\right]$$

$$= \sqrt{70 \cdot 85} + 6 \text{ mm } [= \sqrt{0 \cdot 1143} + 0 \cdot 25 \text{ in}]$$

$$= 8 \cdot 42 + 6 \text{ mm } [= 0 \cdot 338 + 0 \cdot 25 \text{ in}]$$

$$= 14 \cdot 42 \text{ mm } [= 0 \cdot 588 \text{ in}]$$

Adopt M20 [$\frac{3}{4}$ in BSW which has a core diameter of $0 \cdot 622$ in]. (See note at end of worked solution.)

Fulcrum bolt jaw portion.

$$\text{Width of jaw } w_f = 2 d_{fp} + 6 \text{ mm } [0 \cdot 25 \text{ in}]$$

$$= (2 \times 12) + 6 \text{ mm } [= (2 \times 0 \cdot 5) + 0 \cdot 25 \text{ in}]$$

$$= 30 \text{ mm } [1 \cdot 25 \text{ in}]$$

From eqn (6.23):

$$t_f = \frac{F_b}{2f_t(w_f - d_{fp})}$$

Taking $f_t = 35$ MPa [5000 lb/in²] (as before) and substituting known values:

$$t_f = \frac{1948}{2 \times 35\,(30 - 12)} \left[= \frac{449}{2 \times 5000\,(1 \cdot 25 - 0 \cdot 5)} \right]$$

$$= 1 \cdot 55 \text{ mm} \quad [= 0 \cdot 06 \text{ in}]$$

which is absurdly small from practical considerations. As indicated in the text this should not be less than

$$0 \cdot 625\, d_{fp} = 0 \cdot 625 \times 12 \quad [= 0 \cdot 625 \times 0 \cdot 5]$$

$$= 7 \cdot 5 \text{ mm} \quad [= 0 \cdot 3125 \text{ in}]$$

Lever. Assume a width b_e (Fig. 6.12) of 12 mm [0·5 in] and the diameter of the bush

$$d_b = d_{fp} + 5 \text{ mm} \quad [0 \cdot 1875 \text{ in}]$$

$$= 12 + 5 \text{ mm} \quad [= 0 \cdot 5 + 0 \cdot 1875 \text{ in}]$$

$$= 17 \text{ mm} \quad [= 0 \cdot 6875 \text{ in}]$$

Let w_t denote the weight of the overhung portion of the lever (see Fig. 6.13) and take the allowable working stress f for mild steel as 40 MPa [6000 lb/in²] then from eqn (6.24):

$$\text{depth } d_e = \sqrt{\left(\frac{6\,W_o y}{b_e f} + d_b^2 \right)}$$

and substituting known values:

$$d_e = \sqrt{\left(\frac{6 \times 28 \cdot 35 \times 9 \cdot 81\,(600{-}75)}{12 \times 40} + 17^2 \right)}$$

$$\left[= \sqrt{\left(\frac{6 \times 64 \cdot 12\,(24{-}3)}{0 \cdot 5 \times 6000} + 0 \cdot 6875^2) \right)} \right]$$

$$= 45 \cdot 97 \text{ mm} \quad [= 1 \cdot 779 \text{ in}]$$

Adopt 50 mm × 12 mm [2 in × 0·5 in] section, or the nearest larger readily procurable size.

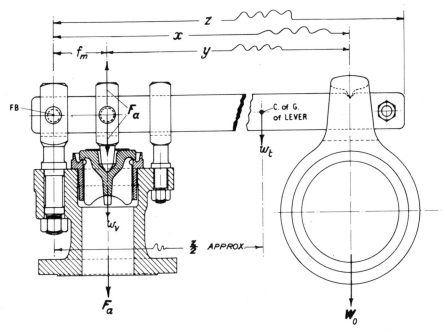

Fig. 6.13 *3 in lever safety/relief valve—design based on worked example*

All the foregoing data are now embodied in Fig. 6.13, giving the general arrangement in detail.

Having established the principal dimensions of the valve let us see what influence the weight of the lever and other moving parts can have on the weight and positioning of the cheeseweight.

Weight of 50 mm × 12 mm [2 in × 0·5 in] mild steel flat bar = 4·68 kg/m [= 3·33 lb/ft] therefore, weight w_t of 640 mm [25·5 in] of such bar

$$= 4·68 \times 0·640 \text{ kg} \left[= \frac{3·33 \times 25·5 \text{ in}}{12} \right]$$

$$= 3 \text{ kg} [= 7·08 \text{ lb}]$$

This may be regarded as acting through the centre of gravity of the 640 mm [25·5 in] length of overhung lever, namely at its mid-point situated 320 mm [12·75 in] from the centre of rotation at FB.

The 25 mm [1 in] length of overhang to the left of FB is unworthy of consideration; having no practical influence to speak of on the positioning or weight of the cheeseweight.

The estimation of the weight of the valve member and stem is an exercise in itself and only calls for a modest knowledge of solid geometry and simple arithmetic. From the design illustrated in Fig. 6.13 the combined weight of these two moving parts work out at 1·9 kg [4·25 lb] and is denoted by w_v.

We have seen from eqn (6.14) that:

$$W_o = \frac{F_T f_m - w_t z/2 - w_v f_m}{x}$$

Substituting known values:

$$W_o = \frac{(2225 \times 75/9 \cdot 81) - (3 \times 320) - (1 \cdot 9 \times 75)}{600} \text{kg}$$

$$\left[= \frac{(513 \times 3) - (7 \cdot 08 \times 12 \cdot 75) - (4 \cdot 25 \times 3)}{24} \text{lb} \right]$$

$$= 26 \cdot 5 \text{ kg} \quad [= 59 \cdot 83 \text{ lb, say } 60 \text{ lb}]$$

a difference of only 1·85 kg [4·29 lb] when the weight of the moving parts is disregarded.

Valves, in common with many other devices of like nature, are almost invariably designed for a pressure *range* and design should be based on catering for the maximum pressure in that range. This accounts in some cases for the scantlings having the appearance of being too generously proportioned for a particular application.

DEADWEIGHT SAFETY VALVES

The simplest of all safety valves is the deadweight pattern, consisting basically of a seating and a mass of metal resting thereon, the latter of sufficient weight to balance the force tending to lift the valve member with something in reserve to secure fluid-tightness across the seating faces in contact.

Due to their extreme simplicity the earliest safety valves were of this pattern and present-day shell boilers often feature this type of valve located near the front end, usually to serve as an additional safeguard, and for this reason alone, almost invariably set to blow off at a pressure somewhat in excess of its spring-loaded companion, so as to come into operation if the latter proves incapable of coping with a sudden excess pressure rise.

The deadweight safety valve is prohibitive for high pressures on account of the bulk of deadweight which would be required. For example, if a 100 mm or 4 in valve for a blowing-off pressure of, say, 1·75 MPa or 250 lb/in^2 was contemplated it would soon be revealed that approximately $1\frac{1}{2}$ tons of deadweight would be required. No survey authority or insurance company would sanction a valve of such bulk on any shell boiler; the spring loaded pattern is the logical alternative.

It is to be noted that in any deadweight safety valve the centre of gravity of the suspensory deadweight must be located well below the seating

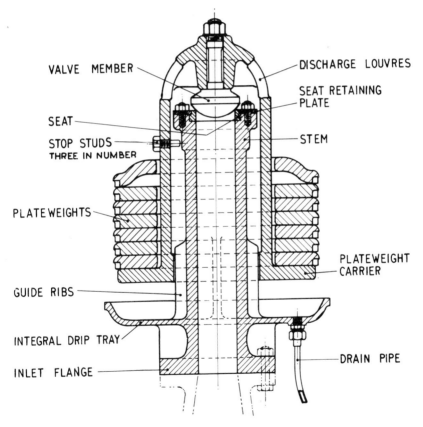

Fig. 6.14 *Simple dead-weight safety/relief valve—open discharge pattern*

surfaces, thereby ensuring that it will be self-centering.

A typical deadweight safety valve, devoid of all embellishments, but retaining all the essential features, is illustrated in Fig. 6.14 an open-discharge pattern, the discharge being direct to atmosphere via the louvres shown. In a more refined version the discharge is controlled, being ordained to leave the valve via a flanged connection to an escape pipe passing out of

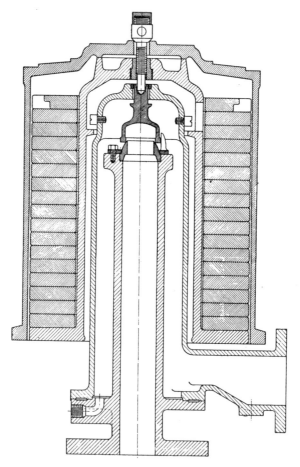

Fig. 6.15 *Hopkinson controlled-flow deadweight safety valve (Courtesy of Hopkinsons Ltd, Huddersfield)*

the boiler room or otherwise discharging well away from the boiler front. Such a valve is illustrated in Fig. 6.15.

Seating members

In order to contribute to the self-centring attribute of the suspensory deadweight it is considered good practice to adopt spherical contoured valve members. The seating member may be pressed into the stem and further secured by means of an annular retaining plate and number of studs and nuts (the nuts preferably non-ferous), as shown in Fig. 6.16 (a) and (b). Three studs, not less than M10 ($\frac{3}{8}$ in BSW), should suffice since they are not called upon to resist any line pressure upthrust by reason of the seating member being pressed into the stem.

Where steam is concerned the Board of Trade rules stipulate that seatings of the type suggested should be secured in this manner and the two alternatives illustrated are equally acceptable, although the bevelled shouldered square-headed set-screw featured at (b) is considered superior by some manufacturers.

With regard to the valve member this may be fashioned with a near hemispherical base as shown at (a) in Fig. 6.17 or with a more oblate contoured base as at (b).

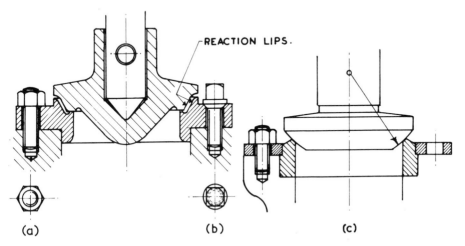

Fig. 6.16 *Alternative modes of securing renewable safety/relief valve seatings*

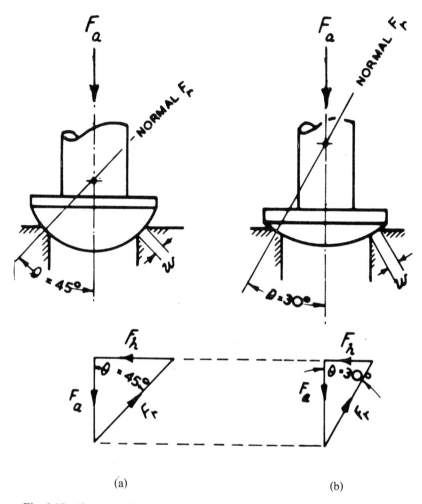

(a)   (b)

Fig. 6.17 *Alternative forms of valve members—dead-weight safety/relief valves*

Consider the forces acting on these respective seatings. There is a down-wardly acting force F_a due to the required deadweight and this force can be resolved into two component forces:

(i) a horizontal force F_h tending to expand the seating and
(ii) a reactionary force F_r whose direction is normal to the seating face.

Obviously

$$F_r = F_a \sec \theta \qquad (6.25a)$$
$$F_h = F_a \tan \Gamma \qquad (6.25b)$$

An examination of the two force diagrams will reveal that both the horizontal component force F_h (the 'expanding' force) and F_r, the reactionary force, diminish with a diminishing angle of incidence θ.

One fact that emerges from this dissertation is that the seat contacting pressure will be greater in the case of spherically contoured seating members than with perfectly flat seatings under identical conditions of axial loading.

To all intents and purposes the width w, being relatively small, may be taken to be the same as for flat seatings (as given in Fig. 6.7) but in checking for permissible surface stress (see Table 6.1) the appropriate value of F_r, the resultant force, must be evaluated.

The angle of incidence θ should by anywhere between the two examples chosen in Fig. 6.17 i.e. between 30° and 45° for preference.

Although the deadweight is made up of a plurality of plates, their supporting carrier, valve member etc, the total deadweight should be calculated (as a preliminary canter, so to speak) on the basis of a hollow mass of metal approximating to the external desired configurations (see Fig. 6.18). Some amount of trial and error calculations is inevitable before the final configurations can be definitely established.

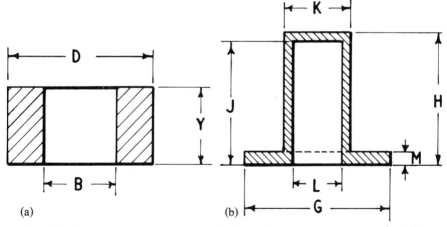

(a)   (b)

Fig. 6.18 *Elementary concept of dead-weight and carrier—dead-weight safety/relief valves*

As before, the width of seat contact w can be taken from Fig. 6.7 (a) or (b) and the *total* deadweight, therefore, will be given by:

$$F_T = 1.025 \frac{\pi}{4} d_m^2 p_b = 0.805 \, d_m^2 p_b \qquad (6.26)$$

(to cater for the additional weight to ensure fluid-tightness at the seatings, as previously explained).

Deadweight

Dealing firstly with the carrier (Fig. 6.18 (b)) the inside diameter L is governed by the outside diameter of the seat-retaining ring (see Fig. 6.14) in the case of the simple deadweight safety valve illustrated. At least 10 mm ($\frac{3}{8}$ in) overall clearance between the two should be arranged so that the mass of deadweight shall be free to swing pendulously without fear of restraint and prevented from undue movement by the guide ribs located near the base of the stem.

The wall thickness is governed more by the exigencies of moulding rather than by the tensile force it is required to resist by the imposition of the deadweight. As the carrier is usually of cast iron a minimum wall thickness of 12 mm or $\frac{1}{2}$ in is deemed advisable and the thickness M of the plate portion about $1\frac{1}{2}$ times this figure. The height H cannot be estimated until we have some idea of the value of Y, the combined height of the stacked plate-weights (shown in 'solidus' in the illustration) but we now have some idea of the value of B, the bore of the centre-hole in the plateweights, since this will be somewhat in excess of K.

Taking the mass of plateweights to represent a hollow cylinder a simple calculation will determine the approximate variables D and Y when the height H of the carrier may be roughly determined.

As will be appreciated some exploratory calculations are inevitable; the results can be adjusted as design finally takes shape.

Stem

This item may be of cast-iron where the steam pressure does not exceed 1 MPa or 150 lb/in^2 of if superheated steam (at any pressure) is not in evidence; otherwise cast steel must be used. Although the stem rightly qualifies as a hollow strut, being axially loaded by the superimposed mass of deadweight plates etc, the compressive stresses are invariably so small (due to limitations of deadweight) as to be inconsequential.

Likewise the wall thickness to counter the line pressure works out so small as to call for enhancement if sound castings are to result. Consequently, the following empirical rules, based on experience, are advocated for determining the wall thickness t_s where d_s is the bore of the stem.

$$t_s = d_s/60 + 12 \text{ mm } [0.5 \text{ in}] \text{ for pressures up to}$$
$$0.15 \text{ MPa } [20 \text{ lb/in}^2] \tag{6.27a}$$

For C.1

$$= d_s/42 + 12 \text{ mm } [0.5 \text{ in}] \text{ for pressures of}$$
$$0.15\text{–}0.35 \text{ MPa } [20\text{–}50 \text{ lb/in}^2] \tag{6.27b}$$

$$= d_s/25 + 12 \text{ mm } [0.5 \text{ in}] \text{ for pressures of}$$
$$0.35\text{–}0.7 \text{ MPa } [50\text{–}100 \text{ lb/in}^2] \tag{6.27c}$$

$$= d_s/16 + 12 \text{ mm } [0.5 \text{ in}] \text{ for pressures of}$$
$$0.7\text{–}1.0 \text{ MPa } [100\text{–}150 \text{ lb/in}^2] \tag{6.27d}$$

For C.S.

$$= d_s/16 + 8 \text{ mm } [0.3 \text{ in}] \text{ for pressures of}$$
$$1.0\text{–}1.4 \text{ MPa } [150\text{–}200 \text{ lb/in}^2] \tag{6.27e}$$

$$= d_s/10 + 8 \text{ mm } [0.3 \text{ in}] \text{ for pressures of}$$
$$1.4\text{–}1.7 \text{ MPa } [200\text{–}250 \text{ lb/in}^2] \tag{6.27f}$$

A worked example follows.

Although no deadweight safety valve may be expected to lift off its seat a distance exceeding 1/24th of the seat diameter the stop studs shown (Figs 6.14 and 6.15) should permit of a lift of one quarter the diameter. This is in order to provide adequate area of escape should an abnormal discharge occur such as severe priming (the carrying over of water) or a very sudden rise in evaporation such as might occur (and has been known to occur) should some misguided person introduce highly flammable material eg, celluloid waste into the boiler furnace.

WORKED EXAMPLE

A low pressure heating boiler, working pressure 0.25 MPa $[35 \text{ lb/in}^2]$ is to be fitted with an additional safety valve of the deadweight pattern, 50 mm [2 in] bore, arranged to blow-off at 0.28 MPa $[40 \text{ lb/in}^2]$.

Determine the essential details based on the open discharge pattern illustrated in Fig. 6.14.

Solution

From the graph in Fig. 6.7 (a) the width of seating annulus $w = 2 \cdot 5$ mm [$0 \cdot 10$ in]; therefore the mean diameter $d_m = 50 + 2 \cdot 5 = 52 \cdot 5$ mm [$2 + 0 \cdot 10 = 2 \cdot 10$ in].

From eqn (6.26) the total deadweight required

$$F_T = 0 \cdot 805 \ d_m^2 p_b$$
$$= 0 \cdot 805 \times 52 \cdot 5^2 \times 0 \cdot 28 \text{N} \ [= 0 \cdot 805 \times 2 \cdot 10^2 \times 40 \text{ lb}]$$
$$= 622 \text{N} \ [= 142 \text{ lb}]$$

For such a low loading the seat width w could be reduced somewhat, say the mean of the two values denoted by the 'curves' in Fig. 6.7 (a), say

$$w = \frac{0 \cdot 5 + 2 \cdot 5}{2} = 1 \cdot 5 \text{ mm} \left[= \frac{0 \cdot 10 + 0 \cdot 02}{2} = 0 \cdot 6 \text{ in} \right]$$

then $d_m = 51 \cdot 5$ mm [$2 \cdot 06$ in]

Accepting this figure, the value of F_T will be reduced somewhat

$$F_T = 0 \cdot 806 \times 51 \cdot 5^2 \times 0 \cdot 28 \ [= 0 \cdot 806 \times 2 \cdot 06^2 \times 40]$$
$$= 598 \text{N} \ [137 \text{ lb}]$$

The seat contacting pressure under this loading is unworthy of investigation since it would fall well under the maximum permissible value.

The outside diameter of the seat retaining ring, allowing for M10 [$\frac{3}{8}$ BSW] studs (and nuts) would be approximately 108 mm [$4 \cdot 25$ in] so the inside diameter L of the carrier (see Fig. 6.18) could be 114 mm [$4 \cdot 5$ in]. Assume a shell thickness of 12 mm [$0 \cdot 5$ in] then the outside diameter K of the shell becomes 138 mm [$5 \cdot 5$ in]. As pointed out certain dimensions will require to be assumed, based on judgement, so we will assume the outside diameter G of the bottom flanged portion to be 300 mm [12 in] and its thickness M to be 20 mm [$0 \cdot 75$ in]. Take the approximate heights J and H to be 228 mm [9 in] and 240 mm [$9 \cdot 5$ in] respectively. Now we have all the data enabling us to calculate the weight of the carrier.

Take the weight of cast iron to be $7 \cdot 1$ mg/mm^3 [$0 \cdot 26$ lb/in^3], the weight of carrier

$$= \frac{7 \cdot 1 \pi}{4 \times 10^6} \left\{ 20 \ (300^2 - 108^2) + 228 \ (132^2 - 108^2) + (132^2 \times 12) \right\}$$
$$= 17 \cdot 23 \text{ kg}$$

$$\left[\text{or} = \frac{0 \cdot 26\pi}{4} \left\{ 0 \cdot 75 \, (12^2 - 4 \cdot 5^2) + 9 \, (5 \cdot 5^2 - 4 \cdot 5^2) + (5 \cdot 5^2 \times 0 \cdot 5) \right\} = 40 \cdot 5 \text{ lb} \right]$$

Therefore weight of plateweights = total deadweight − weight of carrier, etc

$$= 61 - 17 \cdot 23 \text{ kg} \quad [= 137 - 40 \cdot 5 \text{ lb}]$$
$$= 43 \cdot 77 \text{ kg} \quad\quad [= 96 \cdot 5 \text{ lb}]$$

Again referring to Fig. 6.18 we can assume with every justification that the bore B of the deadweight mass to be 150 mm [6 in], the outside diameter could be equal to G, i.e. 300 mm [12 in] and the depth Y can then be established knowing that the weight requires to be $43 \cdot 77$ kg [$96 \cdot 5$ lb] then:

weight of plateweights

$$= \frac{7 \cdot 1}{10^6} \times \frac{\pi}{4} Y (300^2 - 150^2) = 43 \cdot 77 \text{ kg} \left[= 0 \cdot 26 \times \frac{\pi}{4} Y (12^2 - 6^2) = 96 \cdot 5 \text{ lb} \right]$$

whence $Y = \dfrac{4 \times 10^6 \times 43 \cdot 77}{7 \cdot 1\pi \times 67\,500} \quad \left[= \dfrac{4 \times 96 \cdot 5}{0 \cdot 26\pi \, (144 - 36)} \right]$

$$= 116 \cdot 3 \text{ mm} \quad [= 4 \cdot 4 \text{ in}]$$

Thickness of stem. From eqn (6.27b)

$$t_s = d_s / 42 + 12 \text{ mm} \, [0 \cdot 5 \text{ in}]$$
$$= 50/42 + 12 \text{ mm} \, [= 2/42 + 0 \cdot 5 \text{ in}]$$
$$= 1 \cdot 19 + 12 \text{ mm} \, [= 0 \cdot 0476 + 0 \cdot 5 \text{ in}]$$
$$= 13 \cdot 19 \text{ mm, say } 14 \text{ mm} \, [= 0 \cdot 5476 \text{ in, say } \tfrac{9}{16} \text{ in}]$$

SPRING SAFETY VALVES

The erratic behaviour of the deadweight and lever and weight loaded safety valves, originally the vogue on the early locomotive and marine boilers, occasioned by the unavoidable jolting and rolling can well be imagined, and engineers were prompted, in consequence, to concentrate on devising a more satisfactory alternative.

One of the first attempts in this direction was to substitute an anchored tension spring for the cheeseweight on the lever and weight loaded version (Fig. 6.19) and it will be apparent that this would be less prone to spluttering than any of its predecessors relying solely on a mass of metal for loading the valve. A relatively light spring acting through the leverage shown could

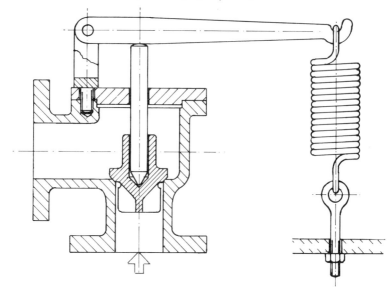

Fig. 6.19 *Spring balance safety/relief valve*

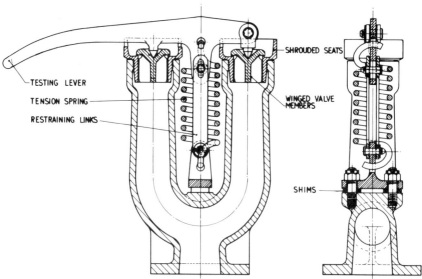

Fig. 6.20 *Ramsbottom spring safety/relief valve*

exert an appreciable load for countering the upthrust due to the line pressure.

An improvement on the foregoing was the dual spring loaded valve illustrated in Fig. 6.20 invented by John Ramsbottom *circa* 1856, and which satisfied the needs of locomotive builders for a considerable number of years until ousted by the more compact 'pop' type safety valve, although the Ramsbottom valve is still favoured for certain classes of boilers, notably those coming under the classification of 'economic' type.

A noteworthy example of the 'pop' type of safety valve is the Ross muffled pop safety valve illustrated in Fig. 6.21.

As the technique of spring making improved apace with the advent of better spring materials the direct spring loaded safety valve caused the lever and spring type to lapse into obscurity.

The Ramsbottom valve is worthy of a little close study, possessing quite a number of commendable features although it has certain shortcomings. The dual valves are equally loaded by the single tension spring and, being of identical diameter, the two should blow off simultaneously, although it is

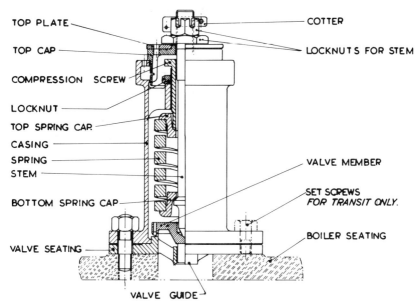

Fig. 6.21 *Ross 'pop' type safety/relief valve*

scarcely conceivable that either valve could lag very much behind the other. This dual arrangement is preferable to employing a single valve of increased diameter to give an equivalent area, and halves the chances of the valve sticking, as can occur if a valve has remained inoperative for a long period, and with untreated boiler water. This fear apparently prompted its originator to extend the lever so as to provide means of easing each valve member off its seat by hand, each thrusting finger acting as the fulcrum according to which of the two valve members it is required to ease off, although normally lift is entirely dependent upon the requisite steam pressure being available and effective.

Provision is made for preventing the valve members being blown out of their seats, (and taking the lever with them) in the event of the spring breaking, by the two flat steel restraining members housed within the coils of the spring.

The purpose of the shrouded seats is to deflect the discharging steam clear of the driver's look-out windows.

With increasing boiler dimensions the Ramsbottom valve occupied too much headroom which is another reason why it was abandoned on locomotive boilers in favour of the Ross type.

In a work of this nature only the more orthodox types of safety valve will be employed as design examples. This should forestall the critics who might be tempted to point out (possibly anxiously) that the *nozzle, high-lift, full-bore* and *torsion-bar* types have received no more than a fleeting reference, lacking detailed description. But these types are the domain of the specialist manufacturer and this work is concerned only with the basic rudiments of valve design.

Two widely differing designs will now receive consideration.

Open discharge type spring safety valve

Figure 6.22 illustrates a simple form of safety valve widely favoured for those installations where discharge direct to atmosphere is inconsequential. It is often chosen for installation on superheater headers.

The winged form of valve member has been obviated in the design chosen by way of illustration and the spring adjusting screw common in other types has been dispensed with in favour of utilising the upper portions of the pillars, double nutted.

The spring is located at its upper end by a collar on the underside

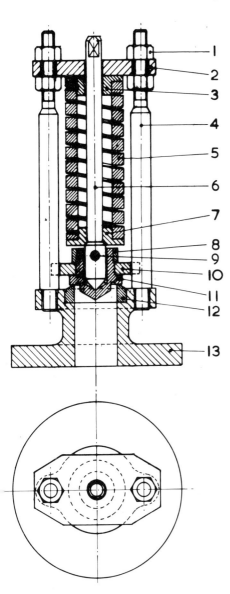

REF NO	DESCRIPTION	MATERIAL.
1	NUT, ADJ.	STEEL or BRASS
2	CROSSHEAD.	MILD STEEL.
3	SPRING CAP.	MILD STEEL.
4	COLUMN.	MILD STEEL.
5	SPRING.	STEEL.
6	STEM.	STAIN STEEL.
7	SPRING PLATE.	MILD STEEL.
8	FERRULE.	MILD STEEL.
9	SPRING PIN.	HARDENED STEEL
10	GUIDE PLATE.	GUN METAL.
11	VALVE DISK.	GM or NICKEL ALLOY
12	SEATING.	"
13	BODY.	CI, GM or STEEL.

Fig. 6.22 *Open discharge spring safety/relief valve*

of the crosshead and by a similar one on the stem at the lower end which is also extended so as to form a sliding guide engaging the pillars, the stem being thereby constrained to keep the valve member in its ordained central position.

Springs for safety valves

For all safety valves of the spring loaded variety destined for steam duties the springs should conform to the rules prescribed by the British Standards Institution, namely BS 759:1975 and by the Board of Trade. The alert designer will avail himself of copies of these publications, especially BS 759:1975.

Much confusion regarding the lift of a safety valve when blowing off at full pressure can be attributed to a mis-interpretation of the term *compression* in the Board of Trade and other formulae. These specifically refer to the *initial compression* to be imparted to the spring in order to produce the necessary axial force to counter the pressure upthrust and other resistances and do not apply to any *subsequent compression* resulting from valve lift, which is very much smaller by comparison.

Clause 22.4 of BS 759:1975 states, *inter alia*, that the springs shall be made from round section bar or wire and that the shear stress q, as determined by the various appropriate equations shall not exceed certain optimum values, given in Table 6.3, subject to the maximum shear stress when the spring might be compressed coil to coil.

This stress q is given by:

$$q = \frac{8\,W\,D\,K\,A}{\pi\,d^3} \qquad (6.28)$$

where W is the force at the set pressure (N)

$\qquad D$ is the mean diameter of the coil (mm)

$\qquad d$ is the diameter of the section (mm)

Note that $K = \dfrac{c + 0.2}{c - 1}$ $\qquad\qquad\qquad$ (6.29)

where $c = D/d$

$$A = \frac{\delta_1 + \delta_2}{\delta_1}$$

Table 6.3 Safety valve springs

Spring material	Permissible shear stress q (eqn 24)		Maximum permissible shear stress when spring compressed solid		Shear modulus (G)	
	MPa	psi	MPa	psi	MPa $(\times 1000)$	psi $(\times 1000)$
High duty oil hardened and tempered steel	450	65 000	750	110 000	80	11 500
High duty cold drawn 0·40/0·85 carbon steel	415	60 000	655	95 000	80	11 500
0·55/0·85 carbon steel 'Music' wire	560	81 000	930	135 000	80	11 500
Oil hardened and tempered carbon and carbon–manganese steel	540	78 000	860	125 000	70	10 000
Chrome nickel rust, acid and heat resisting steel	415	60 000	655	95 000	80	11 500
Nickel chrome molybdenum steel	540	78 000	860	125 000	80	11 500

where δ_1 is the axial deflection due to force W (mm)

$$\delta_2 = \frac{\text{diameter of valve (mm)}}{8}$$ for ordinary and high lift safety valves

and equals the lift (mm) as defined in the appropriate clause previously cited.

q is the shear stress (N/mm²)

Number of working coils

The number of active or free coils may be determined from the following equation.

$$n = \frac{d^4 G \delta_1}{8 D^3 W} \qquad (6.30)$$

where G is the shear modulus (N/mm²)

   n is the number of active coils.

Other symbols are as those given in eqn (6.28).

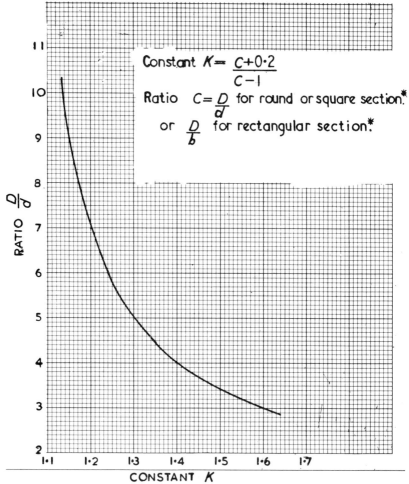

Fig. 6.23 *Graph for value of constant K*

*BS 759:1975 states 'springs shall be made from round section bar or wire'. This would appear to denounce the use of square and rectangular section material which has been favoured for many years.

Note that by active or free coils is meant the actual number of coils which take part in the resistance of the applied load and not the *dead* coils, or portions of coils, at each end of the spring. The latter, being squared off and ground flat to present suitably flat bearing surfaces, cannot be relied upon to take any part in resisting the load. Consequently, these dead coils, usually totalling from $1\frac{1}{2}$ to 2 in any compression spring, must be discounted from the number of complete sections. This is best illustrated in Fig. 6.24 (see part-sectional elevation) in which the number of effective coils may be taken to be *nine*.

Ordinary lift and high lift safety valves. The space between adjacent coils shall be such that when the valve head is lifted a distance $D/8$ this space shall be not less than 1 mm [0·040 in] where D is the minimum bore of the body seat.

Full lift safety valves. The space between adjacent coils shall be such that when the valve head is lifted the amount defined in the appropriate Clause (3) previously cited for full lift safety valves this space shall not be less than 1·5 mm [0·060 in].

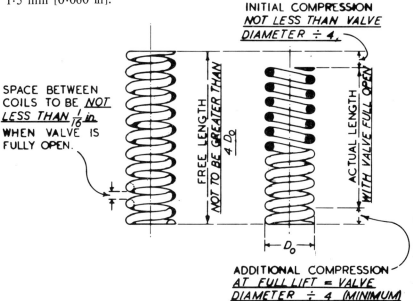

Fig. 6.24 *Safety/relief valve springs*

Having determined n from the appropriate equation (eqn 6.30) the overall free length of the spring may now be determined, having regard to the minimum permissible space between the coils called for in the foregoing clauses and making allowance for the inevitable inclusion of the dead coils to which reference has been made.

WORKED EXAMPLE

Determine the essential dimensions of a 40 mm [$1\frac{1}{2}$ in] diameter open discharge safety valve of the type illustrated in Fig. 6.22 for installation on a superheater and intended to blow off at a pressure of 1·5 MPa, the temperature of the steam being 550°F (288°C).

Solution

For the temperature stated gunmetal as a seating material is ruled out. Adopt a stainless steel seat in conjunction with a nickel–copper–tin alloy (e.g. 'Monel' metal valve member and a stainless steel stem).

From the graph in Fig. 6.7 (b) the width of seating annulus, w is, 2·2 mm; therefore the mean diameter $d_m = 40$ mm + 2·2 mm = 42·2 mm.

From eqn (6.26) the force required to be exerted by the spring will be:

$$F_T = 0\cdot805\, d_m^2 p_b$$
$$= 0\cdot805 \times 42\cdot2^2 \text{ mm}^2 \times 1\cdot5 \text{ MPa}$$
$$= 0\cdot805 \times 42\cdot2^2 \times 1\cdot5 \text{ N}$$
$$= 2150 \text{ N}$$

At zero working pressure the full downward force of the spring would be transmitted to the seating annulus; then from eqn (6.5):

$$\text{intensity of surface stress } u_s = \frac{F_T}{\pi d_m w}$$
$$= \frac{2150}{3\cdot142 \times 42\cdot2 \times 2\cdot2} \text{MPa}$$
$$= 7\cdot371 \text{ MPa}$$

Spring. A spring of round section 'wire' as stipulated in BS 759:1975 will be considered.

We have seen from eqn (6.28) that the maximum permissible stress induced in the spring material is given by the BS expression:

$$q = \frac{8\,W D K A}{\pi\,d^3}$$

where A and K are constants and W (corresponding to F_T in our case) is the spring thrust at the set pressure. D is the mean diameter of the coils and may be taken as 32 mm in this example.

Evaluating the two constants (see nomenclature following eqns (6.28–6.30):

from eqn (6.29) $K = \dfrac{c + 0\cdot2}{c - 1}$ where $c = \dfrac{D}{d}$

Adopting tentatively a section diameter of 9 mm, then $c = \dfrac{32}{9} = 3\cdot555$

whence $K = \dfrac{3\cdot555 + 0\cdot2}{3\cdot555 - 1} = \dfrac{3\cdot755}{2\cdot555} = 1\cdot469$

Now $A = \dfrac{\delta_1 + \delta_2}{\delta_1}$ where δ_1 is the initial deflection to give the required

thrust W (i.e. F_T in the present case) is usually taken as $\dfrac{d_v}{4}$ where d_v is

the nominal diameter of the valve (mm) and δ_2 is given as $\dfrac{d_v}{8}$ in BS 759:1975

then $A = \dfrac{40/4 + 40/8}{40/4} = \dfrac{10 + 5}{10} = 1\cdot5$

Now we have all the 'ingredients' for evaluating eqn (6.28) viz:

$$q = \frac{8 \times 2150 \times 32 \times 1\cdot469 \times 1\cdot5}{3\cdot1416 \times 9^3} = 529\cdot55 \text{ MPa}$$

A suitable grade of spring material may now be selected from Table 6.3 appropriate to this figure.

The remaining essential is to determine the number of active coils. From eqn (6.30):

number of coils $n = \dfrac{d^4 G \delta_1}{8\,D^3 W}$ (refer to previous nomenclature).

Again substitute F_T for W, then, taking G to be 80 000 from Table 6.3,

$$n = \frac{9^4 \times 80\,000 \times 10}{8 \times 32^3 \times 2150}$$

$$= 9\cdot31$$

say 9 coils

Note that the number of coils is not the number of 'sections' as portrayed in a sectional elevation of a spring. The number of 'sections' may be taken to be $1\frac{1}{2}$ or 2 more than the number (n) of complete turns; in short, discounting the redundant spring material for squaring off the ends of the spring the space between adjacent coils shall not be less than 1 mm.

This enables us to now determine the 'free' or uncompressed length of the spring.

No. of coils $= 9$,

then No. of sections $= 9 + 2 = 11$

Solid height of spring $= 11 \times 9 = 99$ say 100 mm.

Adopting a value for the space between the coils of 1 mm, the minimum stipulated, then with 10 spaces between the 11 sections, length of spring when initially compressed by 10 mm

$$= 100 + (10 \times 1)\text{ mm}$$

$$= 110\text{ mm}$$

Adding the initial compression of 10 mm and allowing for a lift of 1/24th of the valve diameter then free length

$$= 110 + 10 + 40/24$$

$$= 121\cdot67\text{ mm}$$

say 122 mm.

Now this value for the space between the coils is a *minimum* value and very small in the extreme.

It is suggested that the free length of the spring be made 133 mm [5·25 in].

Pillars. At all times the pillars will be in tension occasioned by the upward force exerted by the spring on the crosshead. This upthrust will be somewhat in excess of the calculated value of 2150N [483 lb] due to the increased compression of the spring (however slight this may be) at the point of maximum lift on discharge.

For safety valves of 'ordinary' construction a lift of 1/24 of the valve diameter is suggested in BS 759:1967.

This additional upthrust denoted by F_x, will be proportional to the deflexion, or:

$$\frac{\delta_1}{2150}\left[\frac{\delta_1}{483}\right]=\frac{d/24}{F_x}$$

(δ_1 is the initial deflexion to give a thrust of 2150 N [497 lb]).

or $\quad \dfrac{10}{2150}=\dfrac{40/24}{F_x}\left[\dfrac{3/8}{483}=\dfrac{1\cdot5/24}{F_x}\right]$

whence $F_x=\dfrac{2150\times40}{10\times24}\left[=\dfrac{483\times1\cdot5\times8}{24\times3}\right]$

$$=358\cdot3 \text{ N } [=80\cdot5 \text{ lb}]$$

then denoting *total* upthrust by F_T'

we have $F_T'=F_T+F_x$

$$=2150+358\cdot3\,[=483+80\cdot5]$$

$$=2508\cdot3 \text{ N } [=563\cdot5 \text{ lb}]$$

and load to be sustained by each pillar

$$=\frac{2508\cdot3}{2}=1254 \text{ N}\left[\frac{563\cdot5}{2}=282 \text{ lb}\right] \text{ approx.}$$

Equating the core area of each pillar termination times the allowable stress to the load imposed

$$\frac{\pi}{4}d_c^2f_t=\frac{F_T'}{2}\text{ and taking } f_t=70 \text{ MPa } [10\,000 \text{ lb/in}^2]$$

$$d_c=\sqrt{\left(\frac{2\times1254}{\pi\times70}\right)}\quad\left[=\sqrt{\left(\frac{2\times282}{\pi\times10\,000}\right)}\right]$$

$$=3\cdot37 \text{ mm}\qquad[=0\cdot133 \text{ in}]$$

corresponding to say M4 (3/16 BSW). From practical considerations, and allowing for initial tightening stresses, MID on $\frac{3}{8}$ BSF should be regarded as a minimum.

Crosshead. This may be regarded as a 'fixed' beam loaded at the centre (the pillars being double nutted), the force acting being F_T' previously determined, namely 2508 N [563·5 lb]. Owing to the uncertain conditions of

loading and mode of support only an approximate solution to determine its
dimensions appropriate to the stress induced can be expected, and most
designers would proportion this item without much recourse to
mathematical display in a valve of such relatively small proportions. In the
larger valves it is a different story however.

The maximum bending moment will be at the centre of the crosshead and,
having 'fixed' ends, at the points of support and of equal magnitude, the
crosshead being loaded at the centre.

Referring to Fig. 6.25 depicting the crosshead itself the 'span' in the
design shown in Fig. 6.22 worked out at 75 mm [3 in]; then applying the
appropriate beam formula for a beam with fixed ends we have:

$$M = fZ$$

Where M is the bending moment, f the stress incurred and Z the section
modulus which, for a rectangular section is equal to

$$\frac{b_x d_x^2}{6} \text{(see Fig. 6.25) or:}$$

$$M = \frac{F_T' l_x}{8} \text{(for fixed ends)} = \frac{f b_x d_x^2}{6}$$

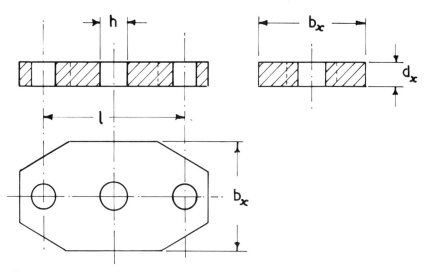

Fig. 6.25 *Crosshead for spring safety/relief valve*

where b_x is the nett width of the crosshead and d_x its depth.

Note that in determining its width account must be taken of the holes for receiving the pillars and the stem. Taking the depth d_x as 12 mm [$\frac{1}{2}$ in] and f, the working stress as 80 MPa [12 000 lb/in²], we have:

$$b_x = \frac{6F_T'l_x}{8fd_x^2}$$

and substituting known values:

$$b_x = \frac{6 \times 2508 \times 75}{8 \times 80 \times 12^2} \quad \left[= \frac{6 \times 563 \cdot 5 \times 3}{8 \times 12\,000 \times 0 \cdot 5^2} \right]$$

$$= 12 \cdot 25 \text{ mm} \quad [= 0 \cdot 423 \text{ in}]$$

Adding this to the diameter of the central hole (9/16 in) for guiding the stem we get:

actual width $= 15 + 12 \cdot 25 = 27 \cdot 25$ mm [$0 \cdot 5625 + 0 \cdot 423 = 0 \cdot 9855$ in], adequate from strength considerations but totally impracticable as will be seen. In a beam with fixed ends (as instanced in the example) and centrally loaded the bending moment is the same at the two supports as at the centre. In the case under consideration the crosshead is also drilled to receive the pillars so the theoretical width at these two points would require to be at least equal to the diameter of the holes (18 mm [11/16 in]) plus 10·5 mm [0·423 in] or $18 + 10 \cdot 5 = 28 \cdot 5$ mm [$0 \cdot 6875 + 0 \cdot 423 = 1 \cdot 111$ in]. Even so, this does not allow coverage for the hexagon nuts and certainly not for the spring plate.

It is suggested, therefore, that the crosshead in this case be cropped from a piece of steel plate or flat 50 mm × 12 mm [2 in × 0·5 in].

Stem. The stem at its lowest extremity is subjected to a compressive force F_T' previously determined, namely 2508 N [563·5 lb], but if its cross-sectional area be determined to resist this force it would work out exceeding small in a valve of this size, even compensating for the loss of area due to the intrusion of the pin securing the stem to the valve member. In the event of the stem being rotated so as to burnish the seat contacting faces (for which purpose provision is made by squaring the upper extremity) it would be subjected at the same time to torsional stresses. It is doubtful whether any attempt to calculate the complex stresses imposed—complicated by the weakening effect of the pin hole—is worthy of the effort: experience must be the guiding factor here, especially in a valve of such relatively small dimensions.

At all events the stem should be turned from stainless steel bar whose enhanced crushing strength calls for no comment. On no account should brass, cast, rolled or extruded be used for this member and for the duty intended.

Chapter Seven
Reducing Valves and Surplus Valves

As the name implies, the function of a reducing valve is to effect a reduction in pressure of the working fluid attempting to pass through the valve. For example, steam intended for supplying a turbine is at too high a pressure for supplying certain auxiliary equipment not requiring high pressure steam yet the one boiler may be required to serve widely varying items of equipment. Shipboard services are notable examples.

Such a valve should effect the required reduction in pressure *automatically*, that is, without resort to manual assistance. Correctly designed and installed (they have been known to be fitted wrong way round and wrong way up) it should give a constant reduced pressure irrespective of any fluctuations in the inlet pressure provided the latter does not fall below the desired outlet pressure, of course.

Although reducing valves vary in design between one make and another they are all identical in the one respect that pressure reduction is effected by the process of *throttling*. Any screw-down valve might be made to function as a reducing valve provided it be permitted to open only by a very small amount but this would involve someone being detailed to manipulate the handwheel, with eyes focused on an obligingly located pressure gauge connected to the downstream side.

With water-tube boilers, which hold a comparatively smaller volume of water than the Lancashire or other 'shell' type boilers, the evaporation is relatively more rapid in consequence and sudden fluctuations in pressure are commonplace. Due to the desirability of maintaining the steam supply to a turbine as nearly as possible at a uniform pressure it is customary to generate steam at a pressure somewhat higher than that required by the turbine and to effect the necessary reduction by means of a reducing valve of a design that is sensitive to these rapid fluctuations in inlet pressure. Moreover, steam, in passing through the narrow confines of a reducing valve seating, suffers a temperature rise in the process which is all to the good of the turbine, relying as it does on superheated steam. Wet steam should never to allowed access.

Whatever type of reducing valve is employed it is most advisable to fit a safety valve on the reduced pressure side, preferably located at a distance downstream of, say, not less than 4 m [12 ft] where practicable, set to blow at a pressure of about 0·4 bar [5 psig] in excess of the desired reduced pressure in order to provide against failure of the reducing valve as might occur in the event of a burst diaphragm.

Additionally, it is expedient to install a steam separator ahead of the reducing valve, serving the dual purpose of precipitating any entrained moisture and acting as a steam receiver.

Consider the design of a simple form of reducing valve illustrated in Fig. 7.1 (a) suitable for use on steam or other hot gases at, say, up to 2·75 MPa and 260°C [400 psig and 500°F] and normally available in sizes up to and including 50 mm [2 in] bore.

The action of such a valve is as follows: the high pressure working medium (eg steam) flows into the valve body in the direction indicated. By compressing the main spring by turning the adjusting screw, the piston pressing on the diaphragm causes this to deflect slightly upwards, raising the distance piece which causes the valve member to lift slightly off its seating member. The slightly open valve imparts a throttling effect to the working fluid thereby causing a diminution in pressure which is exactly what is required of the valve. The extent of opening, slight though it may be, is adjusted until the desired reduction in pressure is achieved.

Should the reduced pressure tend to fall the now compressed main spring meets with less pressure resistance on the top side of the diaphragm and therefore opens up the valve a further amount reducing the throttling effect and thereby causing an increase in pressure on the low pressure side.

Conversely, if the reduced pressure tends to rise, the increase in pressure on the top side of the diaphragm will compress the main spring some-what and the valve member will follow the downward deflexion of the diaphragm, throttling the valve, and assisted in the process by the return spring and thereby causing a diminution in pressure on the reduced pressure side.

The valve portrayed (Fig. 7.1 (a)) is suitable for inlet pressures up to about 2·75 MPa [400 psig] where air, gases, water, oils and other liquids are being controlled, but up to 2 MPa [300 psig] in the case of steam where the temperature does not exceed 260°C (500°F), and in both cases where the

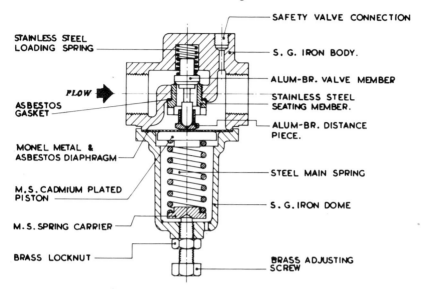

STAINLESS STEEL
LOADING SPRING

FLOW

ASBESTOS
GASKET

MONEL METAL &
ASBESTOS DIAPHRAGM

M.S. CADMIUM PLATED
PISTON

M.S. SPRING CARRIER

BRASS LOCKNUT

SAFETY VALVE CONNECTION

S. G. IRON BODY.

ALUM-BR. VALVE MEMBER

STAINLESS STEEL
SEATING MEMBER.

ALUM-BR. DISTANCE
PIECE.

STEEL MAIN SPRING

S. G. IRON DOME

BRASS ADJUSTING
SCREW

Fig. 7.1 (a) *Simple small bore reducing valve (for steam and other gases)*

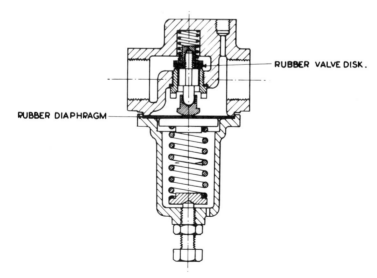

RUBBER VALVE DISK.

RUBBER DIAPHRAGM

Fig. 7.1 (b) *Simple small bore reducing valve (for air, gases, water and liquid generally)*

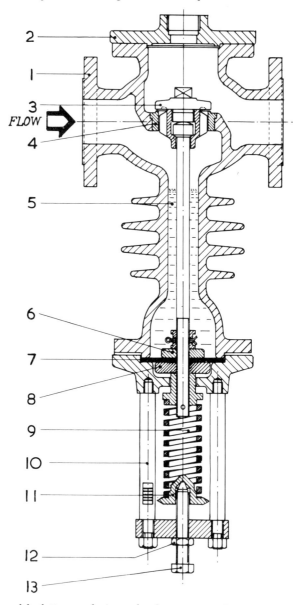

Fig. 7.2 *Flanged body type reducing valve for steam service*

inlet pressures remain reasonably constant and capacities do not vary to any great extent. Reduced pressures in the range 0·07 − 0·8 MPa [10–120 psig] may be expected from this particular type of valve.

For relatively 'cold' applications a diaphragm of composition rubber is substituted for the metallic version employed in high temperature service (eg steam) and the valve member embodies a washer or disk of the same resilient material (Fig. 7.1 (b)).

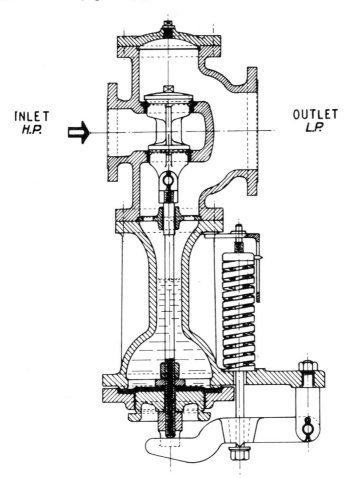

INLET
H.P.

OUTLET
L.P.

Fig. 7.3 *Steam reducing valve. Double beat pattern*

Figure 7.2 depicts a simple flanged-type reducing valve mainly intended for steam service and typical of the type employed on the larger sizes of pipe-lines. It operates exactly on the same throttling principle as the type previously described but in this design a composition rubber diaphragm (7) is employed with advantage—despite its intended duty on *steam*—simply by the incorporation of a condensation leg whereby the accumulation of water therein maintains the diaphragm relatively cool. Such valves have been made suitable for applications where the inlet steam was initially super-heated (eg, to about 450°C (850°F)) by the simple expedient of extending the length of the condensation leg, water being a relatively poor heat conductor.

It should be noted that the piston plate (8) is arranged substantially the same diameter as that of the valve seating (4), thereby placing the valve in equilibrium at all inlet pressures. In short the *upward* pressure exerted on the valve member (3) is counter balanced by the same downward pressure exerted on the piston plate (8).

As in the previous example (Fig. 7.1) the spring (9) is initially compressed so as to 'crack' open the valve member (3) to give the required throttling effect, obviously determined initially by trial.

In the larger sizes of valve, the spring (9) may be arranged in conjunction with a lever mechanism (so as to avoid using a spring of large dimensions) as featured in the design shown in Fig. 7.3. With the same regard for dimensional economy the valve portrayed features a double-beat valve seating arrangement. A single-beat valve would require an inordinately large seating and correspondingly large attendant parts all round.

A valve more sensitively responsive to pressure fluctuations and one expressly intended for large pressure reductions is the one portrayed in Fig. 7.4, featuring *two* diaphragms, both of rubber, each fulfilling its own particular function. The smaller diaphragm (1) has a freely floating piston plate (2) of identical diameter to that of the valve seating (3) attached to its underside, in consequence of which the valve member (4) is at all times in equilibrium under the influence of the inlet pressure, however this may vary, the pressure upthrust balancing the pressure downthrust.

Again the spring (5) may be given a small initial compression through the agency of the adjusting screw (6) causing the valve member (4) to lift off its seating (3) slightly. Thus, air (for example) passing through the narrow annular area presented by this partially open valve will diminish in pressure in consequence. Now this reduced pressure will be exerted on the *top* side of the *larger* diaphragm (7) since it has access via the balance pipe (9), and this downwardly acting force is only opposed by the upwardly acting force imparted by the spring (5). This thrust of the spring is always constant once the valve is set; consequently, it follows that if the reduced pressure tends to fall, the pressure downthrust on the larger diaphragm (7) and piston plate (8) will be insufficient to counter the upthrust of the spring (5), and the valve member (4) will lift slightly more, causing a rise in pressure and thus restoring the desired reduced pressure.

Similarly, if the reduced pressure tends to rise this will have the reverse effect; the spring will become slightly more compressed and the gap between the valve member and the seating will be diminished somewhat, thereby increasing the throttling effect, once again restoring normal reduced pressure conditions.

The rise and fall in the reduced pressure will be minimal in a correctly

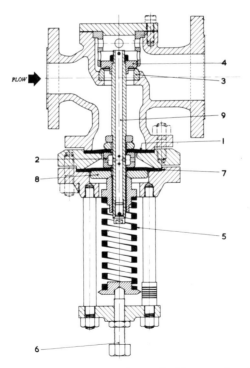

Fig. 7.4 *Air/gas reducing valve. Sensitive or double control pattern*

designed and adjusted valve, the deviation from the required reduced pressure being that just sufficient to motivate the restoring forces.

Proportioning of valve thoroughfares

Whilst it is common practice to supply reducing valves having inlet and outlet connections of identical diameter, this is not in strict accordance with theoretical (or practical) requirements. It must be remembered that steam, for example, in suffering a diminution in pressure, increases in volume during the process; consequently, the outlet connection normally requires to be of larger cross-sectional area than the inlet (although in some instances the difference is not so marked as to justify any alteration to existing patterns).

The *ideal* diameters of the inlet and outlet connections, and also of the seating, may be determined in the following manner, although it will be appreciated that any attempts at precise calculation, involving accurate determination of the condition of the steam, will be negated by the many arbitrary constants which are of necessity employed. For example, the velocity of steam cannot be forecast with exactitude and the values given in Table 7.1, based on customary practice, should be adopted in the absence of more precise information.

Consider first the conditions obtaining at the inlet connection.

Let d = diameter of inlet thoroughfare (mm [in])

W = mass of steam flowing (kg/hr [lb/hr])

v_2 = velocity of entering steam (m/s [ft/sec])

V_{s2} = specific volume of entering steam (m³/kg [ft³/lb])

Then $W = \dfrac{0 \cdot 0036 \, \pi \, d^2 v_2}{V_{s2}} \left[= \dfrac{3600 \, \{ (\pi d^2 v_2)/(4 \times 144) \}}{V_{s2}} \right]$

whence $d = \sqrt{\dfrac{W V_{s2}}{0 \cdot 0036 \, \pi v_2}} \left[= \sqrt{\dfrac{576 \, W V_{s2}}{3600 \times \pi \times v_2}} \right]$

or $\qquad d = 9 \cdot 4 \sqrt{\dfrac{W V_{s2}}{v_2}} \left[= \sqrt{\dfrac{0 \cdot 051 \, W V_{s2}}{v_2}} \right]$ \hfill (7.1)

A value for d corresponding to the nearest convenient pipe size should be adopted.

Where the steam is initially superheated, the specific volume will be higher

Table 7.1 Customary steam velocities in smooth pipes

Nominal bore of pipe		Velocity of steam			
		Saturated steam		Superheated steam	
(mm)	(in)	(m/s)	(ft/sec)	(m/s)	(ft/sec)
up to 75	up to 3.	23	75	30	100
80–225	3·5–9	28	90	37	120
250+	10+	28	90	43	140

and may be calculated from the relation

$$V_{s2} = V_s\left(1 + \frac{t_s C}{347}\right)\left[= V_s(1 + 0\cdot0016\, t_s F)\right]$$

where V_s = specific volume at temperature of saturation (see steam tables)
and $t_s C$ = temperature range of superheat, (°C)
$[t_s F$ = temperature range of superheat, (°F)]

The next step is to determine the bore of seating. In common with the *ordinary* safety valve the lift of the valve member of a reducing valve, in normal operation, is appreciably less than might be imagined, and although provision should be made for it to lift sufficiently to give full bore opening (i.e. one-quarter the diameter of the seating) an average lift on one-sixteenth of the seating diameter is all that may be expected and this figure is adopted in the following calculations.

Now the steam, in passing through such a restricted orifice as that presented by the partial separation of the valve member from its seating, will suffer some amount of superheating, the extent of which will vary according to the reduction in pressure effected. Consequently, the actual condition of the *issuing* steam will require to be ascertained before any calculations on its flow through the seating orifice can be attempted.

Since the *total heat* on both sides of the valve will be practically the same

$$h_2 + L_2 = h_1 + L_1 + K_p(t_4 - t_1) \tag{7.3}$$

where h_2 = sensible heat in entering steam,
L_2 = latent heat in entering steam,

h_1 = sensible heat in issuing steam,

L_1 = latent heat in issuing steam,

t_4 = temperature of issuing steam,

t_1 = saturation temperature of issuing steam corresponding to reduced pressure, and

K_p = average specific heat of steam between the limits t_1 and t_4 (see graph, Fig. 7.5).

Transposing eqn (7.3)

$$t_4 = \frac{h_2 + L_2 - h_1 - L_1}{K_p} + t_1 \qquad (7.4)$$

This expression is for steam *initially dry* and *saturated*; where the entering steam is initially superheated to some temperature, t_3, the following

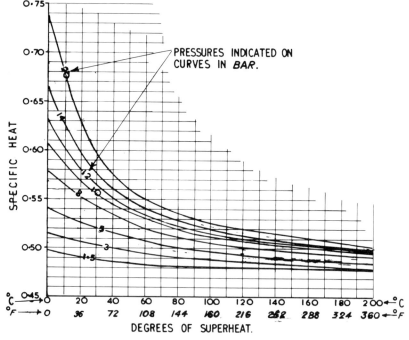

Fig. 7.5 *Specific heat of superheated steam*

similar expression is obtained

$$t_4 = \frac{h_2 + L_2 + K_p(t_3 - t_2) - h_1 - L_1}{K_p} + t_1 \qquad (7.5)$$

where $t_2 =$ saturation temperature of *entering* steam at the initial pressure. It will be noted that in the latter expression K_p occurs twice, but this will have different values corresponding to the temperature ranges under consideration and may be readily interpolated from the graph (Fig. 7.5).

Having determined the conditions of the *issuing* steam from whichever of the two foregoing relations—eqn (7.4) and (7.5)—is applicable, its specific volume may be determined from the expression given previously (eqn 7.2) and, amending the symbols to prevent confusion, we get:

specific volume of *issuing* steam

$$V_{s1} = V_g \{1 + 0 \cdot 0016 \ (t_4 - t_1)\} \qquad (7.6)$$

where V_s is the specific volume of the *issuing* steam corresponding to its temperature of saturation.

Assuming, as stated previously, a maximum lift of the valve member of one-sixteenth of the bore of the seating, and denoting this bore diameter by D:

$$\text{area of escape presented} = \frac{\pi D^2}{16}$$

Now the velocity of steam in flowing into a zone of lower pressure less than three-fifths (approximately) of its initial pressure has a practically constant value of 271 m/s [890 ft/sec]. Adopting a coefficient of discharge of 0·68:

$$W = \frac{0 \cdot 0036 \times 271 \, \pi D^2}{16} \times \frac{0 \cdot 68}{V_{s1}} \ (\text{kg/hr})$$

$$\left[= 3600 \times 890 \times \frac{\pi D^2}{16 \times 144} \times \frac{1}{V_{s1}} \times 0 \cdot 68 \ (\text{lb/hr}) \right]$$

whence

$$D = 0 \cdot 36 \sqrt{(W V_{s1})} \ (\text{mm}) \ \left[= \sqrt{\left(\frac{W V_{s1}}{2750}\right)}(\text{in}) \right] \qquad \text{(approximately)}$$

Where the value of D thus obtained would necessitate a comparatively large seating diameter we have seen that it is sometimes expedient to adopt double seatings of the form shown in Fig. 7.6.

It must be observed, however, that in order to assemble the valve member and seatings within the body casing, the dimensions adopted for these details must be such as to facilitate such assembly. The chief points to observe are: (i) the diameter of the lip on the lower seating must be such as to permit of it being passed through the hole in the body for the reception of the upper seating, and (ii) the lower collar on the valve member must be small enough in diameter to pass through the upper seating whose diameter is denoted by d_m in Fig. 7.6.

These are points which might easily be overlooked in design.

Now if d_a = mean diameter of the double seatings,

then $\frac{\pi}{2} d_a^2 = \frac{\pi}{4} D^2$ very approximately

or $\qquad d_a = \sqrt{\left(\frac{D^2}{2}\right)}$ \hfill (7.8)

The bores of the upper and lower seatings may be more accurately calculated from the relation

$$d_m^2 + d_n^2 = D^2 \qquad (7.9)$$

and this, of course, will probably incur some amount of trial and error, but the determination of d_a in the first place will do much to restrict this to a minimum.

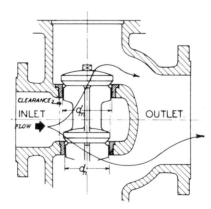

Fig. 7.6 *Double-beat valve seating arrangements (large bore reducing valves)*

After passing through the narrow confines of the central seating (or seatings) the steam will assume comparative quiescence through expansion and, in consequence, will acquire something of its original velocity. The diameter of the outlet branch D_o to suit these conditions may then be determined from the following relation

$$D_o = 9 \cdot 4 \sqrt{\left(\frac{W V_{s1}}{v_s}\right)} \text{ (mm)} \quad \left[= \sqrt{\left(\frac{0 \cdot 0509\, W V_{s1}}{v_s}\right)} \text{ (in)}\right] \qquad 7.10$$

where W = mass of steam flowing (kg/hr [lb/hr]), V_{s1} = specific volume of issuing steam (m³/kg [ft³/lb]), and v_s = velocity of steam in outlet branch (m/s [ft/sec]) which may be obtained from Table 7.1.

SURPLUS VALVES

A surplus valve, as its name implies, is a valve for *automatically* controlling the flow of surplus steam (or gases) on attaining a predetermined pressure, and in some respects is similar in action and appearance to a reducing valve, so much so that it is often mistaken for one until a closer examination reveals its identity.

In a reducing valve, control is effected by the *reduced* pressure, irrespective of any fluctuations in the high pressure, whilst in the case of a surplus valve, the converse obtains, control being affected by the *high* pressure. This difference will be best appreciated when the functional operation of a surplus valve is understood.

A surplus valve is virtually a safety valve wherein the discharge of *surplus* steam is usefully employed or conserved instead of being uselessly discharged to atmosphere, and it is set to open at a pressure somewhat less than that at which the boiler safety valves are set.

Figure 7.7 depicts a surplus valve of simple design embodying a valve closure member of the *single-beat* type. The effective area of the piston on the remote side of the diaphragm is arranged equal to that of the valve seating so that the adjustment of the valve is at all times unaffected by any fluctuations in pressure on the low-pressure side. The thrust-spring, therefore, is only required to impart a thrust of a magnitude determined by the pressure at which the valve is required to lift to pass the surplus steam and will be given by

$$W_1 = \tfrac{1}{4}\pi p_1 d_s^2 \qquad (7.11)$$

where $W_1 =$ load on spring

$p_1 =$ pressure at which valve is required to open

$d_s =$ effective diameter of seating.

(Note that the effective diameter is the *boundary* diameter and not the *bore* of the seating unless this is of the knife-edge type which, of course, is impracticable.)

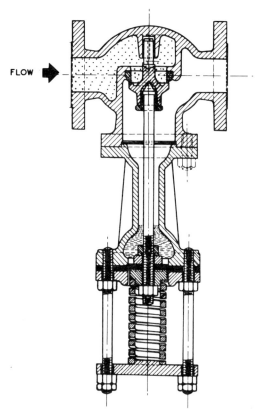

FLOW

Fig. 7.7 *Surplus steam valve (single-beat pattern)*

The valve will commence to open when a pressure is reached sufficient to overcome the upward force of the thrust-spring determined by its initial compression, thus permitting the passage of *surplus* steam to the low-pressure side.

Having determined W_1, the spring may be designed in accordance with the rules for safety and relief valve springs given in Chapter 6, since the surplus valve is virtually a relief valve, differing only in the added refinements of controlled discharge and in the provision of a water-cooling leg (for protecting the diaphragm from the adverse effects of high temperature).

Whilst the flexible rubber diaphragm is primarily to permit of practically unrestricted freedom of movement of the balance-piston (which, in combination with the diaphragm is the simplest device of this nature that could possibly be devised, requiring no rings or precision fits), it ideally fulfils the equally important function of providing a positive seal against leakage of the working medium.

Metallic diaphragms of various materials and diversified configurations have been tried with varying measures of success and in some cases have given results comparable with those obtained from the more obliging rubber diaphragm, but none of these can compete with the latter on the dual scores of simplicity and cheapness. Renewal of the rubber diaphragm is a simple procedure and in cases of emergency a diaphragm cut from insertion rubber may be expected to give temporary service pending receipt of the correct grade and size from the makers. A rubber diaphragm usually gives timely warning of its impending failure by developing a slight leak which is not always arrested by tightening of the flange bolts. Such visible evidence of impending failure should be acted upon without delay and the resourceful engineer will keep a spare diaphragm in stock, in which event it may never be required.

The type of valve portrayed in Fig. 7.7 is one usually encountered in sizes up to 150 mm [6 in]. Above this size, however, adherence to the design shown would inevitably result in a valve inordinately bulky and uneconomical of materials, and for the sake of economy in overall dimensions alone a valve of the *double-beat* type is advocated, as illustrated in Fig. 7.8. Since absolute closure-tightness of a surplus valve is seldom essential, the usual objection to double-beat valves—that of maintaining the two faces steam-tight simultaneously—may be promptly dismissed as being of no material consequence. At all events, whilst the surplus valve is similar in many respects to a safety valve, the former is meant to *pass* steam whilst the latter, in a correctly designed and maintained plant, should really never pass steam at all, being something in the nature of an insurance policy redeemable when the unexpected happens.

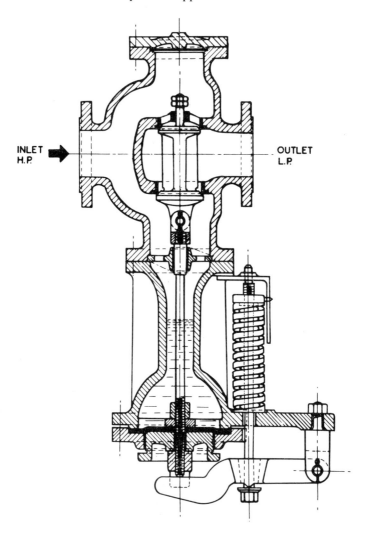

INLET
H.P.

OUTLET
L.P.

Fig. 7.8 *Surplus steam valve (double-beat pattern)*

Surplus valves for the higher capacities in which the valve mechanism is
of the double-beat type as shown in Fig. 7.8 may now be considered. Again,
the valve member is normally constrained to remain in the closed position
mainly due to the thrust of the compression spring acting through the
agency of the lever and rod affixed to the flexible rubber diaphragm and the
piston. The valve will tend to open when a pressure is reached sufficient to
overcome the upward thrust determined by the extent of initial compression
imparted to the spring, thus permitting surplus steam to pass to the low-
pressure side.

Referring to the diagrammatic representation of a valve of the double-
beat type portrayed in Fig. 7.8, the forces acting may be tabulated as
follows:

Closing forces (acting upwards)	Unseating forces (acting downwards)
(i) $F_c = \frac{1}{4} d_m^2 (p_1 - p_2)$ (ii) $W_2 = \dfrac{W_1 l_1}{l_2}$	(iii) $F_u = \frac{1}{4} d_n^2 (p_1 - p_2)$ (iv) $F_d = \frac{1}{4} p_1 d_f^2$

The above takes no account of the weight of the moving parts.

If (i) and (iii) are substantially equal (and the weight of a double-beat
valve and its attendant parts will to some extent offset the 'out-of-balance'
effect due to the necessarily larger effective area of the lower seating) then,
for equilibrium

$$W_2 = F_d$$

or $W_1 \dfrac{l_1}{l_2} = \frac{1}{4} \pi p_1 d_f^2$

whence $W_1 = \frac{1}{4} \pi \dfrac{l_2}{l_1} p_1 d_f^2$ (7.12)

Now l_2 is usually made equal to $2 l_1$.

then $W = \frac{1}{2} \pi p_1 d_f^2$ (7.13)

This is the force to be exerted by the spring and it will be noted that it is
directly proportional to the square of the effective diameter of the

diaphragm; hence it is essential to arrange this diameter as small as possible consistent with practical requirements if an unduly stiff spring, or alternatively an excessive deflection to produce the requisite loading, is to be avoided.

There is little which can be added to aid design of either reducing valves or surplus valves; the rules formulated elsewhere herein for valves of similar construction may be enlisted in the case of the chest, cover plate, etc. The valve thoroughfares may be of equal or unequal diameter, depending upon circumstances of installation, although it would appear undesirable to make the outlet thoroughfare appreciably in excess of the inlet in the case of a surplus valve, since this is only required to pass steam generated *surplus* to requirements and this into a zone of pressure in most cases closely approaching that on the inlet side.

Since actual requirements are so varied and defy any serious attempts to forecast them, surplus valves do not lend themselves to mass production methods of manufacture, and in almost every instance such valves are individually designed. Moreover, there is not a great call for valves of this type, which fact alone is the probable explanation for the scant description accorded to them in most makers' catalogues, some of which make no mention of them whatsoever. This should not be interpreted as an implication that the surplus valve is a dead letter; on the contrary, it is a most essential accoutrement where mixed-pressure boilers contribute their steam to a common main, but the demand for such valves is small compared with that for other valves. By the same token the fire extinguisher is a most useful piece of apparatus at times but is seldom seen in action.

Chapter Eight
Equilibrium Float Valves

WHERE it is desired to maintain a practically constant level in a tank or similar vessel, as for example in boiler feed tanks, make-up tanks, etc, it is essential that this is achieved automatically rather than by manual operation of a stop valve situated in the supply line. Apart from the risk of the vessel becoming devoid of water (as might be occasioned by a forgetful operator) the employment of some form of automatic valve ensures that the water used, or lost by evaporation and other causes, is replenished at the same rate as that at which it is being used, provided the valve is of the right size and sensitively responsive to a diminishing water level.

APPLICATIONS

In the case of air compressors of the water-cooled type the aim should be to arrange for air to be compressed *isothermally* as nearly as is practically possible and this is achieved to some extent by cooling it during compression, either by means of a water jacket enveloping the cylinder and forming an integral part thereof or, in special cases, by means of water sprays discharging into the cylinders themselves, or by a combination of both these methods.

Adiabatic compression is to be avoided since this means increased power required to drive the machine. In practice, compression is neither wholly *isothermal* nor *adiabatic*. The attainment of maximum efficiency is dependent, to some extent, upon an adequate supply of cooling water, not only for the jacket or spray water but also, in some cases, for the intercooler required in the case of multiple-stage compressors. Such water is usually stored in an elevated tank, situated at a convenient height above the machine, although with the larger machines a cooling pond is often necessitated.

In the power house, too, the condenser cooling or injection water system calls for an adequate reserve of make-up water and the consequences of a failure in this supply can be well imagined.

Many other industrial processes demand a constant reserve supply of water necessitating storage in tanks or vessels wherein the level must be maintained reasonably constant and the valve best suited for obtaining this objective is the equilibrium float valve, which may take up a variety of forms, yet remains basically the same in principle.

A typical design of such a valve is portrayed in Fig. 8.1 and Fig. 8.2 shows such a valve controlling the supply of make-up water in an air compressor circulating water tank, complete with ancillary connections.

The auxiliary stop valve shown on the left of the latter illustration is for the purpose of prefilling the tank or for augmenting the supply in the event of the equilibrium float valve being unable to cope with the volume of water required.

The size of valve to be adopted is mainly governed by the amount of make-up water it is required to pass. As a rough guide, this may be taken to equal 3 per cent of the total amount of circulating water required, but as each installation will vary as regards pressure of supply, conditions of mains, size of approach etc, no binding rules can be laid down for determining the size of valve to be installed.

The equilibrium valve belies its title, since it is definitely *out of balance*, admittedly not to any great extent, but sufficient to render it sensitive to fluctuations in water level in the tank whose contents it is required auto-

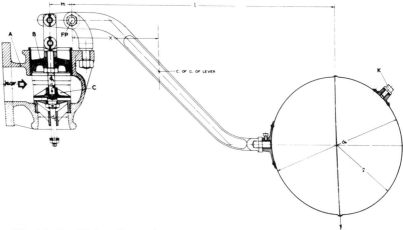

Fig. 8.1 *Equilibrium float valve*

matically to control. This will be best understood by considering its *modus operandi*, together with a study of the forces to which it is subjected in the normal course of operation. Attention is directed to Fig. 8.1.

The valve is connected at A to the main water supply (which may be either town's main or any other pressure supply) and the pressure of this supply acts upwards on the balance-piston B and downwards on the back of the valve plate C. From considerations of assembly it is essential that the cylinder, and consequently the piston, be arranged somewhat larger in diameter than the diameter of the valve plate; otherwise the latter could not be assembled within the body casing.

It will be obvious, therefore, that there will be some amount of *out-of-balance* effect operating in favour of the piston which, in consequence, will be urged upwards and this upward force will be translated into a downward force operating at the ball-float and tending to force it under water. It is this fact which enables the valve to respond to a falling water level and on which design is based.

Neglecting for the moment all frictional resistances (which will be taken into consideration later) and denoting the main's pressure by p it will be

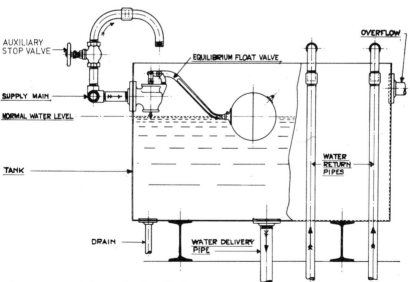

Fig. 8.2 *Typical float valve installation*

evident that the nett upward force acting on the piston will at all times be given by

$$P = \frac{\pi}{4} p(d_1^2 - d_2^2) \qquad (8.1)$$

where d_1 = outside diameter of valve seating face, and

$\quad d_2$ = diameter of piston or cylinder,

and the force on the ball float, tending to force it under water will be given by

$$W = \frac{\pi p m}{4 l}(d_2^2 - d_1^2) \qquad (8.2)$$

where m = fulcrum distance, and

where l = length of lever measured from fulcrum pin to centre line of ball-float, (see Fig. 8.1).

Other dimensions are as before.

It follows, therefore, that to resist this force W, thereby placing the valve in equilibrium, there must be an equal and opposite force operating on the ball-float. This reacting force is supplied by the displacement of the ball-float and, therefore, we have the simple relation

$$W = \text{displacement}$$

To permit of some latitude in design it is desirable to adopt a ball-float of such dimensions as will permit of some reserve displacement. Good practice favours 'half-and-half' immersion; that is to say, the normal water level in the tank should coincide with the centre of the ball-float under operating conditions. Adopting this expedient, and since the volume of a hemisphere $= \frac{2}{3} r 4_b{}^3$, and 1 mm^3 [1 in^3] of water at normal temperature weighs 1 mg [0·0362 lb]

$$W = \frac{2}{3} \pi r_b^3 \times 10^{-6} \text{ kg } [0·0362 \text{ lb}]$$

where r_b = radius of ball-float.

This equation simplifies to

$$W = 2·09 \times 10^{-6} r_b^3 \times 9·81 \text{ N } [=0·0756 \, r_b^3 \text{ lb}] \qquad (8.3)$$

Expressing the dimensions of the ball-float in terms of diameter d_b, then

$$W = 0.0758 \left(\frac{d_b}{2}\right)^3$$

$$= 2.56 \times 10^{-6} d_b^3 \left[= 0.00948 \, d_b^3\right] \tag{8.4}$$

$$\text{whence } d_b = 73 \sqrt[3]{W} \left[= \frac{\sqrt[3]{W}}{0.2115}\right] \tag{8.5}$$

The foregoing formulae will serve to provide some idea of the approximate diameter of ball-flloat required but the effects of friction have not been taken into account. This aspect will be considered later.

WORKED EXAMPLE

It is required to determine the approximate diameter of ball-float on a 75 mm [3 in] bore equilibrium float valve operating on a supply main in which the pressure is constant at 0.7 MPa [100 lb/in^2]. The known dimensions of the valve are as follows:

fulcrum distance, $m = 50$ mm [2 in]

centre line of ball-float to centre line of fulcrum pin $l = 600$ mm [24 in]

diameter of balance-piston $d_2 = 89$ mm [$3\frac{1}{2}$ in]

outside diameter of seating $d_1 = 82$ mm [$3\frac{1}{4}$ in]

Solution

From eqn (8.2)

$$W = \frac{\pi \times 0.7 \times 50}{4 \times 600} (89^2 - 82^2) \left[= \frac{\pi \times 100 \times 2}{4 \times 24} (3.5^2 - 3.25^2)\right]$$

$$= 54.8 \text{N} \ [= 11.05 \text{ lb}]$$

From eqn (8.5)

$$d_b = 73 \sqrt[3]{54.8} = \left[\frac{\sqrt[3]{11.05}}{0.2115}\right]$$

$$= 277 \text{ mm} \quad [= 10.53 \text{ in}]$$

As previously pointed out, the foregoing calculations have not taken the effects of friction into account and, as these tend to hamper the sensitivity of the valve, this aspect must now be considered. Whilst a drop-tight valve is not altogether essential during operation periods, a leaky valve can prove expensive where water has to be paid for.

The unit clamping pressure on the valve seating to ensure fluid-tightness may be taken as $1\frac{1}{4}p$ for leather. Then clamping force F_c to be exerted at the valve seating will be given by

$$F_c = \frac{1\frac{1}{4}\pi p}{4}(d_1^2 - d_0^2)$$

whence $F_c = 0\cdot982\,p\,(d_1^2 - d_0^2)$

say $F_c = p(d_1^2 - d_0^2)$ \hfill (8.6)

The greatest frictional resistance will be set up between the piston-cup and the cylinder and, to a lesser degree, at each of the pin-joints. The latter may be ignored where easy fits are observed, and the correct materials chosen. It is assumed that the designer will not specify mild steel or other corrodable material for the pins, good quality phosphor-bronze, manganese-bronze, or 'Monel' metal being recommended, not necessarily in the order given. It is scarcely conceivable that any calculations can be so precise as to warrant the friction of the pins being taken into account and any such additional resistances would only mean that the ball-float would assume a somewhat increased displacement in order that these may be overcome.

From a preliminary calculation to determine the approximate dimensions of the ball-float, and from consideration of its position in a vertical direction relative to the valve body, some idea of the size of lever to be adopted may be gained and its weight estimated.

Levers are usually made of cast iron in the larger sizes of valves but are more usually of brass or gunmetal in the case of very small valves, say, 12–50 mm [0·5–2 in] bore. Some makers list such valves in sizes up to 600 mm [12 in] bore, but valves of this size are seldom called for. There is no reason against the adoption of even larger valves where circumstances warrant it, although it would be preferable to employ two or more smaller valves in lieu.

The overhanging mass effect of the lever is compensated to some extent by the counterbalance effect of the weight of the valve closure components but it is as well to estimate as accurately as possible the total weight of all moving parts swivelling about the fulcrum pin. The weights of various sizes of complete ball-floats for varying thicknesses of copper sheet* are given in Table 8.1 and intermediate sizes may be readily interpolated from the graphs in Figs 8.3 and 8.4. The former gives particulars of floats up to 300 mm [12 in] in diameter and the latter of sizes 300 mm [12 in] upwards.

Denoting the weight of the ball-float by W_b, the weight of the lever by W_v and the weight of the closure mechanism, including piston, links, etc, by W_m, and equating clockwise and anti-clockwise moments about the fulcrum pin, a more accurate estimate of the forces to be overcome by the buoyancy of the ball-float may now be determined.

The frictional resistance of the piston-cup within the body cylinder cannot be ignored, however, but the behaviour of the cup is open to much speculation since so much depends on:

(a) the degree of 'lubrication' afforded by the water having access,
(b) the stiffness or lack of it exhibited in the material of the cup.

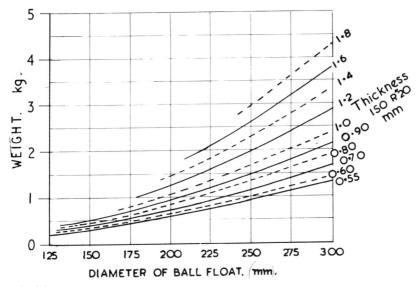

Fig. 8.3

*Copper sheet is the best material to adopt since it is amenable to 'spinning', a process by which such floats are invariably formed into hemispherical shapes from the sheet, the two halves being then brazed or soldered together to form the completed spherical float.

Table 8.1   Weights of spun copper ball floats without caps, etc. (a) metric, (b) Imperial*
(Values tabulated outside the bold lines refer to sizes not recommended)

External Diameter of Ball Float mm	Weight (kg) ISO R" 20											Total Displacement of Ball Float	
	2.0 mm	1.8 mm	1.6 mm	1.4 mm	1.2 mm	1.0 mm	0.9 mm	0.8 mm	0.7 mm	0.6 mm	0.55 mm	Volume m³	Weight of Water kg
125							0.394	0.350	0.306	0.263	0.241	0.0010	1.0148
140							0.495	0.440	0.385	0.330	0.298	0.0014	1.421
150							0.568	0.505	0.442	0.379	0.347	0.0018	1.827
160						0.721	0.649	0.577	0.505	0.432	0.396	0.0021	2.131
180					1.091	0.909	0.818	0.727	0.636	0.545	0.500	0.0031	3.146
200				1.572	1.347	1.123	1.010	0.898	0.786	0.674	0.617	0.0042	4.262
225			2.218	1.940	1.663	1.386	1.247	1.109	0.970	0.832	0.762	0.0060	6.089
250		3.157	2.806	2.455	2.105	1.754	1.579	1.403	1.228	1.052	0.965	0.0082	8.321
300	5.049	4.544	4.039	3.534	3.029	2.524	2.272	2.017	1.767	1.515	1.389	0.0141	14.308
350	6.873	6.185	5.498	4.811	4.124	3.436	3.093	2.749	2.405	2.062	1.890	0.0224	22.731
400	8.978	8.080	7.183	6.285	5.387	4.489	4.040	3.591	3.142	2.694	2.469	0.0335	33.995
450	11.363	10.226	9.090	7.954	6.818	5.681	5.113	4.545	3.977	3.409	3.125	0.0477	48.405
500	14.027	12.624	11.222	9.819	8.416	7.014	6.312	5.611	4.910	4.208	3.858	0.0555	66.468
550	16.972	15.275	13.578	11.881	10.183	8.486	7.638	6.789	5.940	5.092	4.688	0.0871	88.387
600	22.846	18.180	16.160	14.140	12.120	10.100	9.090	8.080	7.070	6.060	5.556	0.1131	114.77
750	31.562	28.406	25.250	22.094	18.937	15.781	14.200	12.625	11.047	9.469	8.681	0.2209	224.17
900	45.443	40.904	36.350	31.814	27.270	22.724	20.750	18.179	15.307	13.635	12.500	0.3817	387.30

External Diameter of Ball Float in.	Weight (lb)											Total Displacement	
	14 S.W.G.	15 S.W.G.	16 S.W.G.	17 S.W.G.	18 S.W.G.	19 S.W.G.	20 S.W.G.	21 S.W.G.	22 S.W.G.	23 S.W.G.	24 S.W.G.	Volume in³	lb wt Water
5								0.75	0.66	0.57	0.52	65.5	2.36
5¼							1.02	0.91	0.79	0.69	0.63	87.1	3.14
6							1.22	1.08	0.95	0.82	0.75	113.1	4.07
6¼						1.59	1.43	1.27	1.11	0.95	0.88	143.8	5.17
7					2.22	1.85	1.66	1.47	1.29	1.11	1.02	179.6	6.47
8				3.35	2.87	2.4	2.16	1.93	1.68	1.45	1.33	268.1	9.65
9			4.85	4.23	3.65	3.1	2.73	2.43	2.12	1.83	1.68	381.7	13.74
10		6.73	6.00	5.24	4.5	3.81	3.38	3.01	2.62	2.26	2.07	523.6	18.85
12	10.8	9.7	8.6	7.6	6.5	5.4	4.87	4.33	3.78	3.26	2.97	904.7	32.57
14	14.7	13.2	11.7	10.3	8.9	7.4	6.6	5.9	5.13	4.43	4.06	1437	51.73
16	19.2	17.3	15.2	13.4	11.6	9.7	8.7	7.7	6.7	5.8	5.3	2145	77.22
18	24.2	25.0	19.4	17.0	14.6	12.2	10.9	9.8	8.5	7.4	6.7	3054	109.9
20	30.0	27.0	23.8	21.0	18.0	15.1	13.6	12.1	10.5	9.1	8.3	4189	150.8
22	36.0	32.5	29.0	25.3	21.8	18.2	16.4	14.6	12.7	11.0	10.0	5570	200.5
24	43.0	38.6	34.4	30.3	26.0	21.7	19.6	17.4	15.1	13.0	11.9	7240	260.6
30	67.2	60.5	53.8	47.2	40.5	33.9	30.5	27.2	23.5	20.4	18.7	14120	508.3
36	97.0	87.0	77.5	68.0	58.2	48.7	43.0	38.8	34.0	29.3	27.0	24250	873.0

*For stainless steel multiply the weights by 0.963.
For 'Monel' metal multiply the weights by 1.027.

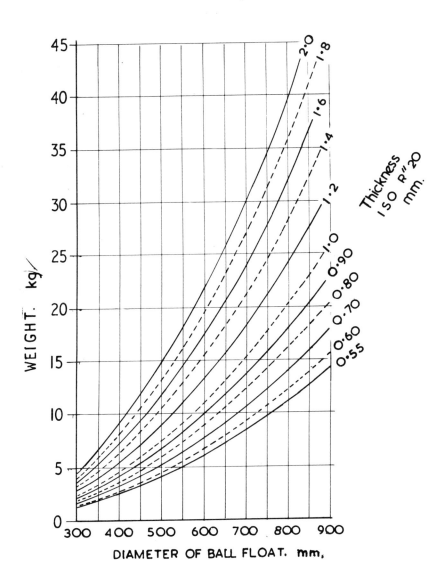

Fig. 8.4

Accordingly, one must rely somewhat on conjecture and the scant information available relating to the behaviour of this simple, but capricious, device.

The following treatment is offered in the absence of anything more specific.

Referring to Fig. 8.5 the inner surface of the piston-cup will be subjected to a uniform pressure p for the whole of its exposed surface between the points A and Z but due to the stiffness of the leather (or other material) and to the fact that the wall of the cup must tend to rotate about the centre of curvature 0, the reaction forces $r_a, r_b \ldots \ldots r_z$ exerted by the cylinder wall will diminish in intensity from a maximum at A (where $r_a = p$) to a minimum at Z where $r_z = 0$ since the cup ceases to make contact at this

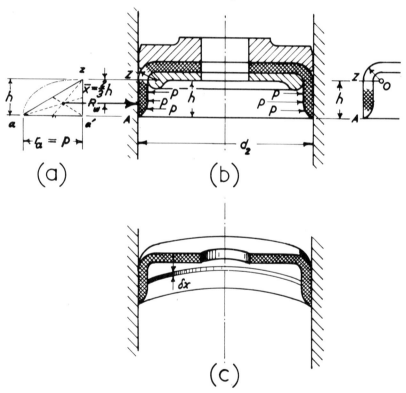

Fig. 8.5 *Piston cup 'leather'*

point. These terminal conditions are indisputable yet one can only conjecture what might be the prevailing conditions intermediately. It would appear logical to infer that the force r, the radial wall reaction, will vary directly as h, the effective depth of the cup, giving rise to a straight line relationship between r and h, as indicated in the supplementary triangular force diagram shown at (a) in Fig. 8.5, but it is equally logical to suppose that the diagram may be anything but triangular in outline. A possible alternative is indicated by a chain dotted line in the diagram.

Since conjecture forms the basis of this argument it will be assumed that a straight-line relationship exists between r and h.

It will be apparent that the cup wall will tend to deflect radially *outwards* about the point of heel O under the influence of the line pressure p exerted on the inner surface thereof and that this tendency will be countered by the wall reaction R_w tending to deflect the cup wall radially *inwards*. Obviously, then, for equilibrium, outwardly and inwardly acting moments must be equal.

Consider an elementary circumferential strip of unit length and of width δx. Let its vertical distance from the centre of rotation O be denoted by x and let d_2 denote the outside diameter of the cup leather. Then

Force due to pressure on unit length of strip $= p\,\delta x$

and moment of force about O $= px\,\delta x$

Then total moment M_o about O $= \Sigma_0^h \pi d_2 p x \delta x$

or M_o $= \pi d_2 p \int_0^h x\,\mathrm{d}x$

$$= \pi d_2 p \left(\frac{x^2}{2}\right)_0^h$$

$$= \tfrac{1}{2}\pi d_2 p h^2 \qquad (8.7)$$

Now for the straight-line relationship assumed, the various wall reaction moments $r_a h_1$, $r_b h_2$, $r_c h_3$, etc, may be replaced by a single force R_w (see Fig. 8.5) whose line of action will pass through the centroid of the triangle $aa'z$ located at a vertical distance $\bar{x} = \tfrac{2}{3}h$ from the point Z.

Note that the force R_w is not concentrated at a single point (as might be supposed from the diagram) but is to be regarded as a continuously applied force concentrated along a line determined by the periphery of the cup leather, such line being vertically distant $\tfrac{2}{3}h$ from the point Z. In short, R_w may be likened to the encircling grip exerted on the cup leather by an imaginary cord or wire of zero thickness or diameter, formed into a ring of diameter equal to that of the enveloping cylinder.

Then the inwardly directed moment M_I will be given by

$$M_I = \tfrac{2}{3} h R_w \qquad (8.8)$$

and since $M_I = M_o$ for equilibrium,

$$\tfrac{2}{3} h R_w = \tfrac{1}{2} \pi d_2 p h^2$$

whence

$$R_w = \tfrac{3}{4} \pi d_2 p h \qquad (8.9)$$

Then obviously the axial force F_2 required to overcome the frictional resistance of the cup leather will be given by

$$F_2 = \mu R_w$$

or

$$F_2 = \tfrac{3}{4} \pi d_2 p h \mu \qquad (8.10)$$

where μ is the coefficient of sliding friction.

Now authorities vary in the values assigned by them to μ for leather on metal. D. A. Low* gives the following values:

dry, $\quad \mu = 0\cdot 56$;

wet, $\quad \mu = 0\cdot 36$;

greased, $\mu = 0\cdot 23$;

oiled, $\quad \mu = 0\cdot 15$.

Experiments carried out by the author some years ago on a proprietary brand of fabric cups used extensively in hydraulic practice yielded a value of $\mu = 0\cdot 15$ in use on cold water.

For design purposes it is recommended that the value of $0\cdot 36$ given by D. A. Low for wet leathers be adopted.

Summarizing the results already obtained:

(i) upward thrust due to unbalanced pressure on piston

$$P = \frac{\pi}{4} p (d_2^2 - d_1^2) \qquad (8.11)$$

(ii) clamping force on valve seating to effect closure-tightness

$$F_c = p(d_1^2 - d_0^2) \qquad (8.12)$$

*LOW, D. A., *A Pocket Book for Mechanical Engineers* 1946 (Longmans Green)

(iii) frictional resistance of cup-leather

$$F_2 = 2 \cdot 35\, d_2 p h \mu \qquad (8.13)$$

It is advisable to evaluate the three foregoing expressions before proceeding to evaluate the required displacement and float diameter; otherwise their subsequent grouping would result in unnecessarily attenuated formulae.

The moment of buoyancy may now be equated to the collective moments of resistance. Taking moments about the fulcrum pin FP (Fig. 8.1)

$$Wl + W_m m = W_b l + W_v x + Pm + F_c m + F_2 m$$

or $\quad W = \dfrac{W_b l + W_v x + m(P + F_c + F_2 - W_m)}{l}$

but, from eqn (8.5)

$$d_b = 73\ \sqrt[3]{W}\ \left[= \frac{\sqrt[3]{W}}{0 \cdot 2115}\ \text{or}\ \sqrt[3]{\left(\frac{W}{0 \cdot 00948}\right)} \right]$$

therefore

$$\left. \begin{array}{l} d_b = 73\ \sqrt[3]{\left(\dfrac{W_b l + W_v x + m(P + F_c + F_2 - W_m)}{l}\right)} \\[4mm] \left[= \sqrt[3]{\left(\dfrac{W_b l + W_v x + m(P + F_c + F_2 - W_m)}{0 \cdot 00948\, l}\right)} \right] \end{array} \right\} \qquad (8.14)$$

In order to demonstrate the increase in diameter of the ball-float necessitated by taking into consideration all factors governing operation, the previously worked out example may be repeated taking into account the refinements included in the foregoing formula, then, from eqn (8.11)

$$P = \pi/4 \times 0 \cdot 7\,(89^2 - 82^2)\ \ [= \pi/4 \times 100\,(3 \cdot 5^2 - 3 \cdot 25^2)]$$
$$= 658\,\text{N}\ \ [= 132 \cdot 5\ \text{lb}]$$

From eqn (8.12)

$$F_c = 0 \cdot 7\,(89^2 - 82^2)\ \ [= 100\,(3 \cdot 5^2 - 3 \cdot 25^2)]$$
$$= 838\,\text{N}\ \ [= 168 \cdot 75\ \text{lb}]$$

From eqn (8.13), letting $h = 8$ mm [5/16 in] and taking $\mu = 0.36$, then

$$F_2 = 2.35 \times 89 \times 0.7 \times 8 \times 0.36$$
$$[= 2.35 \times 3.5 \times 100 \times 0.3125 \times 0.36]$$
$$= 422 \text{ N} \quad [92.5 \text{ lb}]$$

From Table 8.1 take W_b, the weight of the ball-float (assumed 16 in diameter $\times$ 24 SWG thick) to be 2.4 kg [5.3 lb], the weight W_v of the overhanging length of lever to be 1.4 kg [3 lb], centre of gravity to be distance $x = 300$ mm [12 in] from the fulcrum pin, and assume W_m, the weight of the internal working parts to be 2.3 kg [5 lb]. Then from eqn (8.14)

$$d_b = 73 \sqrt[3]{}$$
$$\left(\frac{(2.4 \times 9.81 \times 600) + (1.4 \times 9.81 \times 300) + 50\,(658 + 838 + 422 - (2.3 \times 9.81))}{600} \right)$$
$$= \left[\sqrt[3]{} \left(\frac{5.3 \times 24 + 3 \times 12 + 2\,(132.5 + 168.75 + 92.5 - 5)}{0.00946 \times 24} \right) \right]$$
$$= 419.6 \text{ mm (say 420 mm)}$$
$$= [15.91 \text{ in (say 16 in)}]$$

This clearly demonstrates the inadvisability of relying on approximate calculations, save to gain some idea of the *probable* final dimensions: the originally calculated figure of approximately 277 mm [10.5 in] for the diameter of the ball-float falls somewhat short of the more accurately determined figure of 419.6 mm [15.91 in] calculated above.

Obviously if a small diameter ball-float is desirable, the effective length of the lever must be increased, other things being equal. Thus, by similar calculations, a lever of 750 mm [30 in] effective length would require a 390 mm [15.35 in] diameter ball-float, a 1 m [40 in] lever, a 355 mm [13.5 in] diameter and a 1.5 m [60 in] lever, a 300 mm [12 in] diameter ball-float.

Other ways of reducing ball-float diameter are:

(a) by maintaining the closest possible dimensional parity between the piston/cylinder diameter and the external diameter of the seating face, as near as exigencies of design permit.

(b) by employing accurately moulded and carefully assembled fabric cups of low frictional resistance in the balance piston assembly instead of cup leathers of possible doubtful dimensional accuracy.

In some applications piston rings have been tried successfully, and the toroidal or 'O' ring seems to offer possibilities of successful exploitation.

(c) by employing the lightest possible section for the lever consistent with strength.

(d) by adopting a counterbalance weight to offset the long overhang of the lever in the larger valves.

The detail design of the remaining items of construction may now be considered.

Dealing firstly with the fulcrum pin depicted in Fig. 8.6 this is in double shear under the influence of the buoying effect of the ball-float, and the shearing force will be a maximum in the final stages of closure of the valve. In calculating the value of this shearing force—from which to assign a suitable diameter of pin—the buoying effect should be calculated on the assumption that the float is *fully* immersed since this possibility cannot be entirely ruled out. (For example, one might easily augment the store of water in the tank by admitting water from another source, say, by means of the auxiliary stop valve shown in the arrangement illustrated in Fig. 8.1).

Let S_f denote the total shearing force on the pin occasioned by the buoying effect of a fully-immersed ball-float; then, neglecting the weight of the moving parts

$$S_f = \frac{2W}{m}(l + m) \qquad (8.15)$$

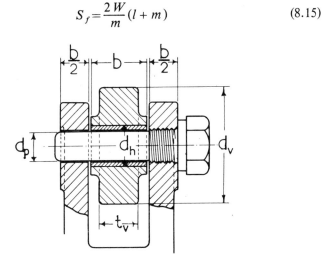

Fig. 8.6 *Non-binding fulcrum pin*

Equating the moment of resistance of the pin (which is in double shear) to the shearing force

$$2 \times \frac{\pi}{4} d_p^2 f_s = S_f$$

whence $d_p = \sqrt{\left(\dfrac{4\,S_f}{2\,\pi f_s}\right)}$

$$= \sqrt{\left(\frac{0\cdot637\,S_f}{f_s}\right)} \tag{8.16}$$

From considerations of the bending action which to some extent will be incurred, particularly in the smaller sizes, it is recommended that the foregoing formula be amended, from practical considerations, by the addition of a constant. Equation (8.16) therefore, might be amended as follows

$$d_p = \sqrt{\left(\frac{0\cdot637\,S_f}{f_s}\right)} + 6 \text{ mm } [\tfrac{1}{4} \text{ in}] \tag{8.17}$$

where S_f = shearing force (determined from eqn (8.15))

f_s = permissible shear stress, say, 45 MPa [6500 lb/in²] for rolled phosphor-bronze or manganese-bronze, 35 MPa [5000 lb/in²] for brass bars, and 55 MPa [8000 lb/in²] for 'Monel' metal.

A noteworthy arrangement of pin assembly is shown in Fig. 8.6. The design shown, which might at first sight appear over-elaborated, rules out the possibility of the two jaws of the fulcrum bolt becoming clamped to the lever and thus rendering the valve inoperative. It will be observed that one end of the pin is a sliding fit in its mating jaw and thus no amount of tightening could result in the two jaws being drawn together, as might result if an ordinary bolt be employed.

Abrasion of the surface of the pin must be reduced to a minimum since rapid wear of this member (or, for that matter, of the hole in the lever) must be obviated if the valve is to work for any length of time without backlash or lost-motion developing. Directing attention once again to Fig. 8.6 the total bearing load transmitted to the lever (which, in the case of cast-iron levers, should be brass bushed as shown) will be given by S_f as previously determined (see eqn (8.15)).

Projected area of pin-hole in lever = $b d_p$
then, if f_b = safe bearing pressure

$$S_f = b d_p f_b$$

whence
$$b = \frac{S_f}{d_p f_b} \qquad (8.18)$$

The safe bearing pressure f_b may be taken equal to 7–10 MPa [1000–1500 lb/in²] of projected area.

Again, this formula might be amended to include a constant in order to cater for those cases where the pin is only lightly loaded, and where strict compliance with the above expression would give an undesirably low value such as would cause the lever to have a sideways tendency to rock.

Equation (8.18) therefore, should read

$$b = \frac{S_f}{d_p f_b} + 6 \text{ mm } [\tfrac{1}{4} \text{ in}] \qquad (8.19)$$

The bending moment in the lever will be a maximum in the region of the fulcrum pin and the lever at this point should be proportioned accordingly. For all practical purposes the maximum bending moment which could occur would be that induced by a fully-immersed ball-float acting through the leverage l.

Thus, the bending moment will be given by the total displacement of the float multiplied by the length of the lever measured from the centre line of the ball-float to the fulcrum bolt or

$$M = \frac{\pi d_b^3}{6} \times l \left[= \frac{\pi d_b^3}{6} \times 0 \cdot 036 \, l \right]$$
$$= 0 \cdot 5236 \, d_b^3 l \; [= 0 \cdot 01885 \, d_b^3 l]$$

where d_b = diameter of ball-float.

Equating this expression to the moment of resistance of the lever at the point referred to above and assuming a strictly rectangular section (from the fundamental relation for bending, $M = fZ$), and

$$Z = f_t \frac{t}{6} (d_v^2 - d_h^2) \qquad \text{(See Fig. 8.6)}$$

then
$$M = 0 \cdot 5236 \, d_b^3 l = f_t Z$$

or
$$9 \cdot 81 \times \frac{0 \cdot 5236 \, d_b^2 l}{10^6} \text{ (mg/mm)} = f_t \frac{t}{6} \,_v (d_v^2 - d_h^2)$$

whence
$$d_v \text{ (mm)} = \sqrt{\left\{ \left(\frac{31 \, d_b^3 l}{f_t t_v \times 10^6} \right) + d_h^2 \right\}} \qquad (8.20a)$$

Similarly $\qquad M = 0 \cdot 5236\, d_b^3\, l\,(\text{lb/in}) = f_t\, Z$

$$= f_t\, \frac{t_v}{6}(d_v^2 - d_h^2)$$

whence $\qquad d_v\,(\text{in}) = \sqrt{\left\{ \left(\dfrac{0 \cdot 1131\, d_b^3\, l}{f_t\, t_v} \right) + d_h^2 \right\}}$. $\qquad\qquad$ (8.20b)

where f_t = safe tensile strength of the lever, say 20 MPa [3000 lb/in²] for good quality cast iron, 35 MPa [5000 lb/in²] for gunmetal, and 70–80 MPa [10 000–12 000 lb/in²] for mild steel bars.

The screwed termination of the lever for attachment of the ball-float calls for some amount of thought. If the lever be made entirely of iron, it is practically useless to arrange the screwed end integral with the lever as the chances are that if would readily break off; a superior method of attachment is that portrayed in Fig. 8.7. The screwed termination is a separate piece, renewable in the event of the thread becoming impaired through any cause, and thus occasioning no necessity to renew the whole of the lever for the sake of a broken end fitting.

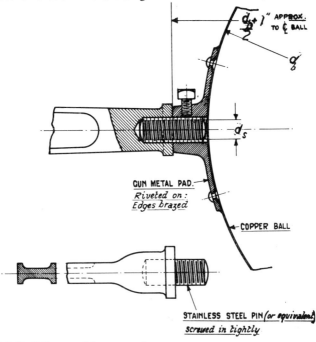

Fig. 8.7 *Ball-float and lever attachment*

This pin will be subjected to a bending moment and a shearing force having a maximum value at the point where the pin enters the lever; for all practical purposes the shearing force may be ignored.

It will be assumed that the amount the pad projects above the surface of the ball-float is 1 in (a correction could be made where there is any appreciable deviation from this amount), then the maximum bending moment at the point indicated will be

$$M_c = D\left(\frac{d_b}{2}\right) + 1 \tag{8.21}$$

where D = displacement of complete ball-float,

and d_b = diameter of ball-float.

The moment of resistance of the pin (at its root diameter) will be

$$Z_p = \frac{\pi}{32} d_s^{3} f_t \tag{6.22}$$

where d_s = root diameter of pin,

and f_t = safe tensile strength of the material of the pin, say 35 MPa [5000 lb/in²] for gunmetal and 70–80 MPa [10 000–12 000 lb/in²] for mild steel or 'Monel' metal.

The latter material is to be strongly recommended for this item on account of its high resistance to corrosion coupled with its high mechanical strength.

Equating the bending moment to the moment of resistance,

$$d_s = \sqrt[3]{\left\{\frac{32 D}{\pi f_t}\left(\frac{d_b}{2} + 1\right)\right\}} \tag{8.23}$$

It must be remembered that d_s thus obtained is the *root* diameter of the thread: the nearest standard size in excess of that obtained by the above formula should, of course, be adopted.

One more detail yet to receive consideration is the fulcrum bolt, a typical example of which is shown in Fig. 8.8. In order to restrict the fulcrum distance to a reasonably small amount it is expedient to crank the jaw portion inwards, as shown, so as to permit of the screwed portion being passed through the cover flange and to be secured by a nut on the underside, thus presenting no difficulties of alignment as would otherwise be occasioned were the bolt to be screwed into the flange, since the chances of it facing the way of the lever would be very remote in the fully tightened position.

The shank is subjected to combined *bending* and *direct tensile* stresses under the influence of the upward force S_f acting on the fulcrum pin. For the sake of simplicity of calculation it is more convenient first to assume a shank diameter d_f and collar diameter d_c and then to compute the *total tensile* stress incurred. Subsequent adjustment may then be made to these dimensions if it is found that the resulting stress is on the high side.

The jaw will tend to heel about the point *0* in Fig. 8.8 hence, *mean tensile force* due to bending may be obtained from the relation

$$Q\frac{d_c}{2} = S_f\left(e + \frac{d_c}{2}\right)$$

or

$$Q = \frac{2S_f}{d_c}\left(e + \frac{d_c}{2}\right)$$

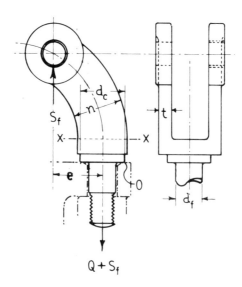

Fig. 8.8 *Fulcrum bolt*

The *direct tensile* force will be S_f; then *total tensile* force F_f will be $S_f + Q$

or

$$F_f = S_f + \frac{2S_f}{d_c}\left(e + \frac{d_c}{2}\right)$$

$$= S_f\left\{1 + \frac{2}{d_c}\left(e + \frac{d_c}{2}\right)\right\} \tag{8.24}$$

Then, *net tensile* stress

$$f_{nt} = \frac{4S_f}{\pi d_f^2}\left\{1 + \frac{2}{d_c}\left(e + \frac{d_c}{2}\right)\right\} \tag{8.25}$$

A suitable value for f_{nt}, in this case, may be taken up to 15 000 lb/in² for a mild steel forging or drop stamping, 80 MPa [12 000 lb/in²] for a steel casting, 50 MPa [7500 lb/in²] for malleable iron and 35 MPa [5000 lb/in²] for gunmetal where the bolt is a good fit in the hole drilled for its reception.

Again referring to Fig. 8.8 it will be appreciated that the jaws of the fulcrum bolt will require to be so proportioned that they will be able to withstand the bending forces incurred in the region of the section denoted by *xx*, at which section the bending moment is a maximum, then

$$S_f e = 2f_t\,\frac{tn^2}{6}$$

$$= \frac{f_t tn^2}{3} \tag{8.26}$$

Now t may be arbitrarily fixed as $0 \cdot 4\ b$ where b is the width of the jaw taken through the boss (see Fig. 8.6) and this readily enables the value of n to be determined.

Transposing eqn (8.24)

$$n = \sqrt{\left(\frac{3S_f e}{f_t t}\right)} \quad \text{or}\quad n = \sqrt{\left(\frac{7 \cdot 5 S_f e}{b f_t}\right)} \tag{8.27}$$

Values for f_t may be taken equal to those which apply in eqn (8.25). There would appear to be no further items calling for detailed stress investigation excepting, perhaps, the body itself and the ball-float. With regard to the former, this is generally made as light as possible consistent with the requirements of moulding since the pressures under which such valves require to operate are usually low. The lug, by means of which the fulcrum bolt is attached to the body, should be fairly robust and suitably ribbed (as shown in Fig. 8.1) as a precaution against breakage; a cast-iron cantilever (for such it would be if unribbed) is unsound practice. (It must be remembered that in the event of such breakage a new body would have to be obtained.)

Regarding the ball-float there does not appear to be any method of correlating metal thickness and diameter with the collapsing pressure. Experience must be the deciding factor here, as any attempt at stress analysis must be fraught with complexity. The slightest departure from the truly spherical form, or the presence of the two pads or the local stiffening presented by the seam where the two halves must necessarily be joined together, would have the inevitable result of adding to the complexity of the problem. It is rather illuminating to find by direct experiment that the collapsing pressure of a spherical float of the form depicted, and subjected to *external* pressure, is generally much higher than one would imagine. A test conducted to establish the collapsing pressure of a stainless steel ball-

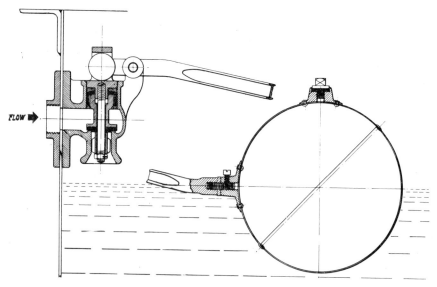

Fig. 8.9 *Improved pattern equilibrium ball-float valve*

float, $5\frac{1}{2}$ in (139·7 mm) in diameter and 20 SWG (0·914 mm) thick, made in two halves electrically welded at the seam, revealed that this could withstand a pressure of 1200 lb/in² (8·26 MPa) before it collapsed.

The provision of a filler-cap is a two-fold necessity; firstly, it permits of some amount of ballasting (should this prove desirable) either by water or lead shot, and secondly, its removal during the process of welding or brazing the two halves together permits the free escape of air from the interior of the float during the final stages of the operation. Anyone who has attempted to join two half-floats in this manner will appreciate the difficulty attending this process, the escape of heated air during the final stages having the effect of blowing the molten metal away from the seam.

It must be borne in mind that the ideal float, from the dual standpoints of maximum buoyancy for a given volume and mechanical strength is one of truly spherical form. Occasionally, one encounters cylindrical, and even box-like, floats, but these are inferior to the spherical float in many ways.

The alternative design shown in Fig. 8.9 may now be examined wherein it will be seen that more thought has been given to the design of the balance-piston than is usually to be found in contemporary designs.

If use is made of a cup *leather* (the italics signifying that leather is not specifically essential; any of the well-known synthetics or bonded-asbestos-rubber compounds would serve equally as well, if not better, under certain conditions of installation) the same care should be expended in an endeavour to make full use of this age-old principle of sealing as would be expended in the best hydraulic practice.

It is useless to jam such a device between two plates and leave it at that; care must be taken to see that it is adequately supported and that it is prevented from curling up at the toe or being subjected to undue flexure at the heel, nothing being more conducive to rapid wear of this member unless

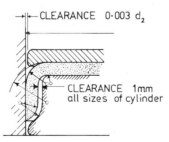

Fig. 8.10 *Cup 'leather' assembly—equilibrium float valves*

it be the presence of abrasives in the working fluid.

The mode of support referred to will be more readily apparent from the additional illustration shown in Fig. 8.10. The provision of 'breather' holes (not shown) is an additional refinement and ensures that ingress of the working fluid, so essential for maintaining the 'leather' in close contact with the cylinder wall, is not restricted. (See Fig. 8.9.)

The top plate (see Fig. 8.10) should be arranged to fit snugly over the 'leather' and should be radiused so as to give the minimum of endplay, a suitable value being 0·003 in per inch of cylinder diameter, on each side.

The bottom support, which forms an integral part of the valve member, should be provided with a more liberal allowance, however, in order to enable entry of the working fluid so as to exert an outward pressure on the walls of the cylinder. A suitable value for the clearance here would be 1/32 in (about 1 mm) per side for all sizes of cylinders.

The valve member is of the winged type but the winged portion is a separate casting which simplifies the task of renewing the rubber or leather facing on the valve and thus obviates the undesirable tendency of the facing to creep during the process of screwing on the winged portion in those valves employing this principle. The bottom nut has a transverse saw-cut for purposes of locking it by means of a light hammer blow (a simple but effective ruse) but the nut is easily removed when required. Concentricity is ensured by the central spindle; the clearance between this and its attendant parts is shown exaggerated in the drawing.

Accidental ingress of water (or other working fluid) to the ball-float during operation is, of course, to be avoided and this calls for there being no uncertainty in the closure-tightness of the filler-cap. Consequently, a leather grummet has been provided in the design shown and arranged in such a manner that the grummet cannot be squeezed out by excessive tightening of the cap. This again is in accordance with usual hydraulic practice.

Too much backlash should not be permitted between the rounded end of the lever and its housing in the head of the piston, although there should be sufficient working clearance (say 1·5 mm or 1/16 in total) to prevent jamming. All roughness on the contacting surfaces should be avoided.

A strict compliance with the aforementioned suggestions should provide a trouble-free valve, calculated to require a minimum of attention or overhaul over a lengthy period of service. It must be remembered that such valves are often installed in some inaccessible position and their presence often forgotten until such time as something goes amiss.

Chapter Nine
Steam Traps and Air Traps

WHILST the steam trap cannot be wholly regarded as a *valve* in the strict sense of the word, it is a device so essential to the effective operation of a variety of steam appliances as to justify an investigation into its fundamental aspects of design; by the same token, the *air* trap is so similar in concept to the steam trap that it will be given equal prominence in the present chapter.

In essence the two traps claiming our attention may be regarded as float-operated automatic valves and singular ones at that, being able to differentiate between *steam* or *air* and *water* when behaving in strict accordance with the designer's intentions.

The designation 'steam trap', for example, now irrevocably and indelibly inscribed in the engineers' vocabulary, is ill-conceived. Judged in the light of true functional interpretation it is really an unhappy marriage of words since the function of the device is to trap the *water* of condensation and then to expel it through the agency of the steam pressure without loss of steam in the process.

The French have a better word—*purgeur*—which is the epitome of functional descriptiveness and one we might have adopted with advantage; albeit by any other tally such devices would now pass *incognito*.

As will be gathered from the foregoing, the function of a trap is to expel unwanted water automatically from any system where its presence would be most undesirable, as, for example, in the steam supply line to an engine or turbine (particularly the latter), in the coils of steam heat exchangers or in the jacket space of a boiling pan. Since it is the *latent* heat in the steam that is required to be given up to the medium to be heated it is imperative that the resulting water of condensation be removed as quickly as possible. This may be accomplished by:

(a) opening a drain valve at frequent intervals;

(b) leaving a valve in the *cracked* (slightly open) position;

(c) arranging a permanent *leak-off* hole in close proximity to the remote end of the coil, etc;

(d) installing a steam trap.

All these expedients save the last one are to be deprecated on the score that live steam in addition to condensate is permitted to flow to waste. In a correctly designed and installed steam trap, expulsion of condensate is effected without loss of *live* steam, although *flash* steam appears (i.e. steam generated when high-temperature condensate meets the atmosphere). This is sometimes mistaken for *live* steam by those unaware of its origin and is the cause of their condemning a trap unwittingly.

With one or two exceptions, steam traps may be broadly classified into two distinct types:

(a) thermostatic traps;

(b) mechanical traps.

In (a) the difference in temperature between live steam and that of the condensate is utilized to effect a change in dimensions of a sensitive element—such as a copper tube, a bellows containing a highly expansible liquid or a bi-metallic strip—constrained to seat or unseat a valve member and thus cut off, or permit, the expulsion of condensate, as the case may be.

All these motivating devices share the common disadvantage of not being instantaneously responsive to sudden changes in temperature, an attribute which militates against prompt opening or closing of the discharge valve, giving rise to dribbling on occasions, with none of that decisive action more commonly associated with the purely mechanical type of trap. This chapter is only concerned with the *mechanical* trap since successful performance of the *thermostatic* trap is more the result of long-term experimentation than that of any mathematical premise. Moreover, manufacturers of the latter type of trap jealously guard the identity of the highly expansible proprietary liquid employed in their bellows actuating element, often the outcome of much costly experiment.

With the *mechanical* type of trap the actuating element generally consists of an open or closed float, the former being sometimes referred to as a bucket, the latter either cylindrical or spherical. The type of float employed is dependent not so much upon the whim of the designer as upon the type of trap preferred for a particular application.

Each *basic* type of *mechanical* trap will be successively dealt with in the
following pages.

DIRECT-ACTING BUCKET STEAM TRAPS

The simplest of all mechanical steam traps is undoubtedly the direct-acting
bucket trap, the very essence of simplicity.

Figure 9.1 portrays diagramatically the elements of construction of such
a trap, stripped of all embellishments in the interests of clarity. Its action will
be understood by most engineers although there is a surprising ignorance of
what is contained 'under the lid', and this alone justifies a brief outline of its
modus operandi. The trap mechanism housed within the casing (D) and lid
(E) comprises an open-topped bucket float (A) to which is attached a valve
member (B), constrained to seat and unseat against a seating orifice (C)
according to the rise and fall of the floating bucket.

Water of condensation gravitates into the trap casing (D) via the inlet
connection (G) and when a sufficient quantity has accumulated in the
bottom of the casing the bucket will float and eventually rise, carrying with
it the valve member (B) on to its seating (C), thus closing off all communication with the outside of the casing. Closure-tightness of this valve will be

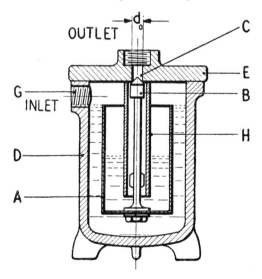

Fig. 9.1 *Elements of construction of a direct-acting bucket steam trap*

enhanced by a force occasioned by the influence of the steam pressure
exerted on the unbalanced area of the seating orifice (C).

This force will be given by

$$U_s = a\,p \qquad (9.1)$$

where a is the effective cross-sectional area of the seating orifice and p the
steam pressure (the valve member (B) is located in a guide or discharge tube
(H)).

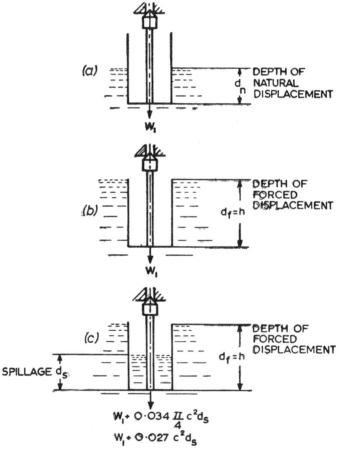

Fig. 9.2 *Forces acting in a direct-acting bucket steam trap*

Water (condensate) continuing to flow into the trap will first creep up the sides of the bucket until the level reaches the top edge of the bucket when it will cascade over the rim. When a sufficient quantity has accumulated therein, the bucket will sink and, in doing so, will pull the valve away from its seating against the combined upthrust of the buoying effect of the surrounding water and that exerted by the steam pressure.

The pressure within the trap casing will then take charge of the situation by acting on the surface of the water in the bucket and forcing some of the water entrapped therein up the guide or discharge tube (H) and through the now open valve (C) to the outside of the trap. When sufficient water has been urged out in this manner to cause the bucket to regain its buoyancy, the bucket will rise and shut off the valve, assisted by the steam pressure acting on the unbalanced area of the seating. The cycle of operations will be repeated so long as water continues to flow into the trap and so long as the steam pressure is of sufficient intensity to effect its ejection.

Consider the forces which are brought into play in a trap of this construction (see the three diagrammatic illustrations (a), (b) and (c) in Fig. 9.2).

At (a) is shown a steam trap bucket with the valve member attached. Assume there is no steam present and the bucket is floating freely, the bucket will sink to a depth corresponding to that at which a condition of equilibrium is established between the upward force induced by the buoying effect of the water and the opposing downward force occasioned by the weight of the bucket and its attendant parts, the depth of displacement being denoted by d_n. Consequently, the weight of water displaced will be equal to the weight of the floating parts (law of Archimedes). From this simple fact the depth of *natural* displacement d_n may be readily calculated. The weight of 1 mm^3 [1 in^3] of water is taken to be 0·94 mg [0·034 lb]

$$0 \cdot 94 \times \frac{\pi}{4} c^2 d_n = W_1 \text{ (mg)} \left[0 \cdot 034 \times \frac{\pi}{4} c^2 d_n = W_1 \text{ (lb)} \right]$$

$$\text{whence } d_n = \frac{4 W_1}{0 \cdot 94 \, \pi c^2} \left[= \frac{4 W_1}{0 \cdot 034 \, \pi c^2} \right]$$

$$= \frac{W_1}{0 \cdot 738 \, c^2} \left[= \frac{W_1}{0 \cdot 027 \, c^2} \right]$$

where W_1 = combined weight of all floating parts and

c = outside diameter of bucket.

The density of water varies according to the temperature and the figure stated is that corresponding to a temperature of approximately 120°C (250°F).

Reverting to Fig. 9.2 (a), assume the position of the bucket with its valve attached to be such that the valve is just making contact with the seating orifice, the level of the water surrounding the bucket corresponding to that at which natural flotation would take place, the depth of such displacement being d_n, and readily calculable from the foregoing equation.

The design of the bucket and its burden of small attendant parts so that their combined weights will not exceed a prescribed weight must be done by trial and error, but the following hints may save much exploratory calculation and speculation. In the first place design should aim at providing a depth of *natural* displacement not exceeding—by any appreciable margin—that of *one-half* the total depth of the bucket. It is better to employ a deep bucket than a shallow one. In short, the depth should be proportionately greater than the diameter.

Table 9.1 gives particulars of an assortment of buckets, together with their weights and displacements, etc, but the displacement values take no account of any other parts attached to the bucket (eg valve member, valve steam, pins, guides, etc) and these should be allowed for in any calculations on displacement. For determining the properties of buckets other than those listed in Table 9.1 reference should be made to the notes contained in the latter part of this section.

Consider the forces acting on the bucket and valve seatings in Fig. 9.2 (a). Assume the pressure within the casing to be atmospheric. Let u_1 be the upward force due to the displacement, D_o the corresponding displacement and W_1 the weight of the bucket and its attendant floating parts, then

$$u_1 = D_0 - W_1 \qquad\qquad (9.3)$$

but, for a freely floating bucket, D_0 and W_1 are equal, whence

$$u_1 = 0 \qquad\qquad (9.4)$$

In other words, when the valve member is just making contact with the seating and with only atmospheric pressure within the casing, the buoying effect of the displaced water does not impart any upward force to the seating.

Now, assume the trap to be subjected to a steam pressure of intensity p, other conditions remaining as before.

Table 9.1 Properties of typical cylindrical copper floats for steam traps

Diameter (c)		Height (h)		Thickness (t)		Weight of float		Natural depth of displacement (d_n)		Ratio			
										h/c		d_n/h	
mm	in	mm	in	mm*	swg	kg	lb	mm	in	SI	Imperial	SI	Imperial
75	3	115	4.5	0.9	20	0.2533	0.56	55.97	2.30	1.53	1.5	0.48	0.512
75	3	140	5	0.9	20	0.3006	0.62	72.21	2.56	1.87	1.67	0.52	0.512
75	3	150	6	0.9	20	0.3196	0.73	76.77	3.02	2.00	2.00	0.51	0.503
100	4	140	5.5	1.2	18	0.5555	1.24	75.06	2.86	1.40	1.38	0.54	0.522
100	4	150	6	1.2	18	0.5891	1.33	79.60	3.07	1.50	1.50	0.53	0.513
100	4	200	8	1.2	18	0.7575	1.72	102.35	3.97	2.00	2.00	0.51	0.496
130	5	160	6.25	1.6	16	1.2254	2.36	84.48	3.52	1.14	1.25	0.53	0.563
130	5	180	7	1.6	16	1.3511	2.60	93.15	3.83	1.29	1.40	0.52	0.548
130	5	250	10	1.6	16	1.7910	3.57	123.47	5.31	1.79	2.00	0.49	0.531
150	6	200	8	2.0	14	1.9989	4.77	120.04	4.92	1.33	1.33	0.60	0.615
150	6	250	10	2.0	14	2.4197	5.50	145.32	5.68	1.67	1.87	0.58	0.568
150	6	300	12	2.0	14	2.8415	6.42	170.59	6.62	2.00	2.00	0.57	0.552
175	7	250	9	2.5	12	3.6054	7.80	159.10	5.90	1.43	1.28	0.64	0.657
175	7	300	12	2.5	12	4.2191	9.95	186.20	7.55	1.71	1.72	0.62	0.630
175	7	350	14	2.5	12	4.8328	11.40	213.20	8.65	2.00	2.00	0.61	0.618

*Conforms to ISO R" 20

We have seen that the upward force u_s due to this pressure acting on the unbalanced area of the seating is given by $u_s = ap$.

If U_a equals the total upward force on the seating due to all influences, then:

$$U_a = \text{displacement} - \text{weight of bucket} + \text{force due to steam pressure}$$
$$= D_0 - W_1 + u_s$$
$$= D_0 - W_1 + ap \tag{9.5}$$

and since

$$u_1 = D_0 - W_1 = 0 \text{ (eqn 9.4)}$$

then

$$U_a = ap \tag{9.6}$$

Still maintaining the conditions shown in Fig. 9.2 (a), now assume that an additional quantity of water is permitted to gain access to the trap casing. As the bucket is unable to rise any further (due to the valve member making contact with the seating), the additional water introduced will build up around the sides of the bucket and the increased displacement occasioned (which will now be termed the *forced* displacement in order to distinguish it from the *natural* or *free* displacement) will have the effect of imparting a small upward force to the seating through the agency of the valve member. Note that the *forced* displacement is inclusive of the *free* displacement.

These conditions are depicted in Fig. 9.2 (b) and it is assumed that the level of the surrounding water has risen up to the level of the rim of the bucket, the depth of *forced* displacement being denoted by d_f and this, of course, will be equal to h, the height of the bucket.

Again if c = the external diameter of the bucket and h = the depth of the bucket (a cylindrical bucket being assumed) the *forced* displacement D_f will be given by

$$D_f = 0.0000098 \frac{\pi}{4} c^2 d_f \; [= 0.034 \frac{\pi}{4} c^2 d_f]$$

$$= 0.0000077 \, c^2 d_f \text{(N)} \; [= 0.027 \, c^2 d_f \text{(lb)}] \tag{9.7}$$
(dimensions in mm)   [(dimensions in in)]

The upward force u_2 due to the *forced* displacement is given by

u_2 = forced displacement – weight of bucket etc.

$= D_f - W$

$= 0.0000098 \dfrac{\pi}{4} c^2 d_f - 9.8\, W_1 \; [= 0.034 \dfrac{\pi}{4} c^2 d_f - W_1]$

$= 0.0000077\, c^2 d_f - 9.8\, W_1 \,(\text{N}) \quad [= 0.027\, c^2 d_f - W_1 \,(\text{lb})] \qquad (9.8)$
(weight in kg) [(weight in lb)]

Hence the total force, say U_b, due to all causes, acting upwards on the valve seating will be given by

$U_b = ap + 0.0000077\, c^2 d_f - 9.8\, W_1 \,(\text{N}) \; [ap + 0.027 c^2 d_f - W_1 \,(\text{lb})] \; (9.9)$

Now consider the third and last case (Fig. 9.2 (c)), where more water has entered the trap casing, crept up the sides of the bucket and spilled over into the bucket, the depth of 'spillage' being denoted by d_s.

Here again, as in Fig. 9.2 (c) the depth of the *forced* displacement is $d_f = h$, and now

u_s = displacement — weight of bucket etc — weight of spillage

$= 0.0000077\, c^2 d_f - 9.8\, W_1 - 0.0000077\, c^2 d_s \,\text{N}$
$[= 0.027\, c^2 d_f - W_1 - 0.027\, c^2 d_s\, \text{lb}]$

and total upward force

$U_c = ap + 0.0000077\, c^2 d_f - 9.8\, W_1 - 0.0000077\, c^2 d_s \,\text{N}$
$[= ap + 0.027\, c^2 d_f - W_1 - 0.027\, c^2 d_s\, \text{lb}] \qquad (9.10)$

These, then, are the conditions which obtain when the trap is under steam and on the point of discharging its contents. Discharge will take place when sufficient 'spillage' has accumulated to upset the equilibrium of the trap mechanism and design should aim at this taking place long before the bucket is completely full; otherwise, the trap will 'hunt' or remain water-logged entirely.

Now U_c must equal zero when the valve is about to unseat (and discharge), or

$ap + 0.0000077\, c^2 d_f - 9.8\, W_1 - 0.0000077\, c^2 d_s = 0$
$[ap + 0.027\, c^2 d_f - W_1 - 0.027\, c^2 d_s = 0] \qquad (9.11)$

From this equation we may readily determine a, the requisite area of the seating orifice, which is what we really set out to do, but some preamble was essential to the process. Then, from the above equation,

$$a = \frac{1}{p}\{9 \cdot 8 \, W_1 + 0 \cdot 0000077 \, c^2 \, (d_s - d_f)\} \; \left[= \frac{1}{p}\{W_1 + 0 \cdot 027 \, c^2 \, (d_s - d_f)\} \right]$$

But $d_f = h$ and, for effective operation, d_s should be taken as $\frac{1}{2}h$, whence

$$a = \frac{1}{p} \left\{ 9 \cdot 8 \, W_1 + 0 \cdot 0000077 \, c^2 \left(\frac{h}{2} - h \right) \right\} \; \text{mm}^2$$

$$\left[= \frac{1}{p} \left\{ W_1 + 0 \cdot 027 \, c^2 \left(\frac{h}{2} - h \right) \right\} \; \text{in}^2 \right]$$

$$= \frac{9 \cdot 8 \, W_1 - 0 \cdot 00000385 \, c^2 h}{p} \; \text{mm}^2 \quad \left[= \frac{W_1 - 0 \cdot 0135 \, c^2 h}{p} \; \text{in}^2 \right] \qquad (9.12)$$

The diameter of the seating orifice d_o may then be determined from

$$d_o = \sqrt{\left(\frac{4}{\pi p} (9 \cdot 8 \, W_1 - 0 \cdot 00000385 \, c^2 h) \right)} \; \text{mm}$$

$$\left[= \sqrt{\left(\frac{4}{\pi p} (W_1 - 0 \cdot 0135 c^2 h) \right)} \; \text{in} \right]$$

which may be reduced to

$$\sqrt{\left(\frac{12 \cdot 5 W_1 - 0 \cdot 0000049 c^2 h}{p} \right)} \; \text{mm} \quad \left[= \sqrt{\left(\frac{1 \cdot 273 W_1 - 0 \cdot 0172 c^2 h}{p} \right)} \; \text{in} \right] \; *$$

$$(9.13)$$

If the result is a negative value this implies that the bucket is insufficiently heavy and would require to be of greater depth so as to accommodate more 'spillage'. Alternatively the bucket may be weighted, although this is not advised.

The foregoing derivations take no account of such minor resistances as are imposed by the friction of pins, guides, etc. Every attempt should be made to reduce friction by adopting reasonable clearances between the various rubbing surfaces. Then one may ignore the effect of such resistances in studying the mechanics of operation (as in the present treatment) and afterwards making such allowances in design as may be deemed expedient.

---

*In using these equations, care must be taken to employ consistent units.

Determination of weight of bucket

It may be necessary to adopt a size of bucket not listed in Table 9.1, to which reference has been made previously, in which case its weight and other properties will require to be calculated and this may be accomplished with reasonable accuracy from considerations of its surface area and weight per unit area of the material employed. This simple expedient takes no account of the additional weight incurred by seaming, welding and/or brazing (if such be the modes of fabrication) and some allowance should be made for this; then neglecting the additive effects of fabrication.

Surface area of bucket

$$a_b = \pi c h + \tfrac{1}{4}\pi c^2 \text{ in}^2$$
$$= \pi c (h + \tfrac{1}{4}c) \text{ in}^2$$

if δ = weight per in^2 and $\varDelta$ the weight per ft^2 of the material of the bucket, then

$$\text{weight of bucket } W_b = \pi \delta c (h + \tfrac{1}{4}c) \text{ lbw} \qquad (9.14)$$

or

$$W_b = \frac{\pi \varDelta c}{144}(h + \tfrac{1}{4}c) \text{ lbw} \qquad (9.15)$$

If w_m = weight in kg/m^2, then weight of bucket

$$W_b = \frac{\pi w_m c}{100\,000}\left(h + \frac{c}{4}\right) \text{ kg} \qquad (9.15a)$$

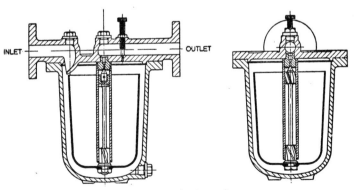

Fig. 9.3 *Typical steam trap (with air eliminator)*

Table 9.2 Weights (m²) of metal sheets (as employed for steam trap floats)

Thickness to ISO R″ 20 mm	Weight kg/m²				High nickel – copper alloy eg approx $\frac{2}{3}$ nickel $\frac{1}{3}$ copper
	Copper	Brass	Steel	Stainless steel	
0·45	4·018	3·875	3·588	3·835	3·991
0·50	4·465	4·273	3·987 ·	4·262	4·421
0·55	4·912	4·701	4·386	4·685	4·628
0·60	5·358	5·128	4·784	5·114	5·916
0·70	6·251	5·982	5·582	5·967	6·206
0·80	7·144	6·837	6·379	6·819	7·064
0·90	8·037	7·691	7·177	7·672	7·933
1·00	8·930	8·576	7·974	8·524	8·814
1·10	9·823	9·400	8·772	9·377	9·708
1·20	10·716	10·255	9·569	10·229	10·574
1·40	12·502	11·964	11·164	11·934	11·356
1·60	14·288	13·673	12·759	13·639	14·133
1·80	16·074	15·383	14·354 ·	15·344	15·914
2·00	17·860	17·692	15·949	17·049	17·635
2·20	19·646	18·801	17·543	18·753	18·755
2·50	22·325	21·365	19·936	21·311	22·101
2·80	25·004	23·929	22·328	23·868	24·734
3·00	26·790	25·638	23·923	25·573	26·501
3·50	31·255	29·911	27·910	29·835	30·934
4·00	35·720	34·184	31·898	34·099	35·320
4·50	40·185	38·757	35·885	38·361	40·020
5·00	44·650	42·730	39·872	42·623	44·159

Table 9.2 will be found useful in the manipulation of the foregoing formulae, noting that the weights given are in kg/m²; thus eqn (9.15a) should be employed in conjunction with Table 9.2.

The weights of the attendant bucket attachments, eg spindle, valve member, guide, etc, will require to be computed, since these have to be carried as 'cargo' by the bucket and taken into account accordingly.

A typical direct-acting bucket steam trap is illustrated in Fig. 9.3.

INDIRECT-ACTING BUCKET STEAM TRAPS

The *direct*-acting bucket trap at best can only present a relatively small area of discharge for the condensate as the formulae outlined in the foregoing section will reveal. It follows, therefore, that if the seating orifice could be enlarged somehow, a more copious discharge would be expected, with a corresponding diminution in the general overall dimensions of the trap, other things being equal. The obvious way to do this is to increase the unseating force operating on the valve. Now we have seen in the previous section that this unseating force is brought about by the requisite amount of spillage accumulating within the bucket and this amount must be appreciably less than the total volumetric capacity of the bucket if the trap is to function over a reasonable pressure range; otherwise, each application would have to be treated strictly on its merits and the seating diameter selected appropriate to the pressure obtaining, which would be ludicrous. Consequently, some other way must be found to increase the unseating force without increasing the spillage. It is simple to do this by introducing a system of leverage in the bucket mechanism. This adds somewhat to the frictional resistance of the moving parts but the addition is negligible if the suggestions previously made regarding clearances are observed.

Figure 9.4 depicts such a lever mechanism, the action of which will be readily understood, and Fig. 9.5 will serve to illustrate the mechanics of operation outlined below.

The lever is arranged to pivot about point 0. Taking moments about the pivot and neglecting friction, at the instant of discharge we have

$$\text{seating moments} = \text{unseating moments}$$

thus

$$\left. \begin{aligned} a p y + 0 \cdot 0000077 \, c^2 d_f x &= x \, (9 \cdot 8 \, W_1 + 0 \cdot 0000077 \, c^2 d_s) \\ [a p y + 0 \cdot 027 \, c^2 d_f x &= x \, (W_1 + 0 \cdot 027 \, c^s d_s)] \end{aligned} \right\} \quad (9.16)$$

whence

$$\left. \begin{aligned} a &= \frac{x}{p y} \left(9 \cdot 8 \, W_1 + 0 \cdot 0000077 \, c^2 \, (d_s - d_f) \right) \\ \left[&= \frac{x}{p y} \left(W_1 = 0 \cdot 027 \, c^2 \, (d_s - d_f) \right) \right] \end{aligned} \right\} \quad (9.17)$$

Now $x/y = v_r$, the *velocity ratio* of the lever arrangement, and $d_f = h$.

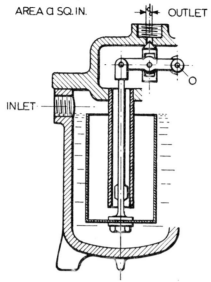

Fig. 9.4 *Simple lever mechanism of an indirect-acting bucket steam trap*

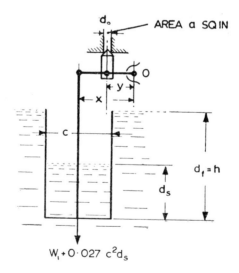

Fig. 9.5 *Forces acting in an indirect-acting bucket steam trap*

Assuming $d_s = h/2$, then

$$a = \frac{v_r}{p}\left(9\cdot8\, W_1 + 0\cdot0000077\, c^2\, \frac{h}{2} - h\right)$$

$$\left[= \frac{v_r}{p}\left(W_1 + 0\cdot027\, c^2\left(\frac{h}{2} - h\right)\right)\right]$$

or

$$a = \frac{v_r}{p}(9\cdot8\, W_1 - 0\cdot00000385\, c^2 h)\left[= \frac{v_r}{p}(W_1 - 0\cdot0135\, c^2 h)\right] \quad (9.18)$$

v_r is usually taken to equal 5 or 6. From this the diameter, d_o, of the seating orifice is found

$$d_o = \sqrt{\left\{\frac{4v_r}{p}(9\cdot8\, W_1 - 0\cdot00000385\, c^2 h)\right\}}$$

$$\left[= \sqrt{\left\{\frac{4v_r}{p}(W_1 - 0\cdot0135\, c^2 h)\right\}}\right]$$

which simplifies to

$$d_o = \sqrt{\left\{\frac{1\cdot273 v_r}{p}(9\cdot8\, W_1 - 0\cdot00000385\, c^2 h)\right\}}$$

$$\left[= \sqrt{\left\{\frac{1\cdot273 v_r}{p}(W_1 - 0\cdot0135\, c^2 h)\right\}}\right] \quad (9.19)$$

By comparing eqns (9.18) and (9.12) it will be seen that the area of the seating orifice in this case is directly proportional to v_r; in other words, the area of the seating orifice of an *indirect-acting* bucket trap (i.e. one with lever operation) may be increased in the same ratio as that of the leverage provided. In short, the orifice may be calculated as for a *direct*-acting trap and the result multiplied by v_r; similarly, the *diameter* will vary as $\sqrt{v_r}$.

Thus the introduction of a simple lever system, other things being equal, enables the size of the orifice—and consequently the discharge characteristics—to be enhanced appreciably.

A trap embodying this principle is illustrated in Fig. 9.6. In an adaptation of the foregoing type of trap the bucket itself is pivoted and, when sufficient spillage has accumulated therein to overcome the force tending to seat the valve, the bucket rotates about the pivot point. The result is that the centre of gravity of the spillage is rapidly displaced outwardly from the centre of rotation, thus progressively increasing the unseating moment. The ever-increasing turning moment occasioned by the progressive filling of the bucket has a pronounced dynamic effect so that the valve member is positively jerked off its seating.

The mechanics of operation, to all intents and purposes, is in accord with the foregoing treatment and calls for no detailed presentation.

INVERTED BUCKET STEAM TRAPS

One of the most reliable and effective of all trap mechanisms is that employing the *inverted bucket* principle. The use of a trap of this type should, however, be restricted to those applications wherein condensation is continuous, eg jacketed pans, heating coils and similar heat-exchange apparatus. In these the condensate has to be expelled rapidly in the interests

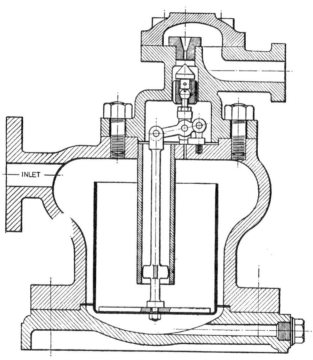

Fig. 9.6 *Indirect acting bucket steam trap*

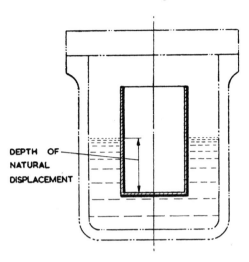

Fig. 9.7 (a) *Freely-floating open-topped bucket*

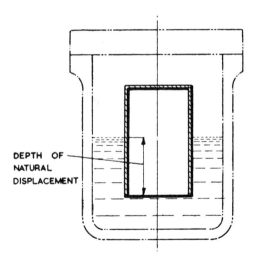

Fig. 9.7 (b) *Freely-floating inverted bucket*

of rapid heat exchange, since the trap is of the pulsating variety and is best kept well supplied with condensate; otherwise, live steam may escape to atmosphere in the absence of condensate. The principle of the inverted bucket mechanism is not universally understood, due, perhaps, to its apparent violation of conventional trap principles, the bucket being upside down and deliberately perforated, in addition. Yet the perforation is essential to its functioning, however paradoxical this might seem. Perforating the bucket can have but one result, to make it sink. And sink it must; but it must likewise be equally capable of flotation, if only for a limited period in its operation.

How, then, can flotation be possible if the bucket is perforated? To answer this question one might reasonably compare the float with a ship that has been holed. If the hole is big enough the ship might sink in a matter of seconds; if small enough it might take hours or even days. (This simile assumes that the pumps are inoperative).

Consider the case of a freely floating bucket as shown diagrammatically in Fig. 9.7 (a). Obviously this bucket will sink until it has displaced a certain quantity of water equal to its own weight. Now invert the bucket as shown in Fig. 9.7 (b) and see what happens. Here again the bucket will float but will tend to turn turtle, suggesting that some restraint must be imposed upon it, either by making it a close fit in the containing vessel (which is undesirable on account of the possibility of wedging) or by providing guides. The displacement will be the same as before.

If the top of the bucket is now perforated, flotation will be possible only as long as the entrained air remains in the bucket, which will continue to sink. The time taken to sink will be completely dependent on how quickly the air can escape through the perforations. Thus the rate of sinking may be controlled by varying the size of the perforations. The sinking will be slow at first, accelerating to a maximum when all the air has been expelled. Now this is what takes place in an inverted bucket trap, except that steam takes the place of air (although any air present in the system would be expelled in the same way), and sinking will be quicker since the steam will become condensed within the bucket. The small amount of steam which leaks off through the perforations into the water surrounding the bucket will also condense.

Thus we have a mechanism which pulsates. The frequency of pulsation is determined by the size of the perforations (rarely exceeding 1·5 mm [1/16 in] in diameter) and with each downward movement of the bucket the valve member is pulled off its seating against the pressure tending to seat it, discharge taking place as a result.

The forces which are brought into play in a trap of this kind may now be considered. Assume that the trap is discharging its contents direct to atmosphere, that is, free from restraint of any kind save that of the frictional resistance of the orifice and outlet which may be disregarded for the moment.

Referring to Fig. 9.8 which is a diagrammatic representation of an inverted bucket mechanism, we have

force urging valve member on to its seating $= ap$

moment of this force about pivot point $O = apm$

Assume the float lever to be balanced.

The apparent weight of float when completely water logged, say W_2, equals the actual weight W_1 *minus* the weight of water, w displaced by the metal of which the float is made, i.e.

$$W_2 = W_1 - \text{w}$$

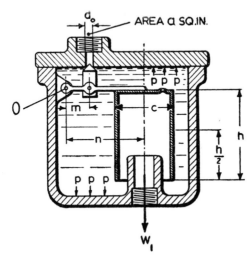

Fig. 9.8 *Diagrammatic representation of an inverted bucket mechanism*

Now W_1 = surface area times weight per unit area of metal (see Table 9.2)
i.e.

$$W_1 = \frac{\pi w_m c}{100\ 000}\left(h+\frac{c}{4}\right)\text{kg}\ \left[=\frac{\pi \varDelta c}{144}\left(h+\frac{c}{4}\right)\text{lb}\right]\qquad \text{(approximately)}$$

This derivation is based on a truly cylindrical float where w_m = weight in kg/m^2 and $\varDelta$ = weight in lb/ft^2 of float material, c, t and h being the diameter, thickness and depth of the float respectively and

$$w = \frac{\pi c t (h + c/4)}{100\ 000}\ \text{kg}\ \left[=0\cdot036\,\pi c t\,(h+c/4)\,\text{lb}\right]$$

then $$W_2 = \frac{\pi w c}{100\ 000}\,(h+c/4)\ \text{kg}\ \left[=\frac{\pi \varDelta c}{144}\,(h+c/4)-0\cdot036\,\pi c t\,(h+c/4)\right.$$

$$\left[=\pi c\,(h+c/4)\,\frac{\varDelta}{144}-0\cdot036\,t\right]\qquad (9.20)$$

Moment of float about pivot point $O = 9\cdot8\ W_2 n$ Nm $[W_2 n$ lb in]. Then, for equilibrium (i.e when valve is about to be pulled away from its seating),

seating moment = unseating moment

or $\qquad apm = 9\cdot8\ W_2 n$ Nm $[= W_2 n$ lb in]

whence $\qquad a = \dfrac{9\cdot8\ W_2 n}{pm}\,\text{mm}^2\ \left[=\dfrac{W_2 n}{pm}\,\text{in}^2\right]$

or $\qquad d_o = \sqrt{\left(\dfrac{4\times 9\cdot8\ W_2 n}{\pi pm}\right)}\,\text{mm}\ \left[=\sqrt{\left(\dfrac{4\ W_2 n}{\pi pm}\right)}\,\text{in}\right]\qquad (9.21)$

The theoretical value of d_o thus derived calls for amendment in order to compensate for the frictional resistance of the pins, swivels, or guides, the clamping pressure at the seating, inertia of the moving parts, etc, all of which are factors which should be taken into account. These, being practically indeterminate, points to the necessity of compensating for them by simply reducing the size of the seating orifice as obtained by the foregoing formula. Experience suggests that the area of the seating orifice may be reduced with advantage to roughly one-third of the calculated values.

The foregoing formulae, therefore, may be amended to give the *empirical* relationship

$$a = \frac{9 \cdot 8\, W_2 n}{3\, p\, m}\mathrm{mm}^2 \left[\frac{W_2 n}{3\, p\, m}\mathrm{in}^2\right] \tag{9.22}$$

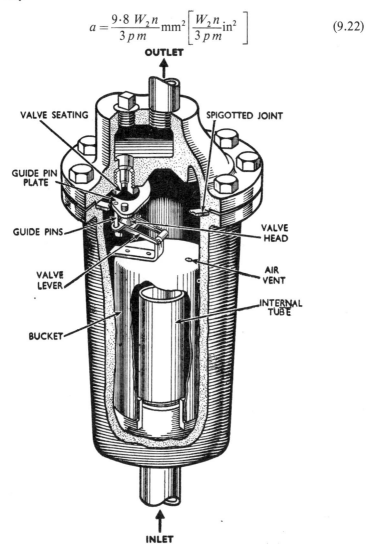

Fig. 9.9 *Drayton Armstrong inverted bucket steam trap (courtesy of Drayton Controls Ltd)*

and

$$d_o = \sqrt{\left(\frac{4 \times 9 \cdot 8 \, W_2 n}{3 \pi p m}\right)} \mathrm{mm} \left[\sqrt{\left(\frac{4 \, W_2 n}{3 \pi p m}\right)} \mathrm{in}\right]$$

or

$$\left.\begin{aligned} &d_o = \sqrt{\left(\frac{4 \cdot 16 \, W_2 n}{p m}\right)} \mathrm{mm} \text{ (where } W \text{ is in kg and } p \text{ in MPa)} \\ &\left[= \sqrt{\left(\frac{0 \cdot 43 \, W_2 n}{p m}\right)} \mathrm{in}\right] \end{aligned}\right\} \quad (9.23)$$

The seatings should be arranged with relatively 'knife-edge' contacting faces or with no perceptible bevelling. As the actual clamping pressure (to secure fluid-tightness) in any steam trap is of a very low order (amounting in most cases to only a few pounds), the vulnerability of 'knife-edge' seatings is more apparent than real. Bevelling obviously has the most undesirable effect of increasing the *unbalanced* area of the seating, thereby calling for a correspondingly greater effort to unseat the valve member. The failure of some traps to operate after an overhaul has frequently been traced to a lavish display of bevelling of the seating, which may be ascribed to a too successful attempt at grinding out erosion marks or to a misconceived idea as to what constitutes a reasonable width of contact face—or to both.

A trap embodying the inverted bucket principle is illustrated in Fig. 9.9.

SLIDE VALVE STEAM TRAPS

Valve designers and others may need no reminding that it requires much less effort to close a valve of the *parallel slide* type than one of the *screw-down* type, size for size and operating at identical pressures, but the reason may possibly escape immediate appreciation. In the parallel slide valve the primary closure force required is that which is just sufficient to overcome the frictional resistance of the disc uniformly loaded by the pressure acting thereon as it is urged across the surface of the seating; in the screw-down valve the closure force is that required to counter the opposing upthrust occasioned by the pressure acting on the effective area of the valve member. Figure 9.10 should make this quite clear, depicting the elements of a *slide* valve in (a) and a *lift* valve in (b) and indicating the principle forces operating thereon.

In (a) $$P_a = \tfrac{1}{4}\pi d_a^2 p \qquad (9.24)$$

and in (b) $$P_b = \tfrac{1}{4}\pi d_b^2 p \qquad (9.25)$$

Now axial force $F_a = \tfrac{1}{4}\pi\mu d_a^2 p$

and $$F_b = P_b = \tfrac{1}{4}\pi d_b^2 p$$

but $$P_a = P_b$$

whence $$F_a : F_b = \mu : 1$$

or $$F_a = \mu F_b \qquad (9.26)$$

Thus, ignoring all secondary resistances, it will be seen that the axial force required to close a valve of the *slide* type is only μ times that required to close a valve of the screw-down type and, obviously, the disparity is greater the lower the value of μ, the coefficient of friction. From this comparison it may be inferred that a trap operating on the slide valve principle should require much less effort on the part of the float mechanism to unseat the valve than one employing a *needle* valve. This claim should not be interpreted to imply that the slide valve principle might be adopted to the exclusion of all others. Individual preferences play their part in the selection of any trap and each has its sphere of application. In order to make this treatment as comprehensive as possible a *slide valve trap* employing a *spherical* float will be considered. Where such a float is contemplated, the thickness of the metal preferred should be chosen with discretion; care should also be taken in joining the two halves together since, unlike the open

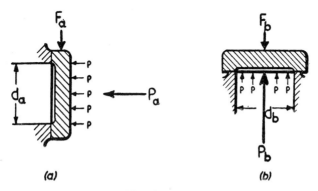

(a)   *(b)*

Fig. 9.10 *Elementary slide and lift valves*

bucket pattern, such a float is liable to collapse prematurely if made of inordinately thin material or if ineffectively brazed or soldered. There is so little published information on the behaviour of ball-floats under the influence of external pressure that design should follow the dictates of practical experience, supported where possible by actual tests rather than by any uncertain venturing into the mathematical field in an attempt to correlate pressure, diameter and thickness. In this connexion the *stainless-steel* ball-float offers many advantages over one of copper, being much stronger in every respect and less liable to indentation, the surest precursor of a collapsed float. A modicum of water (say 1 cm³) is sometimes introduced into a closed float before sealing in order to create an internal steam pressure (when the temperature is favourable) in an attempt to counterbalance the external pressure on the float. This practice might be frowned upon in some circles as one likely to engender an explosion and, therefore, one to be carried out with the utmost discretion.

Consider the forces brought into play in a trap of this type.

Referring to Fig. 9.11, condensate flowing into the trap casing at (A) will accumulate therein and eventually render the ball-float (B) buoyant, causing it to rise. In doing so, the bell-crank lever (C) pivoted at (0) will tend to rotate.

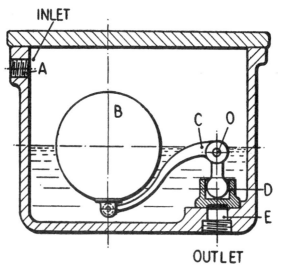

Fig. 9.11 *Elements of construction of a slide valve steam trap*

This will occasion a sideways movement of the short arm of the bell-crank lever which will impart a lateral motion to the valve disc (D), uncovering the outlet or discharge orifice (E). The steam pressure within the casing will instantly urge the condensate into the atmosphere (or elsewhere) through the now open—or partially open—valve. When sufficient condensate has been ejected to cause the ball-float to lose some of its buoyancy, this will commence to fall and the valve disc will return to the closed position.

In order to provide some measure of buoyancy it is customary for the ball-float to be half immersed (as near as may be devised) at the stage when discharge commences.

Reference should now be made to Fig. 9.12 depicting the forces acting on the float mechanism.

Assuming half-immersion of the float at the point of imminent discharge,

$$\text{volume of water displaced} = \frac{\pi b^3}{12}$$

weight of water displaced
(or upthrust due to enforced displacement)

$$= \frac{\pi b^3}{12 \times 10^6} \text{ kg} \left[= \frac{0.034 \, \pi b^3}{12} \text{ lb} \right] = 2.57 \times 10^{-6} \, b^3 \text{ N} \left[= 0.0089 \, b^3 \text{ lb} \right]$$

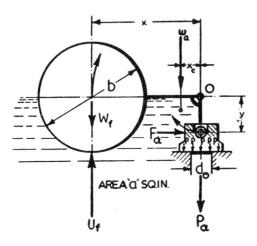

Fig. 9.12 *Forces acting in a slide valve trap*

Ignoring the weight of the lever, net upward force U_f of float will be given by

$$U_f = 2 \cdot 57 \times 10^{-6} b^3 - 9 \cdot 8\, W_f\, \mathrm{N}\; [= 0 \cdot 0089\, b^3 - W_f] \qquad (9.27)$$

where W_f = weight of ball-float (kg [lb])

Now the force P_a holding the disc on to its seating will be given by

$$P_a = a\,p$$
$$= \tfrac{1}{4}\,\pi\,p\,d_o^2$$

and the tangential force F_a required to overcome the resistance to sliding of the disc by

$$F_a = \tfrac{1}{4}\,\pi\,\mu\,p\,d_o^2 \qquad (9.28)$$

Since the system is in equilibrium, the algebraic sum of the moments about the fulcrum point 0 will be equal to zero; then, again ignoring, for the time being, the weight of the float arm,

$$U_f x - F_a y = 0 \qquad (9.29)$$

or, from eqns (9.27) and (9.28)

$$x\,(2 \cdot 57 \times 10^{-6} b^3 - 9 \cdot 8\, W_f) - \frac{\pi}{4}\mu p y d_o^2 = 0$$

$$\left[x\,(0 \cdot 0089\, b^3 - W_f) - \frac{\pi}{4}\mu p y d_o^2 = 0 \right]$$

whence

$$d_o = \sqrt{\left\{ \frac{4\,(2 \cdot 57 \times 10^{-6} b^3 - 9 \cdot 8\, W_f)x}{\pi \mu p y} \right\}}\,\mathrm{mm}$$

$$\left[= \sqrt{\left\{ \frac{4\,(0 \cdot 0089\, b^3 - W_f)x}{\pi \mu p y} \right\}}\,\mathrm{in} \right]$$

$$= 1 \cdot 128 \sqrt{\left\{ \frac{(2 \cdot 57 \times 10^{-6} b^3 - 9 \cdot 8\, w_f)x}{\mu p y} \right\}}\,\mathrm{mm}$$

$$\left[= \sqrt{\left\{ \frac{1 \cdot 273\,(0 \cdot 0089\, b^3 - W_f)x}{\mu y p} \right\}}\,\mathrm{in} \right] \qquad (9.30)$$

Now taking the weight of the float arm into consideration for greater accuracy, denoting its weight by w_a and the distance of its centre of gravity from the fulcrum point 0 by x_c,

$$U_f x - w_a x_c - F_a y = 0 \tag{9.31}$$

thus

$$\left. \begin{array}{l} x\,(2\cdot57 \times 10^{-6}\,b^3 - 9\cdot8\,W_f) - w_a x_c - \pi\,/4\,\mu\,p y d_o^2 = 0 \\[2mm] \left[\,x\,(0\cdot0089\,b^3 - W_f) - w_a x_c - y\,(\pi/4\,\mu\,p d_o^2) = 0\,\right] \end{array} \right\} \tag{9.32}$$

whence

$$\left. \begin{array}{l} d_o = \sqrt{\left\{ \dfrac{(2\cdot57 \times 10^{-6}\,b^3 - 9\cdot8\,W_f)x - w_a x_c}{0\cdot7854\,\mu\,p\,y} \right\}} \\[6mm] \left[= \sqrt{\left\{ \dfrac{x\,(0\cdot0089\,b^3 - W_f) - w_a x_c}{0\cdot7854\,\mu\,y\,p} \right\}} \right] \end{array} \right\} \tag{9.33}$$

WORKED EXAMPLE

A slide valve trap of the type illustrated in Figs 9.11 and (diagrammatically) 9.12, operating at $0\cdot7$ MPa [100 lb/in^2] is actuated by a 100 mm [4 in] diameter ball-float weighing $0\cdot22$ kg [$0\cdot5$ lb] and discharge is direct to atmosphere. The effective lengths of the float arm are 150 mm [6 in] and 37 mm [$1\cdot5$ in] respectively. Determine the requisite diameter of seating orifice: (a) ignoring the weight of the float arm etc., and (b) taking the weight of the lever into account, supposing it to weigh $0\cdot05$ kg [$0\cdot1$ lb], with its centre of gravity situated 32 mm [$1\cdot125$ in] from the fulcrum point 0. Take μ to be $0\cdot2$.

Solution

From eqn (9.30) we have

$$\text{(a)}\quad d_o = 1\cdot128\sqrt{\left\{ \frac{(2\cdot57 \times 10^{-6} \times 100^3 - 9\cdot8 \times 0\cdot22) \times 150}{0\cdot2 \times 0\cdot7 \times 37} \right\}}$$

$$\left[= \sqrt{\left\{ \frac{(1\cdot273 \times 6\,(0\cdot0089 \times 4^3 - 0\cdot5))}{0\cdot2 \times 100 \times 1\cdot5} \right\}} \right]$$

$$= 3\cdot905 \text{ mm } [=0\cdot1331 \text{ in}]$$

and from eqn (9.33) we have

(b) $d_o = \sqrt{\left\{ \dfrac{(150(2\cdot57 \times 10^6 \times 100 - 9\cdot8 \times 0\cdot22) - (0\cdot05 \times 32)}{0\cdot7854 \times 0\cdot2 \times 0\cdot7 \times 32} \right\}}$

$\left[= \sqrt{\left\{ \dfrac{6(0\cdot0089 \times 4^3 - 0\cdot5) - (0\cdot1 \times 1\cdot125)}{0\cdot7854 \times 0\cdot2 \times 1\cdot5 \times 100} \right\}} \right]$

$= 4\cdot15 \text{ mm } [= 0\cdot1139 \text{ in}]$

Now the float when left 'high and dry' must be of sufficient weight, and provide sufficient leverage, to return the valve disc to the closed position against all resistances, chief of which is the friction of the disk on its seating, with which it is maintained in contact by the steam pressure acting on its back. This condition may be expressed as

$$W_f x > \mu\, a\, p\, y$$

Let us see if this is the case in the foregoing example

$W_f x = 0\cdot22 \times 9\cdot8 \times 150 \, [= 0\cdot5 \times 6]$

$ = 323\cdot4 \text{ Nmm } [= 3\cdot0 \text{ lb/in}]$

and

$\mu\, a\, p\, y = 0\cdot2 \times 0\cdot7854 \times 4\cdot15^2 \times 0\cdot7 \times 37$

$ [0\cdot2 \times 0\cdot7854 \times 0\cdot1139^2 \times 100 \times 1\cdot5]$

$ = 70 \text{ Nmm } [0\cdot304 \text{ lb/in}]$

Now, $323\cdot4 > 70$ $[3 > 0\cdot304]$, hence these arrangements would appear most satisfactory and there is little doubt that the valve disk would return to the closed position under conditions of low water and maximum steam pressure.

Actually, with such a preponderance of leverage in favour of the float the valve disk would be returned to its closed position long before the water level had so far receded as to leave the float out of the water, which is most desirable; otherwise there would be no margin of operation to cater for unpredictable resistances, and once the float has been uncovered no reserve of effort would be available for effecting closure.

One meritorious feature of this type of trap is that in the event of partial or complete re-evaporation of the condensate (as sometimes happens on superheated steam) the valve disk is returned to the closed position; thus no live steam is blown to waste. For a method of calculating the weight of ball-floats refer to the section on air traps which concludes this chapter.

Finally, in this type of trap the discharge is secured as a result of a *rising* float. In all types previously described dependence is placed on a *sinking* float. The difference may have escaped notice.

LIFTING PROPENSITIES OF STEAM TRAPS

Steam traps are often required to discharge the condensate against the external resistance incurred in lifting it to some conveniently elevated point from which it may be tapped for any purpose requiring a supply of hot water. It will be apparent that reclamation of the hot condensate—which leaves the trap at a temperature very nearly equal to that of the steam itself—is a highly commendable practice, resulting in the valuable conservation of heat and, therefore, of fuel. Now any steam trap whose construction is such that the live steam has access to the inside of the casing may be relied upon to lift its discharge provided conditions are favourable. The height to which it may do so is dependent upon:

(a) the steam pressure operating in the trap casing,

(b) the back pressure in the discharge pipe,

(c) the frictional resistance to flow presented by the trap seating orifice, adjacent discharge thoroughfares and incidental pipework,

(d) minor mechanical resistances.

Most advertising literature on steam traps will be found to extol the lifting properties of the traps described, usually 2 ft for every lb/in^2 gauge, as if imbued with some special virtue or possessed of some obscure mechanism, cunningly contrived for the purpose of effecting lift. This figure is monotonously repeated, without variation; always 2 ft, but never $1 \cdot 9$ or $2 \cdot 1$ ft per lb/in^2 gauge. As if in expiation for such acts of plagiarism the qualifying adverb *approximately* is sometimes included.

Now why should this round figure of 2 ft for every lb/in^2 gauge be so universally proclaimed and accepted? The answer is simple enough. Suppose no restraint whatsoever be imposed by the full complement of the trap's discharge thoroughfares. Under such ideal conditions of operation one might reasonably expect the lift per lb/in^2 gauge to be $2 \cdot 4$ ft, this being the vertical height of a column of water (at 100°C) which would create a pressure at the base of the column of 1 lb/in^2 gauge (at 200°C) the height would be 2·67 ft owing to the decreasing density with increasing temperature.

The ideal lift of upwards of 2·4 ft per lb/in^2 gauge is impossible of attainment since the frictional resistance imposed by the working parts of the trap and the resistance to flow offered by its ancillary pipework prevent the attainment of this figure, although it may be closely realized by the careful elimination of avoidable resistances.

Every bend and union and every inch of discharge pipe add their quota to the sum total of resistance to be overcome and reduce the ideal figure of 2·4 ft lb/in^2 gauge plus, thus it is normal practice to associate the available lift with the round figure values of 600 mm or 2 ft.

The all too prevalent practice of arranging a number of traps to discharge into a common condensate return line is to be discouraged since it is by no means axiomatic that a battery of heat exchangers, for example, ostensibly of identical design and purpose, will possess identical heat transfer characteristics and yield identical quantities of condensate. Despite the provision of a non-return valve (an essential often omitted) at the discharge side of each individual trap, variations in pressure which obtain between one trap and another may severely impede the flow from a trap which may be found to be working at a somewhat lower pressure than its companion.

Where circumstances permit, it is preferable to arrange a separate discharge line from each individual trap, although this statement may invite a storm of protest from those apparently achieving good results from the arrangement deprecated.

By the same token it is even more undesirable to arrange the discharge from a battery of heat exchangers to be collectively handled by a single trap since this practice will tend to promote the flow of condensate from a zone .of relatively high pressure to one of low. Here again this likelihood may be averted by the inclusion of non-return valves, but these will add to the flow resistance, the extent of which will be dependent upon the type of non-return valve employed. The swinging-disc type is to be recommended.

The factors promoting lift of condensate and its impact on design will now be considered.

Figure 9.13 shows a *direct-acting* bucket trap arranged to lift its condensate to an elevated storage tank. Not every application is as simple in concept as the one here; in the majority of applications the course taken by the discharge pipework is usually more attenuated and tortuous.

At all times during discharge a back-pressure will be exerted on the valve member of the trap, the extent of which will be determined by the height of the column of water of vertical length L. (Note that it is advisable to fit a non-return valve at the base of the column as a precaution against water being sucked back into the trapped vessel during periods of inoperation.)

Let p_b denote the back-pressure in psig corresponding to the vertical height, L, to which the condensate has to be lifted; then in those cases where lift is contemplated, eqn (9.11), previously determined for a *direct*-operating trap (Figs 9.1 and 9.2) correlating seating and unseating forces, will call for modification as follows

$$\left. \begin{aligned} a'p + 0{\cdot}0000077\,c^2 d_f - 9{\cdot}8\,W_1 - 0{\cdot}0000077\,c^2 d_s - a'p_b &= 0 \\ \left[\, a'p + 0{\cdot}027\,c^2 d_f - W_1 - 0{\cdot}027\,c^2 d_s - a'p_b = 0 \,\right] \end{aligned} \right\} \quad (9.34)$$

or

$$a' = \frac{9{\cdot}8\,W_1 + 0{\cdot}0000077\,c^2\,(d_s - d_f)}{p - p_b} \left[\, = \frac{W_1 + 0{\cdot}027\,c^2\,(d_s - d_f)}{p - p_b} \,\right]$$

$$(9.35)$$

Similarly, in the case of an *indirect*-acting bucket trap (Figs 9.4 and 9.5),

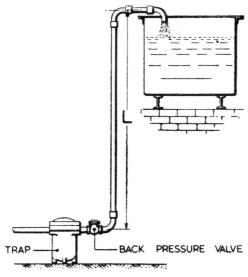

TRAP —————   ————BACK PRESSURE VALVE

Fig. 9.13 *Direct-acting bucket trap arranged to lift its condensate*

eqn (9.16) will call for appropriate modifications:

$$\text{seating moments} = \text{unseating moments}$$

therefore

$$a'py + 0.0000077\, c^2 d_f x = x\,(9.8\, W_1 + 0.0000077\, c^2 d_s) + a'py$$

$$\left[\; a'py + 0.027\, c^2 d_f x = x\,(W_1 + 0.027\, c^2 d_s) + a'py \;\right] \tag{9.36}$$

whence

$$\left.\begin{aligned}
a' &= \frac{x}{y\,(p-p_b)}\left\{9.8\, W_1 + 7.7 \times 10^{-6}\, c^2\,(d_s - d_f)\right\} \text{mm}^2 \\[2mm]
&\left[\; = \frac{0.027\, x}{y(p-p_b)}\left\{\frac{W_1}{0.027} + c^2\,(d_s - d_f)\right\}\text{in}^2 \;\right]
\end{aligned}\right\} \tag{9.37}$$

For an *inverted*-bucket trap (Figs 9.8 and 9.9), again

$$\text{seating moments} = \text{unseating moments}$$

then

$$a'p\,m = W_2 n + a'p_b\, m \tag{9.38}$$

whence

$$a' = \frac{W_2 n}{m\,(p - p_b)} \tag{9.39}$$

The three foregoing cases will suffice to indicate the procedure to be adopted to determine the *modified* orifice area for any other form of trap mechanism; denoting the *modified diameter* by d_0' it may then be readily calculated from

$$d_0' = \sqrt{\frac{4a'}{\pi}} \tag{9.40}$$

The disparity between the area a for a trap discharging to atmosphere and a' for a trap discharging against a back-pressure p_b is not very marked where the pressure differential $(p - p_b)$ is not very great. One fact emerges, however, from the three cases investigated: the size of *orifice* requires to be increased to cater for any back-pressure applied. Mathematically, the various equations for finding the size of the seating orifice would obviously yield results varying according to the working pressure considered, suggesting, perhaps, that there is only one specific orifice diameter appropriate to any specific pressure. Such diversity would be intolerable in practice, as may be imagined, and makers usually adopt one orifice diameter for each pressure increment of 2–4 bar or, say 50 or 25 lb/in² gauge.

A *high* pressure trap will work at a *lower* pressure than that for which it is intended (but giving a correspondingly reduced discharge) but the converse does not hold true. If a specific example would appear to disprove this statement then this is due to the inevitable and unavoidable margin of error separating theoretical aspirations from practical realization. Design should aim at reducing this margin to a minimum.

<h2 style="text-align:center">AIR TRAPS</h2>

As in the case of the *steam* trap the function of an *air* trap is to purge any air vessel or pipeline of its water content automatically, thus preventing moisture gaining access to the tools or machines being supplied with air.

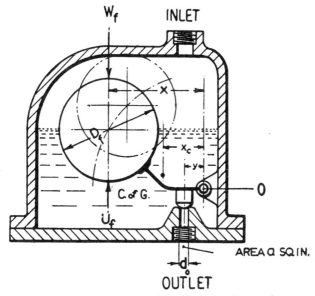

Fig. 9.14 *Elements of construction and forces acting in an air trap*

The mode of expulsion is virtually the same as that employed in a *steam trap*, comprising a float-actuated valve mechanism arranged sensitively responsive to the fluctuating level of the accumulated water content.

The mechanism of operation will be more readily understood when read in conjunction with the diagram in Fig. 9.14. It is customary to employ a sealed ball-float in an air trap and this, and the lever to which it is attached, are free to swivel about the fulcrum point (0) and, in doing so, to open or close the outlet valve alternately. It should be noted that the valve seating is always under water whether the valve is in the open or closed position, thus providing against loss of air. With increasing accumulation of water the ball-float is rendered more and more buoyant until the upthrust thus occasioned—acting through the leverage provided—is ultimately sufficient to lift the valve member against the resistance of the air pressure acting on the unbalanced area of the seating.

As in the case of the other traps previously described, the algebraic sum of clockwise and anti-clockwise moments about fulcrum point 0 will be equal to zero (see Fig. 9.14). Then, using consistent units and neglecting the weight of the necessarily very short lever and other moving parts,

$$U_f x - W_f x - a p y = 0 \tag{9.41}$$

whence

$$U_f = W_f + \frac{a p y}{x} \tag{9.42}$$

where U_f is the upthrust due to the forced displacement of the ball-float, W_f is the weight of the ball-float, p is the working pressure in the trap, and a is the effective area of the seating. Other symbols are given in Fig. 9.14.

It is advisable to arrange the float system to be in equilibrium with the ball-float half immersed, thus providing an ample reserve of buoyancy.

Proceeding on this assumption,

U_f = weight of water displaced (at average atmospheric temperature)

$$= \frac{\pi d_f^3}{12} + \frac{1}{2} \times 10^{-6} \text{ kg} \left[0 \cdot 036 \times \frac{2\pi}{3} \left(\frac{D_f}{2} \right)^3 \text{lb} \right] \tag{9.43}$$

$$= 1 \cdot 28 \times 10^{-6} D_f^3 \text{N} \quad [0 \cdot 0094 \, D_f^3 \text{lb}] \tag{9.44}$$

It is advisable to assume a diameter and metal thickness of ball-float and to make any adjustments found necessary as design proceeds.

Now the weight W_f of any ball-float will be given (very approximately) by

$$W_f = \frac{\pi w}{10^6} D_f^2 \, \text{kg} \left[= \frac{\pi \Delta D_f^2}{144} \text{lb} \right] \tag{9.45}$$

where w is the weight in kg/m² [Δ the weight in lb/ft²] of the material employed.

Then, from eqns (9.42) and (9.44), by substitution,

$$\frac{1 \cdot 28}{10^6} D_f^3 = \left(\frac{\pi w}{10^6} D_f^2 \times 9 \cdot 8 \right) + \frac{apy}{x} \left[0 \cdot 0094 \, D_f^3 = \frac{\pi \Delta}{144} D_f^2 + \frac{apy}{x} \right]$$

whence

$$\frac{1 \cdot 28}{10^6} D_f^3 - \left(\frac{\pi w}{10} D_f^2 \times 9 \cdot 8 \right) = \frac{apy}{x} \left[0 \cdot 0094 \, D_f^3 - \frac{\pi \Delta}{144} D_f^2 = \frac{apy}{x} \right]$$

or

$$a = \frac{x D_f^2}{py} \left(\frac{1 \cdot 28 \, d_f - 30 \cdot 8 \, w}{10^6} \right) \left[= \frac{x D_f^2}{py} \left(0 \cdot 0094 \, D_f - \frac{\pi \Delta}{144} \right) \right] \tag{9.46}$$

from which the diameter of the orifice may be readily determined, as previously demonstrated.

Obviously, the trap as portrayed would not operate under vacuum since the atmospheric pressure would tend to open the valve and to lift the ball-float out of the water. Whilst the ball-float could be ballasted to overcome this tendency the mechanism would not be sensitively responsive to variations in vacuum between 0 and 30 in. Hg, and other means must be employed for draining equipment operating at sub-atmospheric pressure.

The air trap shown in Fig. 9.14 is arranged with the inlet connection situated at the uppermost point of the casing. Provided the pipe from the vessel being drained takes the shortest possible course to the trap and permits free gravitation thereto, this represents the ideal arrangement. There are occasions, however, when it may be desirable to arrange the inlet and outlet connections in line with one another. In this event it is essential to provide a balance-pipe connecting the top of the trap casing to the top of the vessel being drained if the trap is to function satisfactorily.

The exact purpose of this balance-pipe will be better understood by referring to the diagrammatic arrangement shown in Fig. 9.15.

Water entering the trap will tend to drive before it a quantity of air which will be forced into the top of the trap casing, from which there would otherwise be no escape, and thus limit the extent to which the water could rise within the casing, depending upon the static head of water above the inlet connection and upon the air pressure in the vessel. Thus, the ball-float might easily become erratic in action or unresponsive to changes in water-level. The balance-pipe permits any entrapped air to flow freely back in to the vessel and the trap to become completely waterlogged. With the inlet connection at the top this disquieting tendency is obviated since any entrapped air will bubble up through the water column back to the vessel—bubbles are not prone to travel in a downwards direction!

A typical *Spirax* air trap is illustrated in Fig. 9.16.

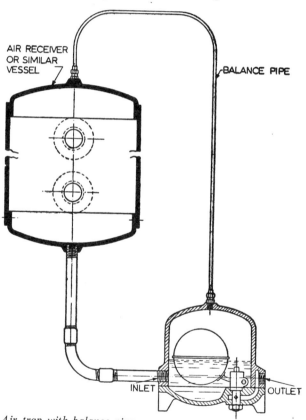

Fig. 9.15 *Air trap with balance pipe*

DISCHARGE CAPACITY OF STEAM TRAPS

In the preceding treatment it has been deemed expedient to determine the diameter of the seating orifice appropriate to the working pressure—with due regard to the particular operating mechanism employed—for traps of varying types, thus presenting a ready means of comparison and one tending to promote a better understanding of the principles involved.

The text of a trap enquiry generally stipulates the amount of condensate to be discharged in a given time. Most trap manufacturers are able to draw freely on past experience for establishing the requisite size of seating to pass the stipulated amount of condensate at the stated pressure; but in a work of this kind it is natural to assume that no precedent exists and to determine the area—or diameter—of the seating from first principles. Once this diameter has been established the key dimensions of the operating mechanism may be correlated with this fundamental dimension and with the operating pressure.

The condensate issuing from a steam trap under pressure obeys the universally accepted laws of hydraulics with the one exception that—being at a temperature exceeding the saturation temperature of steam at atmospheric pressure—it flashes into steam on striking the atmosphere, a phenomenon that often gives rise to the mistaken belief that the trap is passing live steam. The higher the working pressure the more pronounced this illusion and the misgivings of those spectators ill-versed in steam practice are sometimes exceedingly difficult to allay. The seating orifice of a

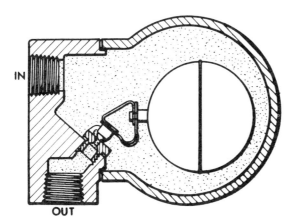

Fig. 9.16 *'Spirax' air trap (courtesy of Spirax–Sarco Ltd)*

steam trap is a typical example—in hydraulic parlance—of a sharp-edged submerged orifice, the pressure of the steam behind the condensate providing the motive power or head for its ejection to atmosphere or elsewhere.

Since the discharge from most traps is intermittent, the period of dormancy varying according to the type of operating mechanism employed, the discharge figures given by most makers are logically displayed on a *continuous rating* basis. It is usually assumed—and not without practical justification—that the *actual* discharge is one third the amount which will be discharged continuously. Thus, the required discharge should be multiplied by three for the purposes of computing the area of the seating orifice.

Now the discharge from a sharp-edged orifice (as exemplified by a steam trap seating) is given by:

$$Q = C A \sqrt{(2 g H)} \qquad (9.47)$$

where Q = volume rate of condensate discharged (continuous rating).

C = coefficient of discharge, say 0·72 for the case under consideration.

A = area of seating orifice.

g = acceleration due to gravity.

H = head.

for any consistent set of units

From eqn (9.47)

$$A = \frac{Q}{C \sqrt{(2 g H)}} \qquad (9.48)$$

Before the foregoing expressions can be evaluated it will be necessary to determine the value of H, the head, corresponding to the pressure at the seating. If the temperature of the issuing condensate were atmospheric it would be sufficient to multiply the pressure in MPa by 102, the head in metres corresponding to 1 MPa at room temperature [the pressure in lb/in^2 by 2·309, the head in ft corresponding to 1 lb/in^2 at that temperature], but at elevated pressures the temperature prevailing will correspond to the saturation temperature of the steam at the appropriate pressure, and the density of the condensate will be progressively lower than at atmospheric pressure and temperature.

Thus, the height H_w of a column of water to give a gauge pressure of p will be given by:

$$H_w = \frac{p}{\rho} \qquad (9.49)$$

where $\rho =$ the density of the water corresponding to the required temperature. (In the absence of other data ρ may generally be assumed to be approximately 0·9 kg/l [0·0325 lb/in³]). Then from eqns (9.48) and (9.49)

$$
\left.
\begin{aligned}
A\ (\text{mm}^2) &= \frac{Q\ (l/s)}{32\ 000 \sqrt{\left(\dfrac{p\ (\text{MPa})}{\rho\ (\text{kg/l})}\right)}} \\[2mm]
\left[A\ (\text{in}^2) \right. &= \frac{144\ Q\ (\text{ft}^3/s)}{0\cdot 72 \sqrt{\left(\dfrac{2 \times 32\cdot2 \times p\ (\text{lb/in}^2)}{12\ \rho\ (\text{lb/in}^2)}\right)}} \left. \right] \\[2mm]
&= \frac{86\cdot35\ Q}{\sqrt{\left(\dfrac{p}{\rho}\right)}} \\[2mm]
\left[\right. &= \frac{200\ Q}{\sqrt{\left(\dfrac{5\cdot366 p}{\rho}\right)}} \left. \right]
\end{aligned}
\right\} \qquad (9.50)
$$

If d_o denotes the *diameter* of the seating orifice in inches, then

$$d_o = \sqrt{\left(\frac{4A}{\pi}\right)} \qquad (9.51)$$

With imperial units the discharge rating is usually stated in cubic feet per *hour* or in gallons per *hour* so that $Q = \dfrac{V}{3600}$ where V is the volume of condensate passed per hour or

$$Q = \frac{G}{3600 \times 6\cdot25} = \frac{G}{22\ 500}$$

where G is the number of gallons of condensate passed per hour.

Then, by substitution in eqn (9.50),

$$A = \frac{200\,V}{3600\sqrt{\left(\dfrac{5\cdot366\,p}{\rho}\right)}} = \frac{V}{18\sqrt{\left(\dfrac{5\cdot366\,p}{\rho}\right)}} \qquad (9.52)$$

Alternatively,

$$A = \frac{200\,G}{22\,500\sqrt{\left(\dfrac{5\cdot366\,p}{\rho}\right)}} = \frac{G}{112\cdot5\sqrt{\left(\dfrac{5\cdot366\,p}{\rho}\right)}} \qquad (9.53)$$

The seating orifice diameter d_o may then be calculated from eqn (9.51).

It is pertinent to repeat that the cross-sectional area A of the seating orifice, as derived from eqn (9.53), will be that required on the basis of *continual discharge*.

PUMPING TRAP OR AUTO TRAP

Most plant engineers are familiar with the steam trap in some form or another, how it functions and its purpose; namely to purge a steam line or vessel of the inevitable but undesirable condensate and to discharge same, either wastefully to atmosphere or drain, otherwise advantageously to some storage tank where its residual heat content may be turned to good account.

Now where it is required to elevate the discharge from a steam trap this may easily impose something of a burden on the trap itself since the motivating force is the line pressure and the area of the valve seating may require to be adjusted accordingly, the column of condensate imposing a back pressure and thereby reducing the discharge capacity of the trap. Where the line pressure is reasonably high this impedance will not be so apparent but definitely so where the pressure is low or if too high a lift is attempted.

Most makers affirm that their traps will raise the condensate about 90 mm/kPa [2 ft/lb/in²] of steam pressure *at the trap*. With 'frictionless' pipes and no other restrictions (both unattainable desirables) these figures would be 701·9 mm [2·303 ft], the height of a column of water at 15°C that would produce a pressure of 1 kPa [1 lb/in²].

The ideal method of lifting condensate is not to rely on the various steam traps performing this function individually but rather to arrange for each trap to discharge by gravity into one common receiver which—it is important to remember—must be vented to atmosphere to prevent any pressure build-up, and the contents then allowed to gravitate (preferably by the shortest possible route) into a pumping trap, alternatively styled an automatic pump since its action—like any steam trap—is entirely automatic, a most commendable attribute.

A typical arrangement of a pumping trap layout is diagrammatically outlined in Fig. 9.17 which gives the barest essentials for better understanding. For example, a screw-down stop valve, preferably of the wedge-gate pattern with its straight through flow characteristics, is advisedly fitted at point A, in order that the flow of condensate may be shut off in case the trap is required to be removed for overhaul or for any other reason.

Further refinements might include pipe line strainers for preventing the ingress of scale to the trap or to its various ancillaries and sight-glass flow indicators, a most useful inclusion, providing visual means of ascertaining if all is going according to plan.

It is now prudent to describe the *modus operandi* of the pumping trap itself as a preliminary to proceeding to the aspects of its design.

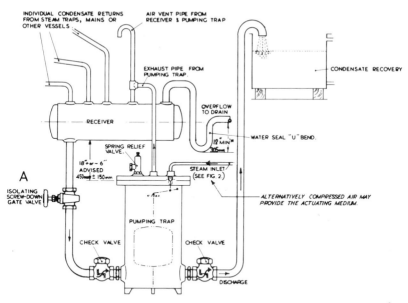

Fig. 9.17 *Diagrammatic lay-out of pumping trap installation. (Refinements such as sight glass fittings and strainers deliberately omitted)*

Action of pumping trap

Condensate following the course from the receiver indicated in Fig. 9.17 gravitates towards the pumping trap and passes through the non-return or check valve (A) (see Fig. 9.18) and into the body (B) housing a cylindrical float (C), closed at both ends, and having a centrally disposed hollow stem (D) enabling it to rise or fall within the body casing guided by a central 'rod' (E) also hollow in the interests of lightness since it is arranged to have some amount of axial displacement so as to rise with the rising float in order to seal the balancing valve (F) on its seating (G).

When the casing (B) progressively fills with condensate the float (C) will rise to such an extent as to strike the collar (H) pinned or otherwise secured to the 'rod' (E) connected to the balancing valve (F) which now seals (at G).

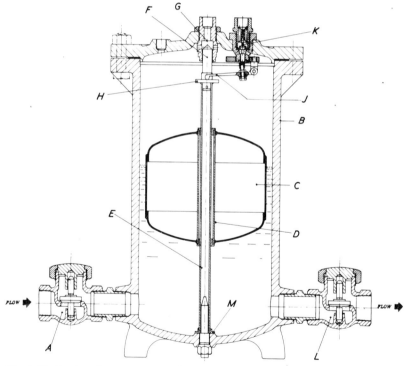

Fig. 9.18 *Sectional arrangement of a typical pumping trap*

Concurrently with this sealing process—or nearly so—the same collar (H) strikes the trigger (J) which then lifts the steam inlet valve (K) (normally held down by the influence of the steam pressure) admitting live steam to the casing (B). The pressure of the now entering steam acting on the surface of the entrained condensate pushes same out through another non-return or check valve (L) (at the same time firmly closing the inlet check valve (A)) and thence along the discharge line to some appointed collecting vessel.

When all the condensate has been forced out of the trap the float (C) will fall to the bottom of the casing (B) and in doing so will strike the collar (M) screwed or otherwise attached to the 'rod' (E), and thereby pulling the balancing valve (F) off its seating (G), thus venting the casing to atmosphere. At the same time the pressure of the live steam exerted on the top of the inlet valve (K) will promptly close it.

The whole cycle of operations will then commence anew.

In one particular make, an ingenious trip mechanism ensures prompt and more decisive opening and closing of both the vent and steam valves, but the foregoing will serve to illustrate the basic principles of the pumping trap as a whole as manufactured by quite a few firms in this country and abroad.

Design aspects

In order to demonstrate the underlying principles of design we will assume a hypothetical trap having 40 mm [1½ in] inlet and outlet condensate connections, a cylindrical body of 250 mm [9¾ in] inside diameter and motivated by steam at a pressure of 1 MPa [150 psig]. The height of the body will emerge as design proceeds but we shall require to make certain *à priori* assumptions, the validity of which can be checked also as the design takes shape.

The first essential is to determine the wall thickness of the body casing to withstand the maximum working pressure of 1 MPa [150 psig] by any of the well-known formulae for the design of pressure vessels. In our case we will settle for the empirical formula prescribed in the Indian Boiler Regulations as being the embodiment of practicality and adopt cast iron.

It gives the following:

$$t = \frac{p\,d_o}{C} + X \tag{9.54}$$

Where t = thickness of wall, d_o = inside diameter of chest, p = the working pressure; C and X are constants according to materials of construction as in the table below:

Casting Material	C		X	
	MPa	psi	mm	in
Cast steel 430–540 MPa [28–35 ton/in²] UTS	88	12 800	6	0·25
Cast iron, at least 140 MPa [9 ton/in²] UTS	35	5120	5	0·1875
Bronze, at least 215 MPa [14 ton/in²] UTS	39	5600	3	0·125

In the design under consideration d_o is 250 mm [$9\frac{3}{4}$ in]; then:

$$t = \frac{1 \times 250}{28} + 5 \quad \left[= \frac{\dfrac{150 \times 9·75}{160}}{32} + 6 \right]$$

$$= 13·92 \text{ mm (say 14 mm)} \quad \left[= \frac{15·14}{32} \text{in (say } \tfrac{1}{2} \text{ in)} \right]$$

Adopt 15 mm [9/16 in] to cater for possible slight inaccuracies in moulding. The dimensions of the cover flanges will receive consideration later as design proceeds.

Float

The inside diameter of the body more or less determines the outside diameter of the float which should fit snugly within the body (but not unduly so) in order to give the optimum buoyancy with minimum height and, what is equally desirable, to give the maximum discharge effect when acted upon by the steam pressure exerted on the top of the float and the surface of the trapped condensate.

We will adopt a float of 230 mm [9 in] outside diameter comfortably accommodated within a body of 250 mm [$9\frac{3}{4}$ in] diameter.

As previously pointed out certain assumptions based on sound judgement are essential, checked later for validity. The float is no exception and we will assume it conforms approximately to the elementary concept outlined in Fig. 9.19.

We require to determine the weight of such a float, which will be much simplified by assuming it to take the elementary form shown in Fig. 9.19 and which should give results sufficiently accurate for our purpose. To estimate the weight on the resulting design of float featured in Fig. 9.18 would prove unnecessarily tedious by comparison.

Surface area of each spherical segmental end $= 2\pi r h_s$

$\quad = 2 \times 3 \cdot 142 \times 220 \times 30\,(\text{mm}^2)\ [= 2 \times 3 \cdot 142 \times 8 \cdot 5 \times 1 \cdot 25\,(\text{in}^2)]$

$\quad = 41\,469\ \text{mm}^2\ [= 66 \cdot 75\ \text{in}^2]$

Surface area of both ends $= 2 \times 41\,469\ \text{mm}^2\ [= 2 \times 66 \cdot 75\ \text{in}^2]$

$\quad\quad\quad\quad\quad\quad\quad\quad = 82\,938\ \text{mm}^2\ [= 133 \cdot 5\ \text{in}^2]$

Surface area of cylindrical portion $= \pi \times 230 \times 140\,(\text{mm}^2)$
$\quad\quad\quad\quad\quad\quad\quad\quad\quad\quad [= \pi \times 9 \times 5 \cdot 5\,(\text{in}^2)]$

$\quad = 101\,159\ \text{mm}^2\ [= 155 \cdot 5\ \text{in}^2]$

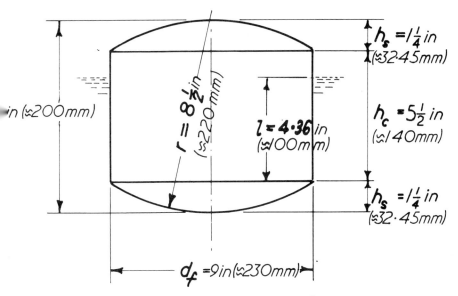

Fig. 9.19 *Diagrammatic arrangement of pumping trap float*

Therefore total surface area $= 101\ 159 + 82\ 938\ (\text{mm}^2)$

$$[= 133 \cdot 5 + 155 \cdot 5\ (\text{in}^2)]$$

$$= 184\ 097\ \text{mm}^2\ (= 0 \cdot 184\ \text{m}^2)\ [= 289 \cdot 0\ \text{in}^2]$$

Assume a metal thickness of $2 \cdot 5$ mm [12 SWG $= 0 \cdot 104$ in] and adopting stainless steel sheet weighing 21 kg/m^2 [$4 \cdot 51$ lb/ft^2] we have:

$$\text{weight of float} = 0 \cdot 184 \times 21 \left[= \frac{289 \times 4 \cdot 51}{144} \right]$$

$$= 3 \cdot 86\ \text{kg}\ [= 9 \cdot 05\ \text{lb}]$$

To this must be added the weight of the central guide tube welded to the float at each end. Adopting tube 34 mm [$1\frac{5}{16}$ in] outside diameter by 27 mm [$1\frac{1}{16}$ in] inside diameter and 220 mm [$8\frac{1}{2}$ in] long, the weight of such tube is $2 \cdot 61$ kg/m [$1 \cdot 349$ lb/ft] whence

$$\text{Weight of tube} = 2 \cdot 61 \times 0 \cdot 22 \left[= \frac{1 \cdot 349}{12} \times 8 \cdot 5 \right]$$

$$= 5 \cdot 75\ \text{kg}\ [= 0 \cdot 955\ \text{lb}]$$

then total weight of complete float $= 3 \cdot 86 + 0 \cdot 575\ [= 9 \cdot 05 + 0 \cdot 955]$

$$= 4 \cdot 435\ \text{kg}\ [= 10\ \text{lb}]$$

Buoyancy of elementary float.

Volume of each spherical end $\qquad = \pi h_s^2 \left(r - \dfrac{h_s}{3} \right) \qquad$ (9.55)

$$= 3 \cdot 142 \times 30^2 \left(220 - \frac{30}{3} \right) \quad \left[= 3 \cdot 142 \times (1 \cdot 25)^2 \left(8 \cdot 5 - \frac{1 \cdot 25}{3} \right) \right]$$

$$= 593\ 761\ \text{mm}^3 \qquad\qquad\qquad [= 39 \cdot 67\ \text{in}^3]$$

Volume of two ends $= 593\ 761 \times 2 \quad [= 39 \cdot 67\ \text{in} \times 2]$

$$= 1\ 187\ 522\ \text{mm}^3 [= 79 \cdot 35\ \text{in}^3]$$

Volume of cylindrical portion $\qquad = \pi h_c \left(\dfrac{d_f}{2} \right)^2$

$$= 3 \cdot 142 \times 145 \times 115^2 \qquad [= 3 \cdot 142 \times 5 \cdot 5 \times 4 \cdot 5^2]$$

$$= 6\ 024\ 396\ \text{mm}^3 \qquad\qquad [= 349 \cdot 9\ \text{in}^3]$$

then total volume of elementary float

= 6 024 396 + 1 187 522   [= 349·9 + 79·35]

7 211 918 mm³ (7·2 l)   [= 429·25 in³]

Depth of immersion.

Weight of complete float (as previously determined) = 4·435 kg [10·00 lb]

Then weight of water displaced when floating freely = weight of float

= 4·435 kg [10·00 lb]

Now the density of water at a temperature of 186°C [366°F] corresponding to a steam pressure of 1 MPa [150 psig] = 0·886 kg/l [0·0315 lb/in³]

then volume of water displaced

$$= \frac{4 \cdot 435}{0 \cdot 886} \left[\frac{10 \cdot 00}{0 \cdot 0315} \right] = 5 \ l \ [317 \cdot 4 \ in^3]$$

Now we have seen that one dome end accounts for 593 761 mm³ [39·67 in³] of this amount of displacement, then the proportion of displacement accorded to the cylindrical portion will be

5 − 0·593761 l [317·4 − 39·67 in³] = 4·406 l [277·7 in³]

Let l = length of cylindrical postion involved (see Fig. 9.19)

then $\frac{\pi}{4} d^2_f l = 4 \cdot 406 \ l \ [277 \cdot 7 \ in^3]$

whence $l = \dfrac{4 \cdot 406 \times 10^6 \times 4}{3 \cdot 142 \times 230^2} \left[= \dfrac{277 \cdot 7 \times 4}{3 \cdot 142 \times 9^2} \right]$

= 106 mm [= 4·365 in]

Strength of float

The float would collapse by crushing and it therefore behoves us to satisfy ourselves that the wall thickness previously assumed (12 SWG) is adequate. Only an approximate solution is possible since there would appear to be no strictly rational formulae for accurately determining the collapsing pressure of externally loaded 'tubes' and similar shells as is exemplified by the present example, but the formula advanced by Saunders and Windenberg* and given by R. J. Roark in his book *Formulas for Stress and Strain*† (Table XVI, 'Q', p.318) is one most worthy of exploitation in the present case since it relates to short thin cylinders with ends held circular but not otherwise restrained and the float in our case would appear to approximate to these conditions. The two dished ends in themselves would offer appreciable restraint to collapse or yielding of the extremities.

The formula is as follows, amended to suit the nomenclature of this presentation.

$$p' = 0.807 \, \frac{E \, t_f^2}{h_c r_c} \, \sqrt[4]{\left\{ \left(\frac{1}{1 - p^2} \right)^3 \frac{t_f^2}{r_c^2} \right\}}$$

(9.56)

Where p' is the *collapsing* pressure.

    E is Young's modulus.

    t_f is shell thickness.

    h_c is length of cylindrical portion (see Fig. 9.19).

    r_c is external radius of cylindrical portion.

    p is Poisson's ratio.

    (consistent units throughout)

Take h_c to be the 'active' length, say 145 mm [$5\frac{1}{2}$ in] r_c is 115 mm [$4\frac{1}{2}$ in], E for stainless steel = 200 000 MPa [30 × 10⁶ lb/in²] and $p = 0.31$. We have assumed $t_f = 2.5$ mm [0.104 in], then substituting known values, we have:

$$p' = \frac{0.807 \times 200\,000 \times 2.5^2}{140 \times 115} \, \sqrt[4]{\left\{ \left(\frac{1}{1 - 0.31^2} \right)^3 \times \left(\frac{2.5^2}{115^2} \right) \right\}}$$

$$\left[= \frac{0.807 \times 30 \times 10^6 \times 0.104^2}{5.5 \times 4.5} \, \sqrt[4]{\left\{ \left(\frac{1}{1 - 0.31^2} \right)^3 \times \left(\frac{0.104^2}{4.5^2} \right) \right\}} \right]$$

$$= 62.65 \, \sqrt[4]{(0.0006849)} \, [= 10\,580 \, \sqrt[4]{(0.000723)}]$$

$$= 62.65 \times 0.16177 \, [= 10\,580 \times 0.1640]$$

$$= 10.135 \text{ MPa} \, [= 10\,580 \times 0.1640]$$

---

*Strength of thin cylindrical shells under external pressure, *Trans. Am. Soc. Mech. Engrs,* 1931, **53**, No. 15, 207.

†ROARK, R. J., *Formulas for Stress and Strain*, 1954 (McGraw-Hill, London).

Now p' is the ultimate collapsing or buckling pressure. If we take a factor of safety of 10, a figure recommended for boiler flue tubes, for example, then a safe working pressure in our case would be $10 \cdot 135/10$ MPa $[1735/10$ lb/in$^2] = 1 \cdot 0135$ MPa $[173 \cdot 5$ lb/in$^2]$ and it will be remembered that the trap featured in Fig. 9.18 was based on a maximum working pressure of 1 MPa [150 psig], so our original assumptions would appear to have been well-merited.

Valve linkage

Consider the diagrammatic arrangement of the steam admission valve linkage outlined in Fig. 9.20 in conjunction with the general arrangement of the trap outlined in Fig. 9.18.

We have seen that progressive ingress of condensate eventually causes the rising float to contact the collar on the central guide tube when a further rise causes the pivoted arm to lift the steam admission valve off its seat against the steam pressure acting upon its back face and normally tending to keep it closed.

Consider the forces operating (see Fig. 9.20).

We have; (a) a downwardly acting force P due to the steam pressure exerted on the back of the valve and tending to rotate the lever in an anticlockwise direction about the pivot point (O), and (b) an upwardly

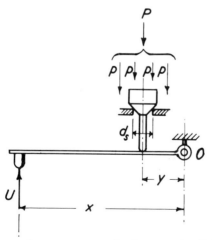

Fig. 9.20 *Diagrammatic arrangement of valve actuating linkage*

acting force U occasioned by the uplifting force exerted by the float and again tending to rotate the lever arm, this time in a clockwise manner, about the pivot point (O).

Now just on the point of opening, the moments of these two forces (neglecting friction, which will be of a very small order if care is taken to allow freedom of movement) will be equal, then

$$Py = Ux \qquad (9.59)$$

$$\text{or } P = \frac{Ux}{y}$$

let $x : y = 4 : 1$, then

$$P = 4U$$

We know U to be $4 \cdot 435$ kg [$10 \cdot 0$ lb], the weight of water displaced when freely floating and

$$P = pa$$

where p is the working steam pressure and a the effective area of the seating. The only unknown quantity is a which can now be readily calculated:

$$a = \frac{P}{p} = \frac{4U}{p}$$

If d_s denotes the required diameter of the seating:

$$\frac{\pi}{4} d_s^2 = a$$

or $\qquad\qquad\qquad d_s = \sqrt{\left(\frac{4a}{\pi}\right)} \qquad (9.60)$

Let us see how this works out in our case.

$$a = \frac{4u}{p} = \frac{4 \times 4 \cdot 435 \times 9 \cdot 80665}{1} \left[= \frac{4 \times 10}{150} \right]$$
$$= 174 \text{ mm}^2 \ [= 0 \cdot 2667 \text{ in}^2]$$

whence

$$d_s = \sqrt{\frac{174 \times 4}{\pi}} \left[= \sqrt{\left(\frac{0 \cdot 2667 \times 4}{\pi}\right)} \right]$$
$$= \sqrt{221 \cdot 5} \ [= \sqrt{0 \cdot 3395}] = 14 \cdot 88 \text{ mm} \ [= 0 \cdot 583 \text{ in}]$$

Adopt 12 mm [$\frac{1}{2}$ in] (or even less) to err on the safe side. At all events it is an easy matter to substitute a seating ring of smaller area.

Further encroachment of condensate up the annular clearance between the float and the body of the trap will result in increasing the upthrust U and, in turn, the unseating force P which is all to the good.

It can be shown that in the design under consideration there is a pleasing amount of reserve buoyancy, viz:

buoyancy when float is fully immersed $= 7\cdot2$ l [429$\cdot$25 in^3]

minimum operative buoyancy $= 5$ l [$= 317\cdot4$ in^3]

Therefore reserve buoyancy $7\cdot2 - 5 = 2\cdot2$ l [$= 429\cdot25 - 317\cdot4 = 111\cdot85$ in^3] or reserve uplift $= 2\cdot2$ kg [$= 3\cdot52$ lb]

Immediately steam is admitted the hollow guide stem carrying the atmospheric vent valve will be forced on to its seating under the combined influence of the steam pressure and the uplifting effect of the float, principally the former. It is essential, however, to make the guide tube as light as possible consistent with adequate rigidity.

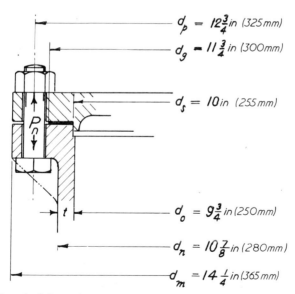

Fig. 9.21 *Detail of flanged cover joint (pumping trap)*

Cover bolts

On inspection it would appear that twelve bolts may be conveniently disported. Referring to Fig. 9.21, which shows the cover joint bolting in detail, it will be noted that the joint is made by a thin sheet of, say, graphited asbestos, bounded by the insides of the bolts or very nearly so, outside diameter d_g, inside diameter d_s.

Now the force tending to lift the cover plate may be supposed (with every justification) to be that occasioned by the line pressure acting on an area A bounded by the spigot, then:

Total load P_T to be sustained by *all* the bolts will be given by:

$$P_T = pA$$

For n bolts the load P_n to be calculated by *each* bolt will be

$$P_n = \frac{P_T}{n}$$

In the present example (see Fig. 9.21)

$$A = \frac{\pi}{4}d_s^2 = 0\cdot7854 \times 250^2 \ [0\cdot7854 \times 10^2]$$

$$= 49\,087 \text{ mm}^2 \ [78\cdot54 \text{ in}^2]$$

Let a_f denote the area of the gasket and η_3 the gasket factor which, for graphited asbestos, may be taken to be $0\cdot26$. In the present example

$$a_f = \frac{\pi}{4}(d_g^2 - d_s^2) = \frac{\pi}{4}(300^2 - 255^2) \left[= \frac{\pi}{4}(11\cdot75^2 - 10^2)\right]$$

$$= 19\,615 \text{ mm}^2 - 29\cdot89 \text{ in}^2]$$

Now it can be shown* that the load per bolt $P_n = \frac{p}{n}(A + a_f\eta_3)$ when, substituting known values,

*PEARSON, G. H., *The Design of Valves and Fittings* (2nd edition) Ch. 18, p.468, eqn (18.8). (Pitman, London).

Load per bolt $p_n = \dfrac{1}{12}$ {49 087 + (19 615 × 0·26)}

$$\left[= \frac{150}{12} \{78\cdot54 + (29\cdot89 \times 0\cdot26)\} \right]$$

$= 4516$ N [= 1079 lb]

From the table* it will be found that an M20 [¾ BSW] bolt of 35 UTS would be suitable.

Cover flanges

The determination of the thickness of bolted flanged joints with due regard to the pressure to be countered is all too often based on intitution ('guestimation') rather than on any analytical investigation, especially where no precedence exists to guide the designer.

The following analytical procedure, at best only to be regarded as a close approximation, is offered in preference to any more involved exposition.

Consider the perspective view of a portion of the body flange shown in Fig. 9.22 (a). The flange may be regarded in the light of a continuous

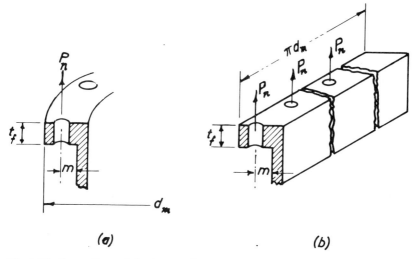

(a) *(b)*

Fig. 9.22 *Cover flange behaviour under pressure*

*Ibid. p.469.

cantilever rigidly supported by the body shell and loaded by the collective tensile forces in the bolts acting through a moment arm m.

In Fig. 9.22 (b) the flange has been assumed to be straightened out, the 'width' of the 'beam' being πd_m and the depth t_f.

This artifice, of taking the flange to be an elongated cantilever, would be more valid if we imagined the flange to be slotted (as indicated) between each bolt.

Then, from the theory of beams we know that

$$M = fZ$$

where M is the bending moment imposed, f the stress induced and Z the section modulus.

This resolves into:

$$P_T m = \frac{f}{6} (\pi d_m t_f^2)$$

where P_T is the collective force exerted by all the bolts (which is equal to pA), m is the moment arm and d_m the outside diameter of the flange, whence: (note that m is $22 \cdot 5$ mm [7/8 in] in the present example)

$$t_f = \sqrt{\left(\frac{6 P_t m}{\pi d_m f}\right)}$$

Substituting known values and taking $f = 28$ MPa [4000 lb/in^2] for, say, grey iron castings:

$$t_f = \sqrt{\left(\frac{6 \times 49\,087 \times 1 \times 22 \cdot 5}{3 \cdot 142 \times 365 \times 28}\right)} \left[= \sqrt{\left(\frac{6 \times 78 \cdot 54 \times 150 \times 0 \cdot 875}{3 \cdot 142 \times 14 \cdot 25 \times 4000}\right)} \right]$$
$$= 14 \cdot 37 \text{ mm } [= 0 \cdot 587 \text{ in}]$$

Adopt 20 or 25 mm [15/16 (0·9375) or 1 in] to compensate for the weakening effect of the recess of the spigoted connection.

Due to the intrusion of the spigot into the body flange and the possible weakening effect it might occasion it might be advisable to introduce a succession of ribs between each bolt as indicated in Figs 9.18 and 9.21.

With regard to the cover plate itself this is complicated somewhat by the intrusion of the two valves—the vent valve and the steam inlet valve—and so experience to some extent must be the guiding factor in determining the thickness, bearing in mind that pressure loaded flat surfaces should be avoided wherever possible. A cambered plate is the more logical alternative. The study of flat plate design is a most absorbing one and draughtsmen should be alerted to the dangers that can result from adopting a nonchalant attitude in their design. Ribs are often introduced in the sometimes mistaken belief that they will strengthen an otherwise weak plate. Unless correctly proportioned with due regard to the section modulus they can actually weaken the plate. Ribs lacking in depth are to be avoided at all costs.

Quite an article in itself could be written on this one subject alone but perhaps sufficient has been stated to prompt the designer to devote more than a cursory glance at this all-important aspect of pressure vessel design.

The pumping trap may be employed for draining turbine casings, oil separators, exhaust steam lines, sump hole pits, excavations etc, provided there are no solids in suspension. If the latter are suspected a strainer should be incorporated in the layout.

Condensed steam is not the only medium lending itself to elevation by means of a pumping trap. Various industrial mobile liquids such as petrol and benzine may be pumped, using compressed air as the motivating agent in lieu of steam (the latter most inadmissible, of course). The versatility of the pumping trap is remarkable. It can also be employed for draining water from a closed vessel under vacuum (eg vacuum boiling pans) in which event the vent pipe must be in communication with the highest point of the vessel being drained.

Its particular virtue lies in its most economical consumption of the motivating agent, whether this be steam or compressed air, since when no more liquid remains to be pumped the flow of the motivating agent is promptly arrested, resuming only when sufficient liquid has gravitated into the trap. Additionally, the pumping trap permits of condensate being returned usefully without imposing any back pressure on individual steam traps, thus improving plant drainage to a marked degree by preventing tiresome waterlogging. It is also a means of effecting air removal.

It is pertinent to point out that the pumping trap is a fitting not exclusively employed for the removal of condensate; it can be used with equal effectiveness for a wide variety of hot, boiling or cold liquids only restricted by consideration of the specific gravity of the liquid (i.e. not too high) or the ability of the materials of construction to withstand the effects of such liquids (or gases).

Appendices

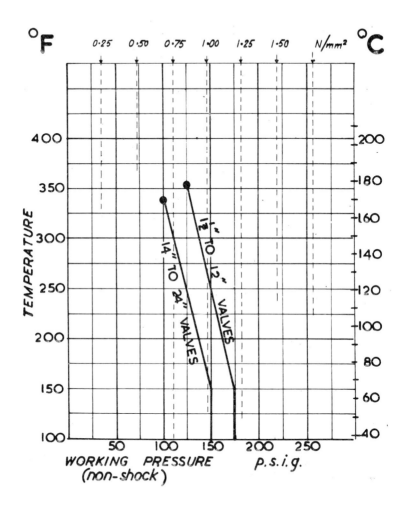

Appendix A Cast iron B.S. 1452 Grade 14
            100 and 125 lb pressure/temperature ratings
            (0·7 and 0·9 N)

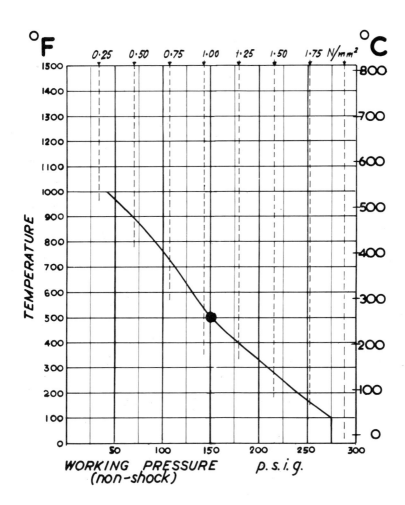

Appendix B Cr . Ni . Steel AISI 3 lb or En 58J
          All grades Cr . Mo . steel. B.S. 3100
          Carbon steel B.S. 592
          150 lb (1 N) pressure/temperature rating

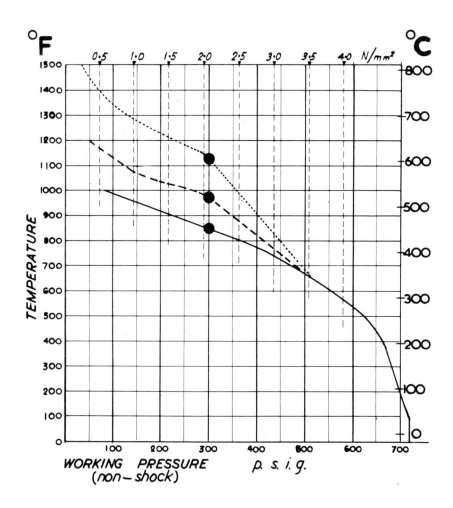

Appendix C Cr . Ni . steel AISI 316 or En 58J (dotted line)
5% Cr . Mo . steel B.S. 3100 (broken line)
Carbon steel B.S. 592 (full line)
300 lb (2 N) pressure/temperature rating

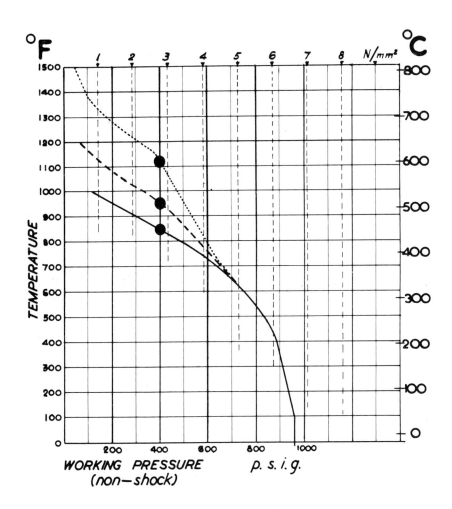

Appendix D Cr . Ni . steel AISI 316 or En 58J (dotted line)
5% Cr . Mo . steel B.S. 3100 (broken line)
Carbon steel B.S. 592 (full line)
400 lb (2·75 N) pressure/temperature rating

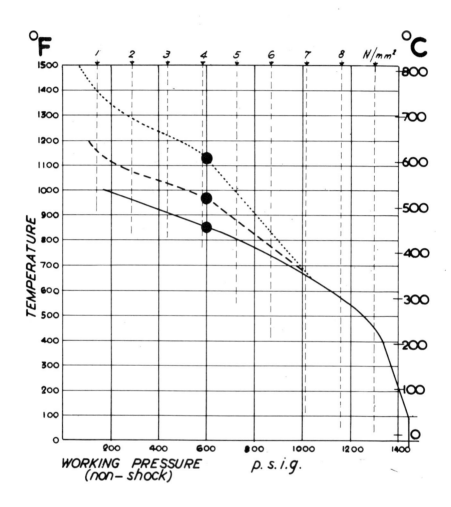

Appendix E Cr . Ni . steel AISI 316 or En 58J (dotted line)
5% Cr . Mo . steel B.S. 3100 (broken line)
Carbon steel B.S. 592 (full line)
600 lb (4 N) pressure/temperature rating

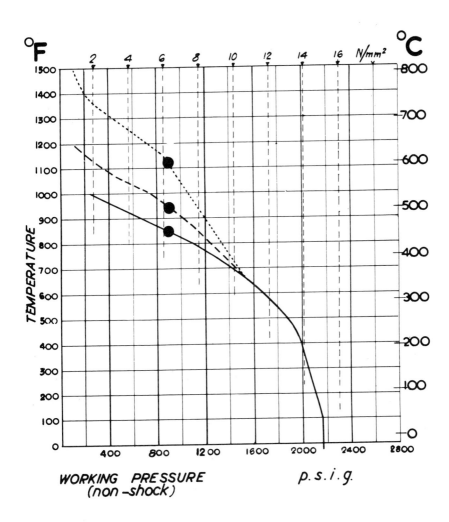

WORKING PRESSURE (non -shock)   p.s.i.g.

Appendix F Cr . Ni . steel AISI 316 or En 58J (dotted line)
5% Cr . Mo . steel B.S. 3100 (broken line)
Carbon steel B.S. 592 (full line)
900 lb (6 N) pressure/temperature rating

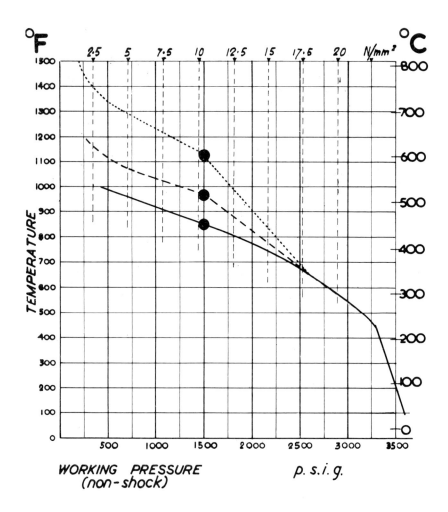

Appendix G Cr . Ni . steel AISI 316 or En 58J (dotted line)
5% Cr . Mo . steel B.S. 3100 (broken line)
Carbon steel B.S. 592 (full line)
1500 lb (10 N) pressure/temperature rating

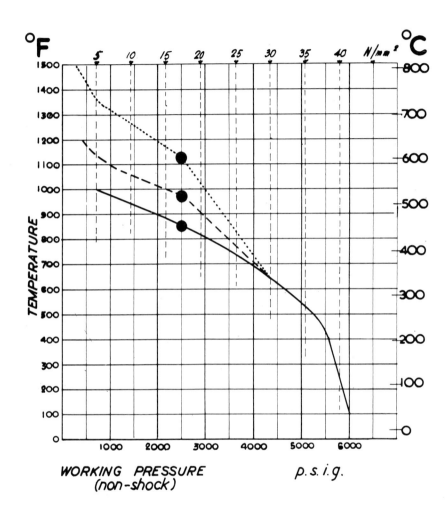

Appendix H Cr . Ni . steel AISI 316 or En 58J (dotted line)
5% Cr . Mo . steel B.S. 3100 (broken line)
Carbon steel B.S. 592 (full line)
2500 lb (17 N) pressure/temperature rating

Appendices

Appendix J Mechanical properties of ferrous and non-ferrous metals at ambient temperatures. (Imperial units)

Material	Character and/or constituents %	Ultimate strength			Recommended Dead Load		
		T	C	S	T	C	S
		psi × 10³			psi × 10³		
Cast iron	Grey, soft	16·0	80·0	17·0	4·00	8·00	3·00
Cast iron	Average quality	22·0	100·0	24·0	5·50	10·00	4·10
Cast iron	Hard	35·0	150·0	38·0	7·00	13·00	5·25
Cast iron	High tensile	45·0	200·0	50·0	7·50	33·35	5·60
Cast iron	Mall	54·0		48·0	9·00		6·75
Iron							
Wrought	Along the grain	47·0	48·0	40·0	14·00	12·00	9·35
Spheroidal graphite	Pearlitic as cast 1 Ni	106·0	157·5	84·0			
Spheroidal graphite	Pearlitic Normalised 1 Ni	123·0	119·0	100·0			
Spheroidal graphite	Ferritic 1 Ni	56·0		50·0			
Spheroidal graphite	Oil quenched & temperred 1 Ni	162·5		108·2			
Steel							
Carbon	Cold drawn 0·20 C	62·5	62·5	43·0	15·63	15·63	9·75
Case hard	0·15/0·25 C, 0·4/0·6 Mn	80·0	80·0	60·0	16·00	16·00	12·00
Castings		70·0	70·0	60·0	14·00	15·00	11·00
Forgings		90·0	70·0		20·00	20·00	15·00
Mild	0·1 C	65·0	60·0	40·0	16·00	15·00	10·00
Rivet		57·0	57·0	44·0			13·00
Structural		60·0	60·0	45·0	12·00	12·00	9·00
Stainless	7·5/9·5 Cr, 0·5 Ni	136·0	136·0		27·20	27·20	
Stainless	18/22 Cr, 6·5/8·5 Ni	120·0	120·0	67·3	24·00	24·00	13·50
Stainless	12/14 Cr, 1 Ni	112·0	112·0	73·7	22·40	22·40	15·00
Stainless softened	17/19 Cr, 8·5/10·5 Ni, 0·7 Ti	95·0	95·0	80·0	19·00	19·00	15·60
Stainless annealed	16·5/18 Cr, 11/13 Ni, 3 Mo	78·5	78·5	87·5	15·70	15·70	10·00

(FERROUS)

Appendix J (continued)

working stress				Modulus of Elasticity		Remarks
Live load						
One kind			Alternate	Dir. 'E'	Transv. 'C'	
T	C	S	T & C			
psi × 10³			psi	psi × 10⁶		
2.00	4.00	1.50	1 350	12		
2.75	5.00	2.00	1 700	16	6.3	Caution! Certain white irons have an ultimate comp. strength of 250 000 psi
4.38	7.50	3.35	2 900	20	7.6	
4.50	20.00	3.38	3 750	25		
5.40		4.10	4 500	25		
8.15	7.00	5.40	5 000	28	10.20	
				25	9.65	Values for ult. & wkg. stress are average: could be ±20% tension ±15% comp'n ±1½% for shear
				25	9.27	Values for ult. & wkg. stress are average: could be ±20% tension ±10% comp'n ±1% for shear
				25	9.47	Values for ult. & wkg. stress are average: could be ±25% tension ±10% comp'n ±1% for shear
				25	9.20	Values for ult. & wkg. stress are average: could be ±12½% tension ±10% comp'n ±1% for shear
10.41	10.41	7.80	7 800	28.9	13.0	Soft open hearth annealed
13.35	13.35	10.00	10 000	30	11.65	
7.50	7.50	5.50	5 000	30	12.0	Note! Heat treated alloy steel castings may have an U.T.S. of 200 000 psi
10.00	10.00	7.50	6 600	30	13.5	
10.00	10.00	6.75	7 500	30	13.0	
		11.00	7 125	29	13.0	
10.00	10.00	7.50	7 500	29	13.0	
22.60	22.60	17.00	17 000	30	11.0	
20.00	20.00	15.00	15 000	28.5	11.0	
18.65	18.65	12.75	12 750	30.3	11.0	
15.80	15.80	12.00	12 000	29	11.3	
12.90	12.90	8.60		29.5		Annealed

Appendix J (continued)

	Material	Character and/or constituents %	Ultimate strength			Recommended Dead Load		
			T	C	S	T	C	S
			psi × 10^3			psi × 10^3		
NON-FERROUS	Aluminium	Cast	13·0		10·0	3·25	2·10	2·00
	Brass							
	Cast		20·0	10·5	30·0	5·00	2·10	6·00
	Naval	Annealed	50·0			8·00		
	Bronze							
	(or G.M.)		32·0		40·0	8·00	8·00	8·00
	Manganese	Parson's No. 1 BS2872 CZ114	80·0	156·8		20·00	39·00	
	Nickel	7 Ni	45·8			11·50		
	Nickel	50 Ni 10 Sn 40 Cu	85·0			21·25		
	Phosphor cast		35·0			8·75		
	Phosphor rolled		60·0	40·0	40·0	14·50	9·00	8·00
	Cupro-Nickel	Annealed 90 Cu 10 Ni	47·0			11·75		
	Duralumin	Heat treated	58·0			12·00		
	Gunmetal	Admiralty 88 Cu 10 Sn 2 Zn	38·0		40·0	9·50		
	Monel	Cast	60·0		36·0	15·00		
	Monel	Wrought	80·0		48·0	20·00		

T = Tension; C = Compression; S = Shear.

The values given relate to properties at ambient temperatures but for all practical purposes these may be regarded as applicable up to 212°F. For values at more elevated temperatures these will fall off appropriately and the suppliers of the material should be consulted where any doubt exists or their relevant literature consulted.

Appendix J (continued)

working stress				Modulus of Elasticity		Remarks
Live Load						
One kind			Alternate	Dir. 'E'	Transv. 'C'	
T	C	S	T & C			
psi × 10³			psi	psi × 10⁶		
2·18		1·75		10·3	3·5	
4·15		5·00		12·0		
8·30				14·3		Rolled and forged
4·25	4·25	6·50	2 750	13·5		
13·30	26·00		7 000	13·4	6·2	Rolled and forged
7·40						
14·00						
5·85			2 850			
7·25	7·25	6·50	4 850	14	5·25	
7·80				18·5		
8·00				11		
6·30				13·5		
9·00				26·0	9·5	
13·00				26·0	9·5	

Appendix K Mechanical properties of ferrous and non-ferrous metals
S.I. Units

Material	Character and/or constituents %	Ultimate strength			Recommended Dead Load		
		T	C	S	T	C	S
		N/mm^2			N/mm^2		
Cast iron	Grey, soft	110	550	117	28	55	21
Cast iron	Average quality	152	690	165	38	69	28
Cast iron	Hard	240	1 180	262	49	90	36
Cast iron	High tensile	310	1 380	344	52	238	39
Cast iron	Mall	370		330	62		47
Iron Wrought	Along the grain	325	330	275	97	83	65
Spheroidal graphite	Pearlitic as cast 1 Ni	730	1 090	580			
Spheroidal graphite	Pearlitic Normalised 1 Ni	850	820	690			
Spheroidal graphite	Ferritic 1 Ni	385		345			
Spheroidal graphite	Oil quenched & tempered 1 Ni	1 125		745			
Steel Carbon	Cold drawn 0·20 C	430	430	295	108	112	67
Case hard	0·15/0·25 C, 0·4/0·6 Mn	550	550	415	110	110	83
Castings		482	480	415	97	104	76
Forgings		620	480			138	103
Mild	0·1 C	450	415	275	110	104	69
Rivet		495	495	295			90
Structural		415	415	310	83	83	62
Stainless	7·5/9·5 Cr, 0·5 Ni	940	940		188	194	
Stainless	18/22 Cr, 6·5/8·5 Ni	830	830	465	165	166	93
Stainless	12/14 Cr, 1 Ni	770	770		164	160	104
Stainless	17/19 Cr 8·5/10·5 Ni	540	540		108	108	69
Stainless softened	17/19 Cr, 8·5/10·5 Ni, 0·7 Ti	650	650	550	131	131	108
Stainless annealed	16·5/18 Cr, 11/13 Ni, 3 Mo	540	540	600	108	108	69

FERROUS

Appendix K (continued)

working stress				Modulus of Elasticity		Remarks
Live load			Alternate			
One kind				Dir. 'E'	Transv. 'C'	
T	C	S	T & C			
N/mm²			N/mm²	N/mm² × 10³		
14	28	10	9	83		
19	35	14	12	110	43	
30	52	23	20	138	53	Caution! Certain white irons have an ultimate comp. strength of 1700 N/mm²
31	138	23	26	172		
38		28	31	172		
56	48	38	34	193	70	
				172	67	Values for ult. & wkg. stress are average: could be ±20% tension ±15% comp'n ±1½% for shear
				172	64	Values for ult. & wkg. stress are average: could be ±20% tension ±10% comp'n ±1% for shear
				172	65	Values for ult. & wkg. stress are average: could be ±25% tension ±10% comp'n ±1% for shear
				172	63	Values for ult. & wkg. stress are average: could be ±12½% tension ±10% comp'n ±1% for shear
72	72	54	54	200	90	Soft open hearth annealed
92	92	69	69	207	81	
52	52	38	35	207	83	Note! Heat treated alloy steel castings may have an U.T.S. of 1400 N/mm²
69	69	52	46	207	93	
69	69	47	52	207	93	
		69	49	200	93	
69	69	52	52	200	93	
156	156	117	117	207	76	
138	138	103	103	197	76	
129	129	88	88	210	76	
89	89	59	67	200	77	Annealed
109	109	83	83	200	77	
89	89	59		203		Annealed

Appendix K (continued)

	Material	Character and/or constituents %	Ultimate strength (N/mm²)			Recommended Dead Load (N/mm²)		
			T	C	S	T	C	S
NON-FERROUS	Aluminium	Cast	90		68	23		14
	Brass							
	Cast		138	72	205	35		42
	Naval	Annealed	345			55		
	Bronze							
	(or G.M.)		220		275	55	15	55
	Manganese	Parson's No. 1 BS2872 CZ114	550	1 080		137	55	
	Nickel	7 Ni	315			80		
	Nickel	50 Ni 10 Sn 40 Cu	585			147		
	Phosphor cast		242			61		
	Phosphor rolled		415	275	275	100	62	55
	Cupro-Nickel	Annealed 90 Cu 10 Ni	325			79		
	Duralumin	Heat treated	400			83		
	Gunmetal	Admiralty 88 Cu 10 Sn 2 Zn	262		275	66		
	Monel	Cast	415		250	104		
	Monel	Wrought	550		330	138		

T = Tension; C = Compression; S = Shear.

The values given relate to properties at ambient temperatures but for all practical purposes these may be regarded as applicable up to 100°C. For values at more elevated temperatures these will fall off appropriately and the suppliers of the material should be consulted where any doubt exists or their relevant literature consulted.

Appendix K (continued)

working stress				Modulus of Elasticity		Remarks
Live load						
One kind			Alternate	Dir. 'E'	Transv. 'C'	
T	C	S	T & C			
N/mm²			N/mm²	N/mm² × 10³		
15		12		71	24	
29		34		83		
57				99		Rolled and forged
28	28	45	19	93		
92	180		48	92	43	Rolled and forged
51						
97						
40			20			
50	50	45	34	97	36	
54				127		
55				76		
44				93		
62				180	66	
90				180	66	

Appendix L Maximum permissible unit surface stresses for valve seatings

Seating material	Max. Brinell Hardness No. (3 000 kg)	Max. unit surface stress u		
		lbf/in²	kgf/cm²	N/mm²
Cast iron	180	1 000	70	7
Fibre composition	—	300	20	2
Gunmetal	75	2 000	140	14
'Monel' metal*	270	9 000	630	62
Nickel bronze (sand cast)	240	6 000	420	42
Nickel chrome steel	440	12 000	850	82
Phosphor bronze	100	3 000	200	20
Polytetrafluoroethylene	—	500	35	3
Stellite	600	15 000	1 000	100

Approximate equivalents

*'Monel' (Regd. Trade Mark), a proprietary alloy of approximately two thirds nickel, one third copper.

Appendix M Gaskets and flange facings data

Gasket Ref.	Sketch	Description	Material and definition
a		Asbestos with suitable binder for conditions	1/32″ (1·0 mm) thick 1/16″ (1·5 mm) thick 1/8″ (3·0 mm) thick
b		Corrugated metal	Aluminium, soft Copper, soft, or Brass Iron or Steel, soft Monel or 4 to 6% Chrome Stainless steels
c		Serrated metal	Aluminium, soft Copper, soft, or Brass Iron or Steel, soft Monel or 4 to 6% Chrome Stainless steels
d		Solid flat metal	Aluminium, soft Copper, soft, or Brass Iron or Steel, soft Monel or 4 to 6% Chrome Stainless steels
e		Flat metal jacketed and asbestos filled	Aluminium, soft Copper, soft, or Brass Iron or Steel, soft Monel 4 to 6% Chrome Stainless steels
f		Elastomer	Without fabric or high percentage of asbestos fibre below 75 shore durometer 75 or higher shore durometer With cotton fabric insertion With asbestos fabric insertion, with or without wire reinforcement → 3-ply → 2-ply → 1-ply
g		Vegetable fibre (millboard)	

Gasket factor η_3	Facing limitations Use only those indicated below
3·50 2·75 2·00	1, 4 and 6 only
2·75 3·00 3·25 3·50 3·75	1(a) only
3·25 3·50 3·75 3·75 4·25	1, 2 and 3 only
4·00 4·75 5·50 6·00 6·50	None
3·25 3·50 3·75 3·50 3·75 3·75	1(a) and 2 only
0·50 1·00	1, 4 and 6 only
1·25	None
2·25 2·50 2·75	
1·75	1, 4 and 6

Facing Ref.	Sketch
1(a)	
1(b)	
2	
3	
4	
5	
6	
7	

Recommended forms of mating flange facings

Gaskets shown diagrammatically double cross-hatched in each example

The above examples do no preclude the adoption of spigot and faucet type joints wherein the actual contact facings shown might still apply

Extracted from American National Standard Steel Pipe Flanges and Flanged Fittings ANSI B 16.5–1968 with the permission of the publisher, The American Society of Mechanical Engineers, United Engineering Center, 345 East 47th Street, New York

Appendix N Safe working loads for the bolts or studs securing the cover plates of pressure vessels

	Diam. of bolt or stud B.S.W.	Core area	Steel of 28 ton/in² U.T.S. Max. Temp. 600°F		
			Safe working load	Corresponding working stress Based on core area	Factor of Safety
	in	in²	lb	lb/in²	
lb-in units	$\frac{1}{2}$*	0·121	250	2 130	29·4
	$\frac{9}{16}$*	0·163	450	2 760	22·8
	$\frac{5}{8}$	0·204	575	2 817	22·2
	$\frac{3}{4}$	0·304	1 000	3 290	19·1
	$\frac{7}{8}$	0·422	1 700	4 055	15·5
	1	0·554	2 500	4 513	13·9
	$1\frac{1}{8}$	0·697	3 500	5 020	12·5
	$1\frac{1}{4}$	0·894	5 250	5 875	10·7
	$1\frac{3}{8}$	1·058	6 500	6 140	10·2
	$1\frac{1}{2}$	1·299	9 000	6 930	9·0
	$1\frac{3}{4}$	1·753	13 000	7 410	8·5
	2	2·311	17 000	7 355	8·5

	Diam. of bolt or stud (and designation)	Core area	Steel of 430 N/mm² U.T.S. Max. Temp. 315°C		
			Safe working load	Corresponding working stress Based on core area	Factor of Safety
	mm	mm²	kN	N/mm²	
S.I. units	M 12	84·3	1·25	14·80	29
	M 16	157	2·81	17·85	24
	M 20	245	5·53	22·62	19
	M 22	303	8·15	26·88	16
	M 24	353	10·90	30·9	14
	M 27	459	15·00	30·7	13
	M 30	561	20·00	35·6	12
	M 36	817	32·00	39·2	11
	M 42	1120	48·20	43·0	10
	M 45	1300	62·20	47·8	9
	M 48	1470	72·50	49·2	8·75
	M 52	1760	89·00	50·5	8·5

*Not recommended for use on steam or on other high temperature services

Steel of 35 ton/in² U.T.S. Max. Temp. 750°F			Steel of 65 ton/in² U.T.S. Max. Temp. 800°F		
Safe working load	Corresponding working stress Based on core area	Factor of Safety	Safe working load	Corresponding working stress Based on core area	Factor of Safety
lb	lb/in²		lb	lb/in²	
375	3 100	25·3	700	5 780	25·2
675	4 140	18·9	1 300	7 975	18·3
900	4 410	17·8	1 800	8 920	16·3
1 600	5 265	14·9	3 250	10 690	13·6
2 500	5 830	13·5	5 250	12 430	11·7
4 000	7 218	10·9	8 500	15 330	9·6
5 500	7 890	9·9	12 000	17 220	8·5
9 000	10 060	7·8	20 000	22 350	6·5
11 000	10 400	7·5	25 000	24 620	5·9
14 000	10 760	7·3	35 000	26 940	5·4
19 000	10 820	7·3	49 000	27 950	5·2
25 000	10 820	7·3	65 000	28 120	5·2

Steel of 535 N/mm² U.T.S. Max. Temp. 400°C			Steel of 1 000 N-mm² U.T.S. Max. Temp. 420°C		
Safe working load	Corresponding working stress Based on core area	Factor of Safety	Safe working load	Corresponding working stress Based on core area	Factor of Safety
kN	N/mm²		kN	N/mm²	
1·81	21·45	25	3·37	37·3	25
4·20	26·75	20	8·70	55·3	18
8·20	33·42	16	17·50	71·7	14
12·50	41·30	13	25·20	83·2	12
15·80	44·5	12	35·3	100·0	10
22·25	47·5	11	51·0	111·2	9
30·00	53·3	10	70·0	124·8	8
54·60	66·9	8	116·8	143·0	7
76·00	66·8	7·75	186·0	166·0	6
92·00	70·7	7·5	236·0	181·0	5·5
109·00	74·3	7·25	280·0	191·0	5·25
135·00	76·8	7	353·0	200·0	5

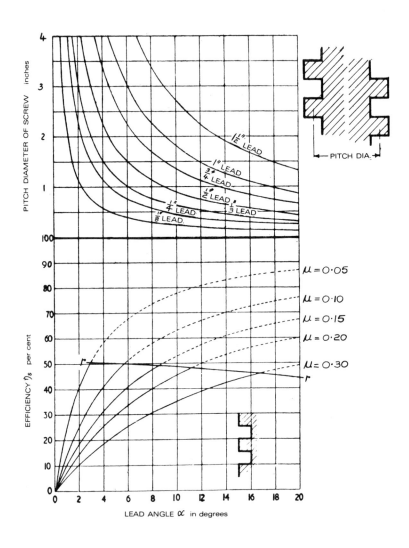

Appendix P Efficiency curves for square section screw threads (inch sizes)

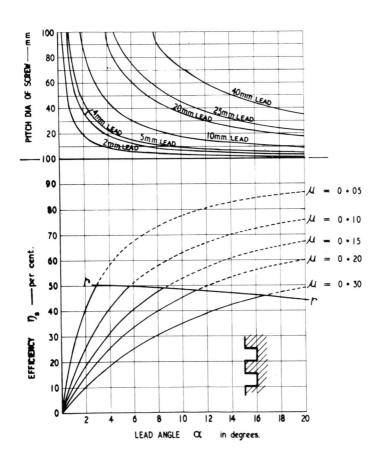

Appendix Q Efficiency curves for square section screw threads (metric sizes)

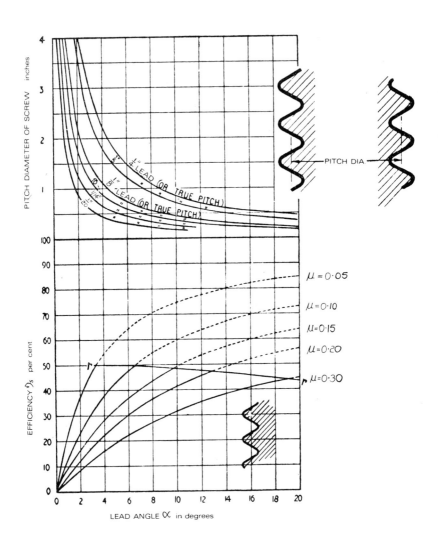

Appendix R Efficiency curves for vee-section screw threads (inch sizes)

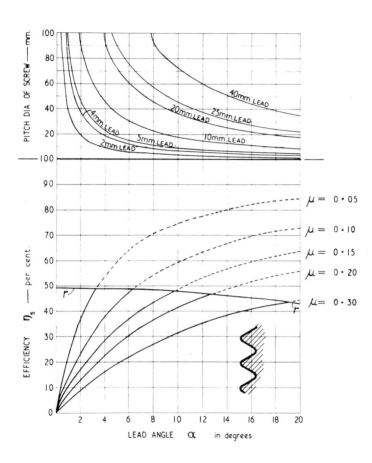

Appendix S Efficiency curves for vee-section screw threads (metric sizes)

Appendix T Allowable working stresses for *solid* valve stems in compression

Ratio: Length* / Min. dia.	Allowable stress f'_c lbf/in^2 of section (based on ultimate buckling load and factor of safety shown in brackets)					
	Cast iron soft (6)†	Cast iron hard close grained (6)†	Wrought iron (4)	Mild steel (5)	Hard steel (5)	Forged mang. bronze
5	10 670	17 335	10 500	12 620	20 060	15 000
10	6 670	10 835	9 300	11 260	15 880	11 000
15	5 400	7 000	7 800	9 400	12 000	8 750
20	2 670	4 335	6 400	7 100	8 660	5 650
25	2 200	3 000	5 750	4 120	4 920	3 560
30	1 335	2 170	4 200	3 900	3 850	2 600
35	1 000	1 550	3 600	3 150	4 000	2 500
40	785	1 270	2 850	2 680	3 080	1 900
45	600	1 000	2 300	2 200	2 500	1 500
50	517	833	2 000	1 840	2 060	1 275

Imperial units

Ratio: Length* / Min. dia.	Allowable stress f'_c N/mm² of section (Based on ultimate buckling load and factor of safety shown in brackets)					
	Cast iron soft (6)†	Cast iron hard close grained (6)†	Wrought iron (4)	Mild steel (5)	Hard steel (5)	Forged mang. bronze
5	73·6	119·5	70·2	87·0	142·0	103·3
10	46·0	74·8	60·4	77·8	109·5	75·8
15	37·2	48·2	53·7	65·0	82·7	60·4
20	18·5	29·9	44·2	48·9	59·7	38·9
25	15·2	20·7	39·6	28·5	34·0	24·8
30	9·2	14·9	29·0	26·9	26·7	17·9
35	6·9	10·7	24·9	21·7	27·6	17·2
40	5·4	8·8	19·7	18·5	21·2	13·1
45	4·1	6·9	15·9	15·2	17·2	10·3
50	3·6	5·7	13·8	12·7	14·2	8·8

SI units

*Root diameter in the case of screwed stems
†Cast iron stems are often stipulated for valves used on caustic liquors

Appendix U Proportions of valve stuffing boxes appropriate to various stem diameters and primary service pressure ratings

The Imperial and Metric values are not true equivalents but rounded off for convenience

Spec.	Primary Service Pressure		Valve dia.		Valve dia.		Valve dia.		Valve dia.	
	lb/in²	kN/m²	mm	in	mm	in	mm	in	mm	in
BS.1735 1966	100 125	700 850	40	1½	50	2	80	3	100	4
API.600	150	1 000			50, 65	2, 2½	80	3	100	4
API.600	300	2 000			40, 65	1½, 2 2½	80	3	100	4
API.600	400	2 750	25, 32	1, 1¼	40, 65	1½, 2	65	2½	80	3
API.600	600	4 000	25, 32	1, 1¼	40, 65	1½, 2	65	2½	80	3
API.600	900	6 250			25, 32	1, 1¼	40	1½	50	2
API.600	1 500	10 000			25, 32	1, 1¼	40	1½	50	2

Spec.	Primary Service Pressure		Valve dia.		Valve dia.		Valve dia.	
	lb/in²	kN/m²	mm	in	mm	in	mm	in
BS.1735 1966	100 125	700 850	150	6	200	8	250	10
API.600	150	1 000	150	6	200	8	250	10
API.600	300	2 000			150	6	200	8
API.600	400	2 750	100	4	400		150	6
API.600	600	4 000	100	4	600			
API.600	900	6 250	80	3	100	4		
API.600	1 500	10 000	65	2½	80	3	100	4

Appendix U (continued)

Spec.	Primary Service Pressure		Valve dia.		Valve dia.		Valve dia.	
	lb/in²	kN/m²	mm	in	mm	in	mm	in
BS.1735 1966	100 125	700 850	300	12			250	14
API.600	150	1 000	300	12	350	14	400	16
API.600	300	2 000	250	10	300	12	350	14
API.600	400	2 750	200	8			250	10
API.600	600	4 000	150	6	200	8		
API.600	900	6 250			150	6		
API.600	1 500	10 000					150	6

Spec.	Primary Service Pressure		Valve dia.		Valve dia.		Valve dia.	
	lb/in²	kN/m²	mm	in	mm	in	mm	in
BS.1735 1966	100 125	700 850	400	16	450	18		
API.600	150	1 000	450	18	500	20		
API.600	300	2 000	400	16	450	18	500	20
API.600	400	2 750	300, 350	12, 14	400	16		
API.600	600	4 000		10	300	12		
API.600	900	6 250	200	8			250	10
API.600	1 500	10 000						9

Appendix U (continued)

Spec.	Primary Service Pressure		Valve dia.		Valve dia.		Valve dia.	
	lb/in²	kN/m²	mm	in	mm	in	mm	in
BS.1735 1966	100 125	700 850	500	20	550	22	600	24
API.600	150	1 000	600	24	550	22		
API.600	300	2 000			600	24		
API.600	400	2 750	450	18				
API.600	600	4 000	350	14	400	16	450	18
API.600	900	6 250	300	12	350	14	400	16
API.600	1 500	10 000					250	10

Appendix U (continued)

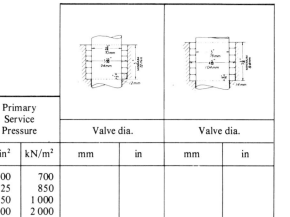

Spec.	Primary Service Pressure		Valve dia.		Valve dia.	
	lb/in²	kN/m²	mm	in	mm	in
BS.1735	100	700				
1966	125	850				
API.600	150	1 000				
API.600	300	2 000				
API.600	400	2 750	600	24		
API.600	600	4 000	500	20	600	24
API.600	900	6 250			450	18
API.600	1 500	10 000	300	12	350, 400	14, 16

Appendix V Stop valve handwheels—dished spoke pattern

	A	B	C	D	E	F	G	H	J	K	L
Inches*	5	$\frac{3}{4}$	1	$\frac{7}{8}$	$\frac{3}{4}$	$\frac{3}{32}$	$\frac{7}{16}$	$\frac{1}{4}$	$\frac{3}{4}$	Acc. to torque	None
	6	$\frac{3}{4}$	$1\frac{1}{16}$	$\frac{15}{16}$	$\frac{3}{4}$	$\frac{3}{32}$	$\frac{7}{16}$	$\frac{1}{4}$	$\frac{3}{4}$	do	None
	7	$\frac{13}{16}$	$1\frac{1}{8}$	$1\frac{1}{16}$	$\frac{13}{16}$	$\frac{3}{32}$	$\frac{7}{16}$	$\frac{1}{4}$	$\frac{13}{16}$	do	None
	8	$\frac{7}{8}$	$1\frac{1}{8}$	$1\frac{3}{16}$	$\frac{7}{8}$	$\frac{3}{32}$	$\frac{7}{16}$	$\frac{1}{4}$	$\frac{13}{16}$	do	Eight
	9	1	$1\frac{1}{4}$	$1\frac{3}{8}$	1	$\frac{3}{32}$	$\frac{1}{2}$	$\frac{5}{16}$	$\frac{7}{8}$	do	Twelve
	10	$1\frac{1}{16}$	$1\frac{5}{16}$	$1\frac{1}{2}$	$1\frac{1}{16}$	$\frac{3}{32}$	$\frac{1}{2}$	$\frac{5}{16}$	1	do	Twelve
	12	$1\frac{1}{8}$	$1\frac{1}{2}$	$1\frac{5}{8}$	$1\frac{1}{8}$	$\frac{3}{32}$	$\frac{1}{2}$	$\frac{5}{16}$	$1\frac{1}{16}$	do	Fifteen
	15	$1\frac{3}{16}$	$1\frac{3}{4}$	$1\frac{3}{4}$	$1\frac{1}{16}$	$\frac{1}{8}$	$\frac{5}{8}$	$\frac{3}{8}$	$1\frac{1}{8}$	do	Twenty
mm*	125	19	25	22	19	3	10	6	20	do	None
	150	19	27	24	19	3	10	6	20	do	None
	180	20	29	27	20	3	10	6	21	do	None
	200	22	29	30	22	3	10	6	21	do	Eight
	230	25	32	35	25	3	12	8	22	do	Twelve
	250	27	38	38	27	3	12	8	25	do	Twelve
	300	28	38	42	28	3	12	8	27	do	Fifteen
	380	30	44	44	33	4	15	10	28	do	Twenty

*Not necessarily complementary equivalents but close approximations

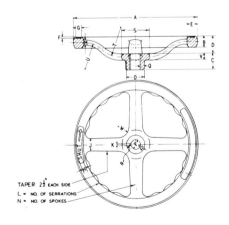

TAPER $2\frac{1}{2}°$ EACH SIDE
L = NO. OF SERRATIONS
N = NO. OF SPOKES

M	N	O	P	Q	R	S	T	U	V	W	X	Y	Z
$\frac{5}{16}$	Three	According to dia. of stem		$\frac{11}{32}$	$\frac{5}{16}$	$1\frac{3}{4}$	$\frac{5}{8}$	$\frac{5}{8}$	$\frac{3}{8}$	$\frac{3}{4}$			
$\frac{11}{32}$	Three	do		$\frac{11}{32}$	$\frac{5}{16}$	$1\frac{7}{8}$	1	1	$\frac{13}{32}$	$\frac{3}{4}$			
$\frac{11}{32}$	Three	do		$\frac{11}{32}$	$\frac{11}{32}$	2	$1\frac{3}{4}$	$1\frac{3}{4}$	$\frac{13}{32}$	$\frac{13}{16}$			
$\frac{3}{8}$	Four	do		$\frac{11}{32}$	$\frac{11}{32}$	$2\frac{1}{8}$	$1\frac{7}{8}$	$1\frac{7}{8}$	$\frac{7}{16}$	$\frac{13}{16}$			
$\frac{1}{2}$	Four	do		$\frac{13}{32}$	$\frac{13}{32}$	$2\frac{3}{8}$	2	2	$\frac{5}{8}$	$\frac{7}{8}$			
$\frac{1}{2}$	Four	do		$\frac{13}{32}$	$\frac{7}{16}$	$2\frac{1}{2}$	$2\frac{1}{4}$	$2\frac{1}{4}$	$\frac{5}{8}$	1			
$\frac{9}{16}$	Five	do		$\frac{7}{16}$	$\frac{1}{2}$	$2\frac{3}{4}$	3	3	$\frac{11}{16}$	$1\frac{1}{16}$			
$\frac{5}{8}$	Five	do		$\frac{1}{2}$	$\frac{9}{16}$	3	6	6	$\frac{3}{4}$	$1\frac{1}{8}$			
8	Three	do		9	8	44	16	16	10	20			
9	Three	do		9	8	47	25	25	11	20			
9	Four	do		9	9	50	44	44	11	21			
10	Four	do		9	9	54	48	48	12	21			
12	Four	do		10	11	60	50	50	14	22			
13	Four	do		10	12	63	57	57	16	25			
14	Five	do		11	13	70	75	75	17	27			
16	Five	do		12	14	76	150	150	19	28			

Appendix W Stop valve handwheels—flat spoke pattern

	A	B	C	D	E	F	G	H	J	K	L
Inches*	9	1	$1\frac{3}{16}$	$\frac{3}{32}$	1	$\frac{3}{32}$	$\frac{1}{2}$	$\frac{5}{16}$	$\frac{7}{8}$	Acc. to torque	Twelve
	12	$1\frac{1}{16}$	$1\frac{1}{4}$	$\frac{3}{32}$	1	$\frac{3}{32}$	$\frac{1}{2}$	$\frac{5}{16}$	1	do	Fifteen
	15	$1\frac{1}{8}$	$1\frac{3}{8}$	$\frac{1}{8}$	$1\frac{1}{16}$	$\frac{3}{32}$	$\frac{1}{2}$	$\frac{5}{16}$	$1\frac{1}{16}$	do	Twenty
	18	$1\frac{1}{4}$	$1\frac{3}{4}$	$\frac{1}{4}$	$1\frac{1}{16}$	$\frac{1}{8}$	$\frac{1}{2}$	$\frac{3}{8}$	$1\frac{1}{8}$	do	Twenty Five
	20	$1\frac{5}{16}$	$1\frac{7}{8}$	$\frac{1}{4}$	$1\frac{1}{16}$	$\frac{1}{8}$	$\frac{1}{2}$	$\frac{3}{8}$	$1\frac{3}{16}$	do	Thirty
	22	$1\frac{3}{8}$	2	$\frac{5}{16}$	$1\frac{1}{8}$	$\frac{1}{8}$	$\frac{5}{8}$	$\frac{1}{2}$	$1\frac{1}{4}$	do	Thirty
	25	$1\frac{1}{2}$	$2\frac{3}{16}$	$\frac{11}{32}$	$1\frac{3}{8}$	$\frac{3}{16}$	$\frac{5}{8}$	$\frac{1}{2}$	$1\frac{1}{2}$	do	Thirty
	30	$1\frac{5}{8}$	$2\frac{3}{8}$	$\frac{3}{8}$	$1\frac{1}{2}$	$\frac{3}{16}$	$\frac{3}{4}$	$\frac{1}{2}$	$1\frac{3}{4}$	do	Thirty
Milli-metres*	230	25	30	2·5	25	2·5	12	8	22	do	Twelve
	300	27	32	2·5	25	2·5	12	8	25	do	Fifteen
	380	28	36	4	27	2·5	12	8	27	do	Twenty
	450	32	44	6	27	3	12	8	28	do	Twenty Five
	500	33	47	7	27	4	12	8	30	do	Thirty
	550	35	51	8	28	4	15	12	32	do	Thirty
	650	38	56	9	35	5	15	12	38	do	Thirty
	750	42	62	10	38	5	19	12	44	do	Thirty

*Not necessarily complementary equivalents but close approximations

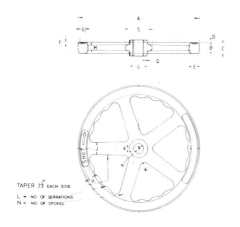

TAPER 2½° EACH SIDE
L = NO. OF SERRATIONS
N = NO. OF SPOKES

M	N	O	P	Q	R	S†	T	U	V	W	X	Y	Z
		According to dia. of stem											
$\frac{1}{2}$	Four	According to dia. of stem		$\frac{1}{4}$	$\frac{5}{16}$	$2\frac{1}{4}$				$1\frac{1}{2}$			
$\frac{9}{16}$	Five	do		$\frac{9}{32}$	$\frac{11}{32}$	$2\frac{1}{2}$				$1\frac{1}{2}$			
$\frac{5}{8}$	Five	do		$\frac{5}{16}$	$\frac{3}{8}$	3				$1\frac{5}{8}$			
$\frac{5}{8}$	Five	do		$\frac{13}{32}$	$\frac{15}{32}$	$3\frac{1}{2}$				$1\frac{5}{8}$			
$\frac{5}{8}$	Five	do		$\frac{7}{16}$	$\frac{9}{16}$	4				$1\frac{3}{4}$			
$\frac{11}{16}$	Six	do		$\frac{1}{2}$	$\frac{5}{8}$	$4\frac{1}{2}$				$1\frac{3}{4}$			
$\frac{3}{4}$	Six	do		$\frac{1}{2}$	$\frac{5}{8}$	5				$2\frac{1}{8}$			
$\frac{7}{8}$	Six	do		$\frac{9}{16}$	$\frac{11}{16}$	$5\frac{1}{2}$				$2\frac{1}{8}$			
12	Four	do		7	8	57				38			
14	Five	do		7	9	64				40			
16	Five	do		8	10	76				42			
16	Five	do		10	12	88				43			
16	Five	do		12	15	100				44			
18	Six	do		13	16	115				45			
20	Six	do		14	16	127				50			
22	Six	do		15	18	140				55			

†Approximate

Appendix X Gate valve handwheels—dished spoke pattern

	A	B	C	D	E	F	G	H	J	K	L
Inches*	5	$\frac{3}{4}$	$\frac{7}{8}$	$\frac{7}{8}$	$\frac{3}{4}$	$\frac{3}{32}$	$\frac{7}{16}$	$\frac{1}{4}$	$\frac{3}{4}$	Acc. to torque	None
	6	$\frac{3}{4}$	$1\frac{1}{16}$	$\frac{15}{16}$	$\frac{3}{4}$	$\frac{3}{32}$	$\frac{7}{16}$	$\frac{1}{4}$	$\frac{3}{4}$	do	None
	7	$\frac{13}{16}$	$1\frac{3}{8}$	$1\frac{1}{16}$	$\frac{13}{16}$	$\frac{3}{32}$	$\frac{7}{16}$	$\frac{1}{4}$	$\frac{13}{16}$	do	None
	8	$\frac{7}{8}$	$1\frac{5}{8}$	$1\frac{3}{16}$	$\frac{7}{8}$	$\frac{3}{32}$	$\frac{7}{16}$	$\frac{1}{4}$	$\frac{13}{16}$	do	Eight
	9	1	$1\frac{7}{8}$	$1\frac{3}{8}$	1	$\frac{3}{32}$	$\frac{7}{16}$	$\frac{1}{4}$	$\frac{7}{8}$	do	Twelve
	120	$1\frac{1}{16}$	$2\frac{1}{16}$	$1\frac{1}{2}$	$1\frac{1}{16}$	$\frac{3}{32}$	$\frac{1}{2}$	$\frac{5}{16}$	1	do	Twelve
	12	$1\frac{1}{8}$	$2\frac{1}{8}$	$1\frac{5}{8}$	$1\frac{1}{8}$	$\frac{3}{32}$	$\frac{1}{2}$	$\frac{5}{16}$	$1\frac{1}{16}$	do	Fifteen
	15	$1\frac{3}{16}$	$2\frac{1}{2}$	$1\frac{3}{4}$	$1\frac{5}{16}$	$\frac{1}{8}$	$\frac{5}{8}$	$\frac{3}{8}$	$1\frac{1}{8}$	do	Twenty
Milli-metres*	125	19	22	22	19	3	10	6	20	do	None
	150	19	25	24	19	3	10	6	20	do	None
	180	20	35	27	20	3	10	6	21	do	None
	200	22	41	30	22	3	10	6	21	do	Eight
	230	25	48	35	25	3	12	8	22	do	Twelve
	250	27	50	38	27	3	12	8	25	do	Twelve
	300	28	54	42	28	3	12	8	27	do	Fifteen
	380	30	64	44	33	4	15	10	28	do	Twenty

*Not necessary complementary equivalents but close approximations

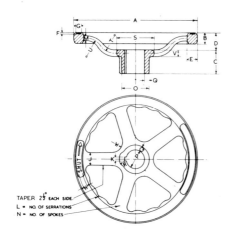

TAPER $2\frac{1}{2}°$ EACH SIDE
L = NO. OF SERRATIONS
N = NO. OF SPOKES

M	N	O	P	Q	R	S	T	U	V	W	X	Y	Z
$\frac{5}{16}$	Three	According to dia. of stem		$\frac{11}{32}$	$\frac{3}{8}$	$2\frac{1}{4}$	$\frac{1}{2}$	$\frac{5}{8}$	$\frac{3}{8}$	$\frac{3}{4}$			
$\frac{11}{32}$	Three	do		$\frac{11}{32}$	$\frac{3}{8}$	$2\frac{1}{4}$	$\frac{7}{8}$	1	$\frac{13}{32}$	1			
$\frac{11}{32}$	Three	do		$\frac{11}{32}$	$\frac{3}{8}$	$2\frac{1}{2}$	$1\frac{1}{4}$	$1\frac{5}{8}$	$\frac{13}{32}$	$1\frac{1}{8}$			
$\frac{3}{8}$	Four	do		$\frac{11}{32}$	$\frac{3}{8}$	$2\frac{3}{4}$	$1\frac{1}{8}$	$1\frac{3}{4}$	$\frac{7}{16}$	$1\frac{1}{4}$			
$\frac{1}{2}$	Four	do		$\frac{13}{32}$	$\frac{7}{16}$	$2\frac{7}{8}$	$1\frac{3}{8}$	$1\frac{7}{8}$	$\frac{5}{8}$	$1\frac{1}{4}$			
$\frac{1}{2}$	Four	do		$\frac{13}{32}$	$\frac{7}{16}$	$3\frac{1}{16}$	$2\frac{1}{4}$	$2\frac{1}{4}$	$\frac{5}{8}$	$1\frac{1}{4}$			
$\frac{9}{16}$	Five	do		$\frac{7}{16}$	$\frac{1}{2}$	$3\frac{3}{8}$	$2\frac{3}{4}$	3	$\frac{11}{16}$	$1\frac{1}{4}$			
$\frac{5}{8}$	Five	do		$\frac{1}{2}$	$\frac{9}{16}$	$3\frac{3}{8}$	$4\frac{1}{2}$	5	$\frac{3}{4}$	$1\frac{3}{8}$			
8	Three	do		9	10	57	12	16	10	20			
9	Three	do		9	10	57	22	25	11	25			
9	Three	do		9	11	64	38	42	11	28			
10	Four	do		9	11	70	41	44	12	32			
12	Four	do		10	12	75	45	47	14	32			
13	Four	do		10	13	78	57	57	16	32			
14	Five	do		11	14	80	69	75	17	32			
16	Five	do		12	15	85	115	125	19	35			

Appendix Y Gate valve handwheels—flat spoke pattern

	A	B	C	D	E	F	G	H	J	K	L
Inches*	9	1	$1\frac{7}{8}$	$\frac{3}{32}$	1	$\frac{3}{32}$	$\frac{1}{2}$	$\frac{5}{16}$	$\frac{7}{8}$	Acc. to torque	Twelve
	12	$1\frac{1}{16}$	$2\frac{1}{8}$	$\frac{3}{32}$	1	$\frac{3}{32}$	$\frac{1}{2}$	$\frac{5}{16}$	1	do	Fifteen
	15	$1\frac{1}{8}$	$2\frac{1}{2}$	$\frac{1}{8}$	$1\frac{1}{16}$	$\frac{3}{32}$	$\frac{1}{2}$	$\frac{5}{16}$	$1\frac{1}{16}$	do	Twenty
	18	$1\frac{1}{4}$	$2\frac{3}{4}$	$\frac{1}{4}$	$1\frac{1}{16}$	$\frac{1}{8}$	$\frac{1}{2}$	$\frac{3}{8}$	$1\frac{1}{8}$	do	Twenty Five
	20	$1\frac{5}{16}$	$2\frac{3}{4}$	$\frac{1}{4}$	$1\frac{1}{16}$	$\frac{1}{8}$	$\frac{1}{2}$	$\frac{3}{8}$	$1\frac{3}{16}$	do	Thirty
	22	$1\frac{3}{8}$	$2\frac{7}{8}$	$\frac{5}{16}$	$1\frac{1}{8}$	$\frac{1}{8}$	$\frac{5}{8}$	$\frac{1}{2}$	$1\frac{1}{4}$	do	Thirty
	25	$1\frac{1}{2}$	3	$\frac{11}{32}$	$1\frac{3}{8}$	$\frac{3}{16}$	$\frac{5}{8}$	$\frac{1}{2}$	$1\frac{1}{2}$	do	Thirty
	30	$1\frac{5}{8}$	$3\frac{1}{4}$	$\frac{3}{8}$	$1\frac{1}{2}$	$\frac{3}{16}$	$\frac{3}{4}$	$\frac{1}{2}$	$1\frac{3}{4}$	do	Thirty
Milli-metres*	230	25	48	2·5	25	2·5	12	8	22	do	Twelve
	300	27	54	2·5	25	2·5	12	8	25	do	Fifteen
	380	28	64	4	27	2·5	12	8	27	do	Twenty
	450	32	70	6	27	3	12	8	28	do	Twenty Five
	500	33	70	7	27	4	12	8	30	do	Thirty
	550	35	73	8	28	4	15	12	32	do	Thirty
	650	38	76	9	35	5	15	12	38	do	Thirty
	750	42	82	10	38	5	19	12	44	do	Thirty

*Not necessarily complementary equivalents but close approximations

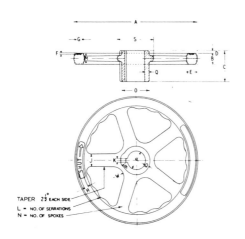

TAPER 2½° EACH SIDE
L = NO. OF SERRATIONS
N = NO. OF SPOKES

M	N	O	P	Q	R	S†	T	U	V	W	X	Y	Z
$\frac{1}{2}$	Four	According to dia. of stem		$\frac{1}{4}$	$\frac{5}{16}$	3				$1\frac{1}{4}$			
$\frac{9}{16}$	Five	do		$\frac{9}{32}$	$\frac{11}{32}$	$3\frac{1}{8}$				$1\frac{1}{4}$			
$\frac{5}{8}$	Five	do		$\frac{5}{16}$	$\frac{3}{8}$	$3\frac{3}{8}$				$1\frac{3}{8}$			
$\frac{5}{8}$	Five	do		$\frac{13}{32}$	$\frac{15}{32}$	$4\frac{1}{4}$				$1\frac{3}{8}$			
$\frac{5}{8}$	Five	do		$\frac{7}{16}$	$\frac{9}{16}$	$4\frac{1}{2}$				$1\frac{1}{2}$			
$\frac{11}{16}$	Six	do		$\frac{1}{2}$	$\frac{5}{8}$	$4\frac{3}{4}$				$1\frac{1}{2}$			
$\frac{3}{4}$	Six	do		$\frac{1}{2}$	$\frac{5}{8}$	$5\frac{1}{4}$				2			
$\frac{7}{8}$	Six	do		$\frac{9}{16}$	$\frac{11}{16}$	$6\frac{1}{2}$				2			
12	Four	do		7	8	76				32			
14	Five	do		7	9	80				33			
16	Five	do		8	10	85				35			
16	Five	do		10	12	108				36			
16	Five	do		12	15	115				37			
18	Six	do		13	16	120				40			
20	Six	do		14	16	132				50			
22	Six	do		15	18	165				50			

Appendix Z   Ultimate and permissible shear strength (in double shear) of plain and 'Spirol' pins. Metric units

SOLID PLAIN PINS Based on 0·1% carbon steel of 28 kgf/mm² ult. shearing strength 274 N/mm² ult. shearing strength					HEAVY			
Nom. dia. of pin mm	Ult. shear strength kgf	Safe working load kgf	Ult. shear strength kN	Safe working load kN	Ult. shear strength kgf		Safe working load kgf	
					SAE 302	SAE 1070 420	SAE 302	SAE 1070 420
1·0	48·5	7	0·48	0·07				
1·5	112	16	1·11	0·16	160	200	22·7	28·5
2·0	197	28	1·95	0·28	250	320	36	46
2·5	306	44	3·05	0·43	360	450	54	64
3·0	445	63	4·40	0·63	500	640	72	91
4·0	788	112	7·80	1·11	1100	1350	157	194
5·0	1230	176	12·20	1·76	1600	2000	230	286
6·0	1780	255	17·60	2·51	2100	2600	300	370
8·0	3160	454	31·30	4·47	4100	5200	585	745
10·0	4830	690	48·70	6·26	6400	8000	920	1140
12·0	7070	1010	70·00	10·00	8000	10000	1140	1430

Appendix Z (continued)

'SPIROL' PINS

DUTY				STANDARD DUTY							
Ult. shear strength kN		Safe working load kN		Ult. shear strength kgf		Safe working load kgf		Ult. shear strength kN		Safe working load kN	
SAE 302	SAE 1070 420	SAE 302	SAE 1070 420	SAE 302	SAE 1070 420	SAE 302	SAE 1070 420	SAE 302	SAE 1070 420	SAE 302	SAE 1070 420
				44	55*	6·3*	7·8	0·43	0·54	0·06	0·08
1·57	1·97	0·22	0·28	110	135	16·6	19·4	1·08	1·32	0·15	0·19
2·45	3·16	0·35	0·45	170	215	24·3	31	1·67	2·10	0·24	0·30
3·52	4·44	0·50	0·63	250	320	36	45	2·45	3·14	0·35	0·45
4·90	6·30	0·70	0·90	340	430	48	62	3·34	4·22	0·48	0·60
10·75	13·33	1·53	1·90	700	875	100	126	6·87	8·55	0·98	1·22
15·80	19·70	2·26	2·81	1000	1250	143	178	9·81	12·22	1·40	1·74
20·58	25·60	2·74	3·66	1400	1750	200	250	13·72	17·12	1·96	2·44
40·20	51·30	5·74	7·33	2800	3500	400	500	27·50	34·20	3·93	4·88
62·70	78·80	8·96	11·26	4000	5000	572	715	39·30	49·0	5·61	7·00
78·00	98·06	11·14	14·00	5500	7000	785	1000	54·00	68·5	7·71	9·80

Appendix Z (continued) Imperial units

Nom. dia. of pin in	SOLID PLAIN PINS Based on 0·1% carbon steel of 40 000 lb/in² ultimate shearing strength		HEAVY		'SPIROL' PINS MEDIUM		LIGHT	
	Ult. shear strength lb	Safe working load lb	Ult. shear strength lb	Safe working load lb	Ult. shear strength lb	Safe working load lb	Ult. shear strength lb	Safe working load lb
1/16 (·0625)	245	35	450	65	300	43	170	25
5/64 (·0781)	385	55	700	100	475	68	275	38
3/32 (·0937)	550	77	1 000	145	700	100	375	54
1/8 (·1250)	960	137	2 100	300	1 250	177	675	96
5/32 (·1562)	1 540	220	3 000	430	1 925	275	1 100	157
3/16 (·1875)	2 200	317	4 400	630	2 800	400	1 500	215
7/32 (·2187)	3 010	430	5 700	815	3 800	545	2 100	300
1/4 (·2500)	3 975	568	7 700	1 100	5 000	715	2 700	385
5/16 (·3125)	6 150	879	11 500	1 645	7 700	1 100	4 400	630
3/8 (·3750)	8 850	1 264	17 600	2 515	11 200	1 600	6 000	860
7/16 (·4375)	12 080	1 726	22 500	3 215	15 200	2 170	8 400	1 200
1/2 (·5000)	15 750	2 250	30 000	4 285	20 000	2 860	11 000	1 575

INDEX